TEACHER RESO

Chemical Interactions

Second Edition

Developed at the Lawrence Hall of Science, University of California, Berkeley
Published and Distributed by Delta Education

FOSS Lawrence Hall of Science Team
Larry Malone and Linda De Lucchi, FOSS Project Codirectors and Lead Developers
Jessica Penchos, Middle School Coordinator; Kathy Long, FOSS Assessment Director; David Lippman, Program Manager; Carol Sevilla, Publications Design Coordinator; Susan Stanley, Graphic Production; Rose Craig, Illustrator
FOSS Curriculum Developers: Alan Gould, Teri Lawson, Ann Moriarty, Virginia Reid, Terry Shaw, Joanna Snyder
FOSS Technology Developers: Susan Ketchner, Arzu Orgad
FOSS Multimedia Team: Kate Jordan, Senior Multimedia; Christopher Keller, Multimedia Producer; Jonathan Segal, Designer; Christopher Cianciarulo, Designer; Dan Bluestein, Programmer; Shan Jiang, Programmer

Delta Education Team
Bonnie A. Piotrowski, Editorial Director, Elementary Science
Project Team: Mathew Bacon, Jennifer Apt, Sandra Burke, Tom Guetling, Joann Hoy, Angela Miccinello, Paulette Miley, Jennifer Staltare

Content Reviewer
John Staver, Ed.D., Professor of Science, Education, and Chemistry
Purdue University

Thank you to the FOSS Middle School Revision Trial Teachers and District Coordinators
Frances Amojioyi, Lincoln Middle School, Alameda, CA; Dean Anderson, Organized trials for Boston Public Schools, Boston, MA; Thomas Archer, Organized trials for ESD 112, Vancouver, WA; Lauresa Baker, Lincoln Middle School, Alameda, CA; Bobbi Anne Barnowsky, Canyon Middle School, Castro Valley, CA; Christine Bertko, St. Finn Barr Catholic School, San Francisco, CA; Stephanie Billinge, James P. Timilty Middle School, Roxbury, MA; Jerry Breton, Ingleside Middle School, Phoenix, AZ; Robert Cho, Timilty Middle School, Boston, MA; Susan Cohen, Cherokee Heights Middle School, Madison, WI; Malcolm Davis, Canyon Middle School, Castro Valley, CA; Marilyn Decker, Organized trials for Milton PS, Milton, MA; Jenny Ernst, Park Day School, Oakland, CA; Marianne Floyd, Spanaway Middle School, Spanaway, WA; Sarah Kathryn Gessford, Journeys School, Jackson, WY; Charles Hardin, Prairie Point Middle School, Cedar Rapids, IA; Jennifer Hartigan, Lincoln Middle School, Alameda, CA; Sheila Holland, TechBoston Academy, Boston, MA; Nicole Hoyceanyls, Charles S. Pierce Middle School, Milton, MA; Bruce Kamerer, Donald McKay K-8 School, East Boston, MA; Carmen Saele Kardokus, Reeves Middle School, Olympia, WA; Janey Kaufman, Organized trials for Scottsdale USD, Scottsdale, AZ; Erica Larson, Organized trials for Grant Wood AEA, Cedar Rapids, IA; Lindsay Lodholz, O'Keeffe Middle School, Madison, WI; Robert Mattisinko, Chaparral High School, Scottsdale, AZ; Brenda McGurk, Prairie Point Middle School, Cedar Rapids, IA; Tim Miller, Mountainside Middle School, Scottsdale, AZ; Thomas Miro, Lincoln Middle School, Alameda, CA; Spencer Nedved, Frontier Middle School, Vancouver, WA; Joslyn Olsen, Lincoln Middle School, Alameda, CA; Stephanie Ovechka, Cedarcrest Middle School, Spanaway, WA; Barbara Reinert, Copper Ridge School, Scottsdale, AZ; Stephen Ramos, Lincoln Middle School, Alameda, CA; Gina Rutenbeck, Prairie Point Middle School, Cedar Rapids, IA; John Sheridan, Boston Public Schools (Boston Schoolyard Initiative), Boston, MA; Barbara Simon, Timilty Middle School, Boston, MA; Lise Simpson, Alcott Middle School, Norman, OK; Autumn Stevick, Thurgood Marshall Middle School, Olympia, WA; Ted Stoeckley, Hall Middle School, Larkspur, CA; Lesli Taschwer, Organized trials for Madison SD, Madison, WI; Paula Warner, Alcott Middle School, Norman, OK; Darren T. Wells, James P. Timilty Middle School, Boston, MA; Kristin White, Frontier Middle School, Vancouver, WA

Photo Credits: © Kenneth Keifer/Shutterstock (cover); © Delta Education

Published and Distributed by Delta Education, a member of the School Specialty Family
The FOSS program was developed in part with the support of the National Science Foundation grant nos. ESI-9553600 and ESI-0242510. However, any opinions, findings, conclusions, statements, and recommendations expressed herein are those of the authors and do not necessarily reflect the views of NSF. FOSSmap was developed in collaboration between the BEAR Center at UC Berkeley and FOSS at the Lawrence Hall of Science. Score analysis is done through the BEAR Center Scoring Engine.

Chemical Interactions, Second Edition — Teacher Toolkit, 1465640
Teacher Resources, 1465691
978-1-62571-204-2
Printing 2 – 6/2017
Patterson Printing, Benton Harbor, MI

WARNING — This set contains chemicals that may be harmful if misused. Read cautions on individual containers carefully. Not to be used by children except under adult supervision.

This warning label is required by the U.S. Consumer Product Safety Commission. The chemicals in the FOSS Chemical Interactions kit are ascorbic acid, calcium carbonate, calcium chloride, calcium hydroxide, citric acid, magnesium sulfate (Epsom salts), sodium bicarbonate (baking soda), sodium carbonate (washing soda), sodium chloride (kosher salt), and hydrochloric acid.

TABLE OF CONTENTS

FOSS Middle School Introduction

FOSS Middle School Introduction

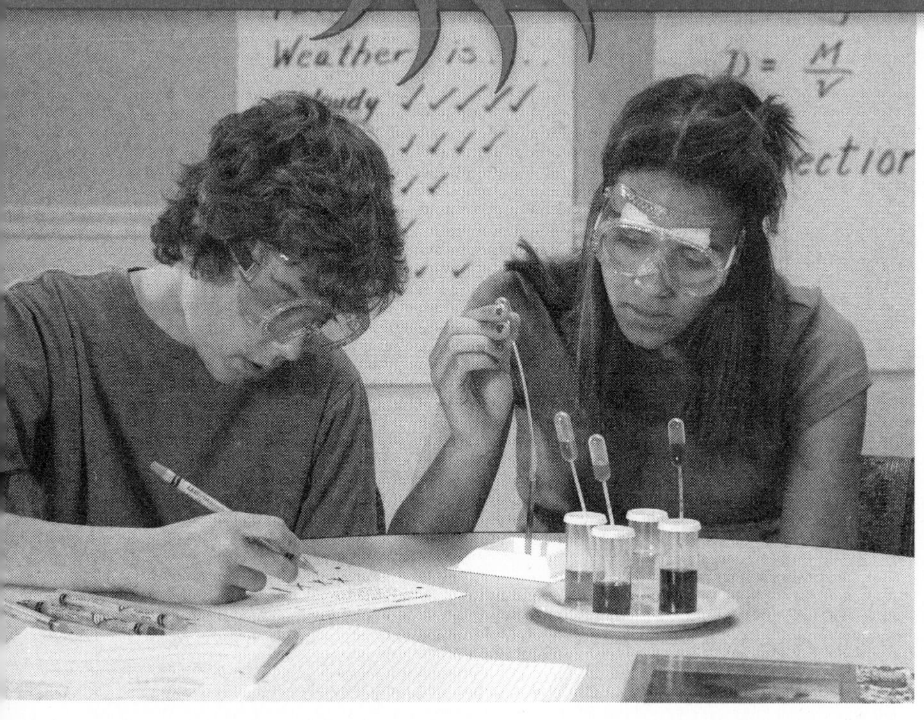

Contents

INTRODUCTION

The Full Option Science System™ has evolved from a philosophy of teaching and learning at the Lawrence Hall of Science that has guided the development of successful active-learning science curricula for more than 40 years. The FOSS Program bridges research and practice by providing tools and strategies to engage students and teachers in enduring experiences that lead to deeper understanding of the natural and designed worlds.

Science is a creative and analytic enterprise, made active by our human capacity to think. Scientific knowledge advances when scientists observe objects and events, think about how they relate to what is known, test their ideas in logical ways, and generate explanations that integrate the new information into understanding of the natural world. Engineers apply that understanding to solve real-world problems. Thus the scientific enterprise is both what we know (content knowledge) and how we come to know it (practices). Science is a discovery activity, a process for producing new knowledge.

The best way for students to appreciate the scientific enterprise, learn important scientific and engineering concepts, and develop the ability to think well is to actively participate in scientific practices through their own investigations and analyses. FOSS was created to engage students and teachers with meaningful experiences in the natural and designed worlds.

GOALS OF THE FOSS PROGRAM

FOSS has set out to achieve three important goals: scientific literacy, instructional efficiency, and systemic reform.

Scientific Literacy

FOSS provides all students with science experiences that are appropriate to students' cognitive development and prior experiences. It provides a foundation for more advanced understanding of core science ideas that are organized in thoughtfully designed learning progressions and prepares students for life in an increasingly complex scientific and technological world.

The National Research Council (NRC) in *A Framework for K–12 Science Education: Practices, Crosscutting Concepts, and Core Ideas* and the American Association for the Advancement of Science (AAAS) in *Benchmarks for Scientific Literacy* have described the characteristics of scientific literacy:

- Familiarity with the natural world, its diversity, and its interdependence.
- Understanding the disciplinary core ideas and the crosscutting concepts of science, such as patterns; cause and effect; scale, proportion, and quantity; systems and system models; energy and matter—flows, cycles, and conservation; structure and function; and stability and change.
- Knowing that science and engineering, technology, and mathematics are interdependent human enterprises and, as such, have implied strengths and limitations.
- Ability to reason scientifically.
- Using scientific knowledge and scientific and engineering practices for personal and social purposes.

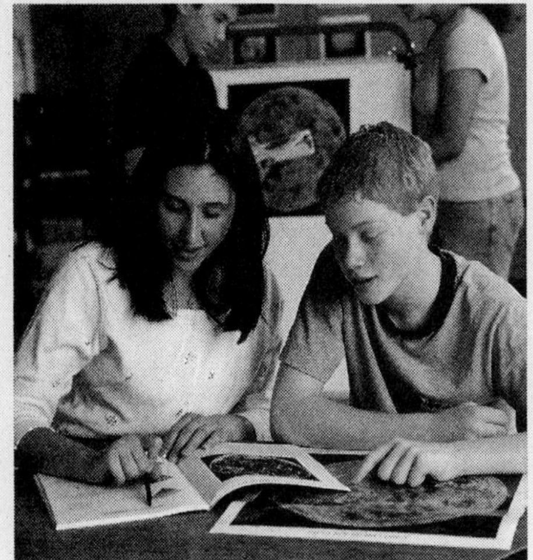

The FOSS Program design is based on learning progressions that provide students with opportunities to investigate core ideas in science in increasingly complex ways over time. FOSS starts with the intuitive ideas that primary students bring with them and provides experiences that allow students to develop more sophisticated understanding as they grow through the grades. Cognitive research tells us that learning involves individuals in actively constructing schemata to organize new information and to relate and incorporate the new understanding into established knowledge. What sets experts apart from novices is that

experts in a discipline have extensive knowledge that is effectively organized into structured schemata to promote thinking. Novices have disconnected ideas about a topic that are difficult to retrieve and use. Through internal processes to establish schemata and through social processes of interacting with peers and adults, students construct understanding of the natural world and their relationship to it.

The target goal for FOSS students is to know and use scientific explanations of the natural world and the designed world; to understand the nature and development of scientific knowledge and technological capabilities; and to participate productively in scientific and engineering practices.

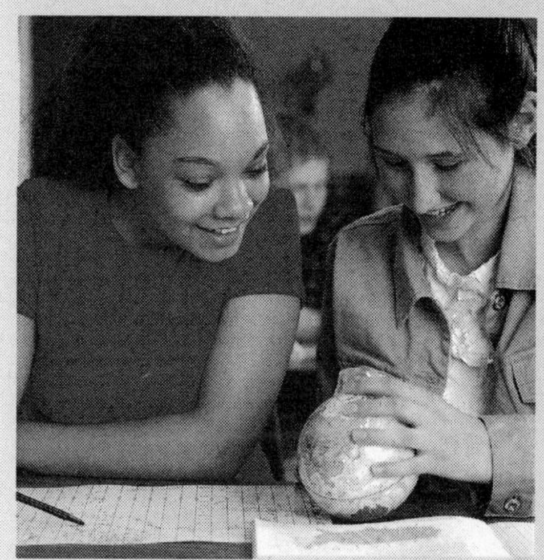

Instructional Efficiency

FOSS provides all teachers with a complete, cohesive, flexible, easy-to-use science program that reflects current research on teaching and learning, including student discourse, argumentation, writing to learn, and reflective thinking, as well as teacher use of formative assessment to guide instruction. The FOSS Program uses effective instructional methodologies, including active learning, scientific practices, focus questions to guide inquiry, working in collaborative groups, multisensory strategies, integration of literacy, appropriate use of digital technologies, and making connections to students' lives.

FOSS is designed to make active learning in science engaging for teachers as well as for students. It includes these supports for teachers:

- Complete equipment kits with durable, well-designed materials for all students.
- Detailed *Investigations Guide* with science background for the teacher and focus questions to guide instructional practice and student thinking.
- Multiple strategies for formative assessment.
- Benchmark assessments with scoring guides.
- Strategies for use of science notebooks for novice and experienced users.
- *FOSS Science Resources*, a book of course-specific readings.
- The FOSS website with course-integrated online activities for use in school or at home, suggested extension activities, and extensive online support for teachers.

Systemic Reform

FOSS provides schools and school systems with a program that addresses the community science-achievement standards. The FOSS Program prepares students by helping them acquire the knowledge and thinking capacity appropriate for world citizens.

The FOSS Program design makes it appropriate for reform efforts on all scales. It reflects the core ideas to be incorporated into the next-generation science standards. It meets with the approval of science and technology companies working in collaboration with school systems, and it has demonstrated its effectiveness with diverse student and teacher populations in major urban reform efforts. The use of science notebooks and formative-assessment strategies in FOSS redefines the role of science in a school—the way that teachers engage in science teaching with one another as professionals and with students as learners, and the way that students engage in science learning with the teacher and with one another. FOSS takes students and teachers beyond the classroom walls to establish larger communities of learners.

BRIDGING RESEARCH INTO PRACTICE

The FOSS Program is built on the assumptions that understanding core scientific knowledge and how science functions is essential for citizenship, that all teachers can teach science, and that all students can learn science. The guiding principles of the FOSS design, described below, are derived from research and confirmed through FOSS developers' extensive experience with teachers and students in typical American classrooms.

Understanding of science develops over time. FOSS has elaborated learning or content progressions for core ideas in science for kindergarten through grade 8. Developing the learning progressions involves identifying successively more sophisticated ways of thinking about core ideas over multiple years. "If mastery of a core idea in a science discipline is the ultimate educational destination, then well-designed learning progressions provide a map of the routes that can be taken to reach that destination" (National Research Council, *A Framework for K–12 Science Education*, 2011).

Focusing on a limited number of topics in science avoids shallow coverage and provides more time to explore core science ideas in depth. Research emphasizes that fewer topics experienced in greater depth produces much better learning than many topics briefly visited. FOSS affirms this research. FOSS courses provide long-term engagement (10–12 weeks) with important science ideas. Furthermore, courses build upon one another within and across each strand, progressively moving students toward the grand ideas of science. The core ideas of science are difficult and complex, never learned in one lesson or in one class year.

FOSS K–8 Module Sequences

	PHYSICAL SCIENCE		EARTH SCIENCE		LIFE SCIENCE	
	MATTER	ENERGY AND CHANGE	DYNAMIC ATMOSPHERE	ROCKS AND LANDFORMS	STRUCTURE/ FUNCTION	COMPLEX SYSTEMS
8	Electronics		Planetary Science		Human Brain and Senses	
	Chemical Interactions	Force and Motion	Weather and Water	Earth History	Diversity of Life	Populations and Ecosystems
	Mixtures and Solutions		Earth and Sun		Living Systems	
		Energy		Soils, Rocks, and Landforms	Environments	
	Motion and Matter		Water and Climate		Structures of Life	
	Solids and Liquids			Pebbles, Sand, and Silt	Insects and Plants	
		Sound and Light	Air and Weather		Plants and Animals	
K	Materials and Motion		Trees and Weather		Animals Two by Two	

FOSS Middle School Introduction

Science is more than a body of knowledge. How well you think is often more important than how much you know. In addition to the science content framework, every FOSS course provides opportunities for students to engage in and understand scientific practices, and many courses explore issues related to engineering practices and the use of natural resources. FOSS uses these scientific and engineering practices.

- Asking questions (for science) and defining problems (for engineering)
- Planning and carrying out investigations
- Analyzing and interpreting data
- Developing and using models
- Using mathematics, information and computer technology, and computational thinking
- Constructing explanations (for science) and designing solutions (for engineering)
- Engaging in argument from evidence
- Obtaining, evaluating, and communicating information

Science is inherently interesting, and children are natural investigators. It is widely accepted that children learn science concepts best by doing science. Doing science means hands-on experiences with objects, organisms, and systems. Hands-on activities are motivating for students, and they stimulate inquiry and curiosity. For these reasons, FOSS is committed to providing the best possible materials and the most effective procedures for deeply engaging students with scientific concepts. FOSS students at all grade levels investigate, experiment, gather data, organize results, and draw conclusions based on their own actions. The information gathered in such activities enhances the development of scientific and engineering practices.

Education is an adventure in self-discovery. Science provides the opportunity to connect to students' interests and experiences. Prior experiences and individual learning styles are important considerations for developing understanding. Observing is often equated with seeing, but in the FOSS Program all senses are used to promote greater understanding. FOSS evolved from pioneering work done in the 1970s with students with disabilities. The legacy of that work is that FOSS investigations naturally use multisensory methods to accommodate students with physical and learning disabilities and also to maximize information gathering for all students. A number of tools, such as the FOSS syringe and balance, were originally designed to serve the needs of students with disabilities.

Formative assessment is a powerful tool to promote learning and can change the culture of the learning environment. Formative assessment in FOSS creates a community of reflective practice. Teachers and students make up the community and establish norms of mutual support, trust, respect, and collaboration. The goal of the community is that everyone will demonstrate progress and will learn and grow.

Science-centered language development promotes learning in all areas. Effective use of science notebooks can promote reflective thinking and contribute to lifelong learning. Research has shown that when language-arts experiences are embedded within the context of learning science, students improve in their ability to use their language skills. Students are motivated to read to find out information, and to share their experiences both verbally and in writing.

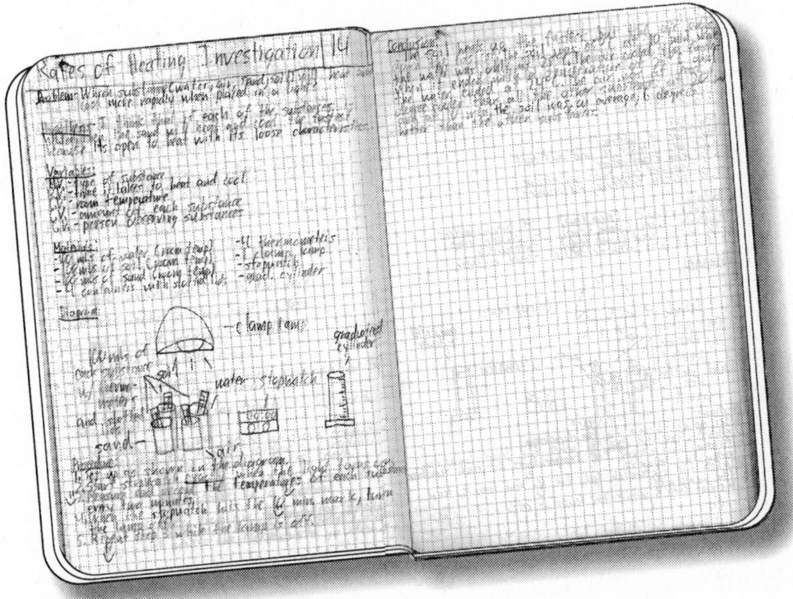

Experiences out of the classroom develop awareness of community. By extending classroom learning into the local region and community, FOSS brings the science concepts and principles to life. In the process of extending classroom learning to the natural world and utilizing community resources, students will develop a relationship with learning that extends beyond the classroom walls.

FOSS MIDDLE SCHOOL COMPONENTS

Teacher Toolkit

The *Teacher Toolkit* is the most important part of the FOSS Program. It is here that all the wisdom and experience contributed by hundreds of educators has been assembled. Everything we know about the content of the course and how to teach the subject in a middle school classroom is presented, along with the resources that will assist the effort. Each middle school *Teacher Toolkit* has three parts.

Investigations Guide. This spiral-bound document contains these chapters.

- Overview
- Materials
- Investigations

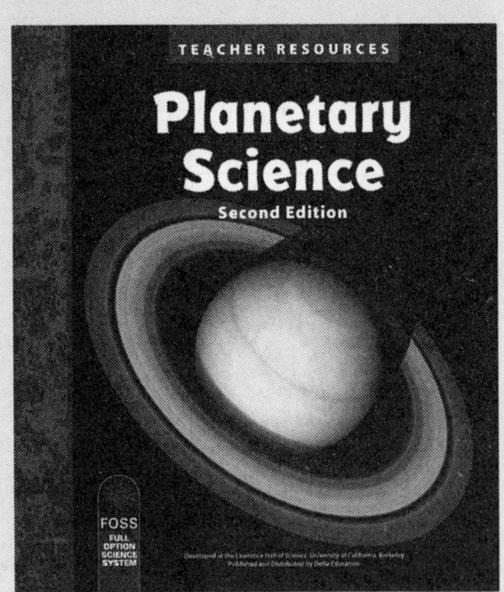

Teacher Resources. This collection of resources contains these chapters.

- FOSS Middle School Introduction
- Assessment
- Science Notebooks in Middle School
- Science-Centered Language Development in Middle School
- FOSSweb and Technology
- Science Notebook Masters
- Teacher Masters
- Assessment Masters
- Notebook Answers

The chapters contained in *Teacher Resources* can also be found on FOSSweb (www.FOSSweb.com).

FOSS Science Resources book. One copy of the student book of readings, images, and data is included for the teacher.

Equipment Kit

The FOSS Program provides the materials needed for the investigations in sturdy, front-opening drawer-and-sleeve cabinets. Inside, you will find high-quality materials packaged for a class of 32 students. Consumable materials are supplied for five sequential uses (five periods in one day) before you need to restock. You will be asked to supply small quantities of common classroom items.

FOSS Science Resources Books

FOSS Science Resources is a book of original readings developed to accompany each course, along with images and data to analyze during investigations. The readings are referred to as articles in the *Investigations Guide*. Students read the articles in the book as they progress through the course, sometimes during class and sometimes as homework. The articles cover a specific concept usually after that concept has been introduced in an active investigation.

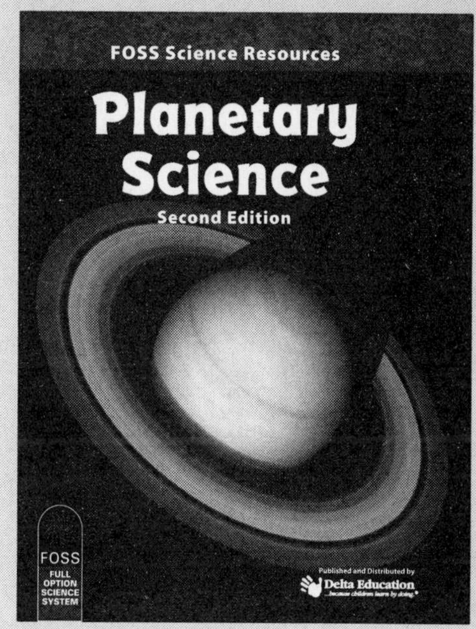

The articles in *FOSS Science Resources* and the discussion questions in the *Investigations Guide* help students make connections to the science concepts introduced and explored during the active investigations. Concept development is most effective when students are allowed to experience organisms, objects, and phenomena firsthand before engaging the concepts in text. The text and illustrations help make connections between what students experience concretely and the ideas that explain their observations.

FOSSweb and Technology

The FOSS website opens new horizons for educators, students, and families, in the classroom or at home. Each course has an interactive site where students can find instructional activities, interactive simulations, virtual investigations, and other resources. FOSSweb provides resources for professional development, materials management, general teaching tools for FOSS, purchasing links, contact information for the FOSS Program, and technical support. You do not need an account to view this general FOSS Program information. In addition to the general information, FOSSweb provides digital access to PDF versions of the *Teacher Resources* component of the *Teacher Toolkit* and digital-only resources that supplement the print and kit materials.

Additional resources are available to support FOSS teachers. With an educator account, you can set up a customized homepage that will provide easy access to the digital components of the courses you teach, and allow you to create class pages for your students.

Ongoing Professional Development

The Lawrence Hall of Science and Delta Education are committed to supporting science educators with unrivaled teacher support, high-quality implementation, and continuous staff-development opportunities and resources. FOSS has a strong network of consultants who have rich and experienced backgrounds in diverse educational settings using FOSS. Find out about professional-development opportunities on FOSSweb.

FOCUS QUESTION

What causes Moon phases?

TEACHING NOTE

Teaching notes appear in this location as needed throughout the investigation.

FOSS INSTRUCTIONAL DESIGN

Each FOSS investigation follows a similar cycle to provide multiple exposures to science concepts. The cycle includes these pedagogies.

- Active investigation, including outdoor experiences and online simulations
- Recording in science notebooks to answer the focus question
- Reading in *FOSS Science Resources*
- Assessment to monitor progress and motivate student reflection on learning

In practice, these components are seamlessly integrated into a continuum designed to maximize every student's opportunity to learn. An instructional sequence may move from one pedagogy to another and back again to ensure adequate coverage of a concept.

Investigation Organization

Courses are subdivided into **investigations**. Investigations are further subdivided into two to four **parts**. Each part of each investigation is driven by a **focus question**. The focus question, presented as the part begins, signals the challenge to be met, mystery to be solved, or principle to be uncovered. The focus question guides students' inquiry and makes the goal of each part explicit for teachers. Each part concludes with students preparing a written answer to the focus question in their notebooks.

Investigation-specific **scientific and historical background** information for the teacher is presented in each investigation chapter. The content discussion is divided into sections, each of which relates directly to one of the focus questions. This facilitates finding the exact information you need for each part of the investigation.

The **Getting Ready** and **Guiding the Investigation** sections have several features that are flagged or presented in the sidebar. These include several icons to remind you when a particular pedagogical method is suggested, as well as concise bits of information in several categories.

Teaching notes appear in blue boxes in the sidebar. An arrow points to the place in the lesson where the note applies. These notes constitute a second voice in the curriculum—an educative element. The first (traditional) voice is the message you deliver to students. It supports your work teaching students at all levels, from management to inquiry. The second educative voice is designed to help you understand the science content and pedagogical reasoning at work behind the instructional scene.

The small-group **discussion** icon asks you to pause while students discuss data or construct explanations in their groups. Often a Reporter shares the group's conclusions with the class.

The **vocabulary** icon indicates where students should record vocabulary in their science notebooks, often just before preparing for a benchmark assessment.

The **recording** icon points out where students should make a science notebook entry. Students can record on prepared notebook sheets or on plain sheets in a bound notebook.

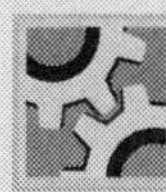

The **engineering** icon indicates opportunities for addressing engineering practices—applying and using scientific knowledge. These opportunities include developing a solution to a problem, constructing and evaluating models, and using systems thinking.

The **reading** icon signals when the class should read a specific article or refer to data in *FOSS Science Resources*. Some readings are critical to instruction and should take place in class. A reading guide is provided for each such reading.

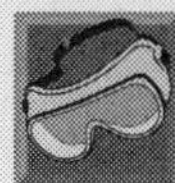

The **safety** icon alerts you to a potential safety issue. It could relate to the use of a chemical substance, such as salt, requiring safety goggles, or the possibility of an allergic reaction when an investigation might expose the students to latex, legumes, or wheat.

The **assessment** icon appears when there is an opportunity to assess student progress or performance. The assessment is usually one of three kinds: observation of students engaged in scientific and engineering practices, review of a notebook entry, or review of students' work on a prepared assessment tool.

The **technology** icon indicates when to have one or more computers available for accessing FOSSweb to use the online resources. The online activities are not optional.

The **homework** icon indicates science learning experiences that extend beyond the classroom. Some of the readings are suggested as homework. In that case, you will see two icons by that step.

The **outdoor** icon indicates science learning experiences that extend into the schoolyard.

To help with scheduling, you will see icons for **breakpoints**. Some breakpoints are essential, and others are optional.

POSSIBLE BREAKPOINT

Active Investigation

Active investigation is a master pedagogy. Embedded within active learning are a number of pedagogical elements and practices that keep active investigation vigorous and productive. The enterprise of active investigation includes

- context: questioning and planning;
- activity: doing and observing;
- data management: recording, organizing, and processing; and
- analysis: discussing and writing explanations.

Context: questioning and planning. Active investigation requires focus. The context of an inquiry can be established with a focus question or challenge from you or, in some cases, from students. At other times, students are asked to plan a method for investigation. This might start with a teacher demonstration or presentation. Then you challenge students to plan an investigation. In either case, the field available for thought and interaction is constrained. This clarification of context and purpose results in a more productive investigation.

Activity: doing and observing. In the practice of science, scientists put things together and take things apart, they observe systems and interactions, and they conduct experiments. This is the core of science—active, firsthand experience with objects, organisms, materials, and systems in the natural world and designed worlds. In FOSS, students engage in the same processes. Students often conduct investigations in collaborative groups of four, with each student taking a role to contribute to the effort.

The active investigations in FOSS are cohesive, and build on each other and the readings to lead students to a comprehensive understanding of concepts. Through the investigations, students gather meaningful data.

Online multimedia activities throughout the course provide students with the opportunity to collect data, manipulate variables, and explore models and simulations beyond what can be done in the classroom. Seamless integration of the multimedia forms an integral part of students' active investigations in FOSS.

Data management: recording, organizing, and processing. Data accrue from observation, both direct (through the senses) and indirect (mediated by instrumentation). Data are the raw material from which scientific knowledge and meaning are synthesized. During and after work with materials, students record data in their notebooks. Data recording is the first of several kinds of student writing.

Students then organize data so that they will be easier to think about. Tables allow efficient comparison. Organizing data in a sequence (time) or series (physical property) can reveal patterns. Students process some data into graphs, providing visual display of numerical data. They also organize data and process them in the science notebook.

Analysis: discussing and writing explanations. The most important part of an active investigation is extracting its meaning. This constructive process involves logic, discourse, and existing knowledge. Students share their explanations for phenomena, using evidence generated during the investigation to support their ideas. They conclude the active investigation by writing a summary of their learning in their science notebooks as well as questions raised during the activity.

Science Notebooks

Research and best practice have led FOSS to place more emphasis on the student science notebook. Keeping a notebook helps students organize their observations and data, process their data, and maintain a record of their learning for future reference. The process of writing about their science experiences and communicating their thinking is a powerful learning device for students. And the student notebook entries stand as a credible and useful expression of learning. The artifacts in the notebooks form one of the core elements of the assessment system.

You will find the duplication masters for middle school presented in a notebook format. They are reduced in size (two copies to a standard sheet) for placement (glue or tape) in a bound composition book. Student work is entered partly in spaces provided on the notebook sheets and partly on adjacent blank sheets. Full-size duplication masters are also available on FOSSweb for projection.

TEACHING NOTE

The Science Notebooks in Middle School chapter includes guidance on how to structure a student-centered notebook in terms of organization, content, and classroom logistics. Reading that chapter will help you consider your instructional practices for notebooks and incorporate new techniques supported by research about student learning.

Reading in *FOSS Science Resources*

Reading is a vital component of the FOSS Program. Reading enhances and extends information and concepts acquired through active investigation.

Some readings can be assigned as homework or extension activities, whereas other readings have been deemed important for all students to complete with a teacher's support in class.

Each in-class reading has a reading guide embedded in the Guiding the Investigation section. The reading guide suggests breakpoints with questions to help students connect the reading to their experiences from class, and recommends notebook entries. Additionally, each of these readings includes one or more prompts that ask students to make additional notebook entries. These prompts should help students who missed the in-class reading to process the article in a meaningful way. Some of the most essential articles are provided as notebook masters. Students can highlight the article as they read, add notes or questions, and add the article to their science notebooks.

Assessing Progress

The FOSS assessment system includes both formative and summative assessments. Formative assessment monitors learning during instruction. It measures progress, provides information about learning, and is generally diagnostic. Summative assessment looks at the learning after instruction is completed, and it measures achievement.

Formative assessment in FOSS, called **embedded assessment**, occurs on a daily basis. You observe action during class or review notebooks after class. Embedded assessment provides continuous monitoring of students' learning and helps you make decisions about whether to review, extend, or move on to the next idea to be covered.

Benchmark assessments are short summative assessments given after one or two investigations. These I-Checks are actually hybrid tools: they provide summative information about students' achievement, and because they occur soon after teaching an investigation, they can be used diagnostically as well. Reviewing a specific item on an I-Check with the class provides another opportunity for students to clarify their thinking.

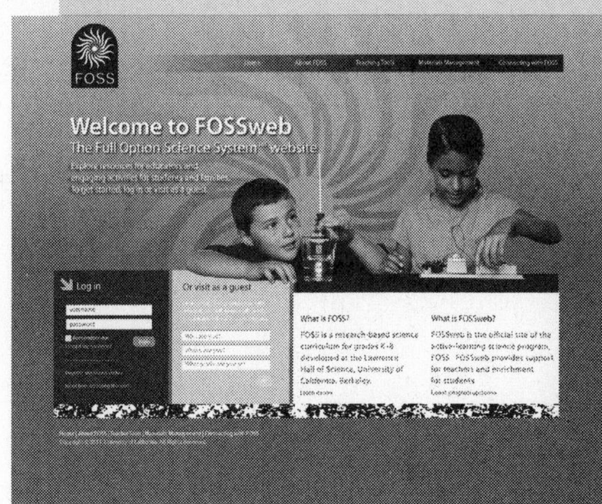

FOSSweb and Technology

FOSS is committed to providing a rich, accessible technology experience for all FOSS users. FOSSweb is the Internet access to FOSS digital resources. It provides enrichment for students and support for teachers, administrators, and families who are actively involved in implementing and enjoying FOSS materials.

Technology to Engage Students at School and at Home

Online multimedia activities. These include models, simulations, and activities that extend the active investigations.

Class pages. Teachers with a FOSSweb account can set up class pages with notes and assignments for students and families to access online.

Recommended books and websites. FOSS has reviewed print books and digital resources that are appropriate for students and prepared a list of these media resources.

FOSS Science Resources. As premium content, *FOSS Science Resources* is available as an eBook.

Technology to Support Teachers

Investigations eGuide. The eGuide is the complete *Investigations Guide* component of the *Teacher Toolkit* in an electronic web-based format, allowing access from any Internet-enabled computer.

Resources by investigation. This digital listing provides online links to notebook sheets, assessment and teacher masters, and online activities for each investigation of a course, for projection in the classroom.

Science-notebook masters and teacher masters. All notebook masters and teacher masters used in the courses are available digitally on FOSSweb for downloading and for projection during class.

Assessment masters. The benchmark assessment masters (I-Checks and Survey/Posttest) are available through FOSSweb.

Materials Safety Data Sheets (MSDS). These sheets have information from materials manufacturers on handling and disposal of materials.

Course summary. The summary describes each investigation in a course, including major concepts developed.

Course updates and course notes. These are updates related to the teacher materials, student equipment, and safety guidelines.

Teacher Resources *chapters.* FOSSweb provides PDF files of the chapters in *Teacher Resources*.

FOSS K–8 SCOPE AND SEQUENCE

Grade	Physical Science	Earth Science	Life Science
6–8	Electronics Chemical Interactions Force and Motion	Planetary Science Earth History Weather and Water	Human Brain and Senses Populations and Ecosystems Diversity of Life
5	Mixtures and Solutions	Earth and Sun	Living Systems
4	Energy	Soils, Rocks, and Landforms	Environments
3	Motion and Matter	Water and Climate	Structures of Life
2	Solids and Liquids	Pebbles, Sand, and Silt	Insects and Plants
1	Sound and Light	Air and Weather	Plants and Animals
K	Materials and Motion	Trees and Weather	Animals Two by Two

FOSS is a research-based science curriculum for grades K–8 developed at the Lawrence Hall of Science, University of California, Berkeley. FOSS is also an ongoing research project dedicated to improving the learning and teaching of science. The FOSS project began over 25 years ago during a time of growing concern that our nation was not providing young students with an adequate science education. The FOSS Program materials are designed to meet the challenge of providing meaningful science education for all students in diverse American classrooms and to prepare them for life in the 21st century. Development of the FOSS Program was, and continues to be, guided by advances in the understanding of how people think and learn.

With the initial support of the National Science Foundation and continued support from the University of California, Berkeley, and School Specialty, Inc., the FOSS Program has evolved into a curriculum for all students and their teachers, grades K–8. The current editions of FOSS are the result of a rich collaboration among the FOSS/Lawrence Hall of Science development staff; the FOSS product development team at Delta Education; assessment specialists, educational researchers, and scientists; and dedicated professionals in the classroom and their students, administrators, and families.

We acknowledge the thousands of FOSS educators who have embraced the notion that science is an active process, and we thank them for their significant contributions to the development and implementation of the FOSS Program.

Assessment

THE FOSS ASSESSMENT SYSTEM *for Middle School*

The assessment materials in this chapter are designed to be used throughout the **Chemical Interactions Course**. They can be used to monitor progress during the investigations and as evaluation tools at the end of the course. For the purpose of assessment, we have identified two overarching goals for the program—science content and scientific practices. Science content consists of the "facts and concepts" of science that students learn throughout the course. Scientific practices comprise experimental design and the skills needed for successfully engaging in science inquiry.

FOSS makes an important distinction between formative and summative assessments. Formative assessments are embedded throughout the course to provide diagnostic information that you can use to inform decisions about instruction for individual students and for the class. In general, FOSS suggests that these **embedded assessments** not be graded, although we provide several assessment tools such as *Embedded Assessment Notes* and *Science and Engineering Practices Checklist* to keep a running record of students' progress. It is important to keep in mind that all embedded assessments are intended to give you greater insight into students' thinking so you have information upon which to base instructional decisions.

Benchmark assessments are given before instruction (the survey/posttest can be used as a survey to assess prior knowledge), after most investigations (I-Checks), and when instruction is complete (posttest). The I-Checks and posttest are forms of summative assessment used when students have had opportunities to gather and process information. Understanding the "big ideas" of science requires students to construct relationships among many different pieces of evidence. It is important that students have time to build these higher levels of understanding before they are assessed. The I-Checks are hybrid tools that can provide summative information about student achievement and, because they occur within the instructional flow of the module, can be used formatively as well. Reviewing specific items on an I-Check with the class provides opportunities for students to review and clarify their thinking.

Check FOSSweb for updates to the assessments for this course.

Contents

EMBEDDED ASSESSMENT

In FOSS middle school, the unit of instruction is the course—a sequence of conceptually related learning experiences that leads to a set of learning outcomes. A science notebook gives students a place to record their thinking and develop deeper understanding of the course content by articulating relationships, patterns, and conclusions, as well as by asking questions that will guide further exploration. Science notebook entries give both you and your students opportunities to review and reflect on students' thinking.

From the assessment point of view, a science notebook is a collection of student-generated artifacts that exhibit student learning. You can informally assess student skills, such as ability to use charts to record data, while students are working with materials. At other times, you collect the notebooks and review them for insights or errors in conceptual understanding. The displays of data and analytical work provide a measure of the quality and quantity of student learning.

As you progress through the course, you will see different strategies used throughout the *Investigations Guide*. These will be marked with the notebook or assessment icons. As you try these strategies, take note of the positive effect that keeping notebooks can have on students' work, as students continually practice expressing their conceptual development in writing, and the way embedded assessments can help you better understand and address students' misconceptions.

Assessment Opportunities

Notebook entries serve as assessment opportunities for learning. Each part of each investigation is driven by a **focus question**. Each part usually concludes with students writing or revising an answer to the focus question in their notebooks. Their answers reveal how well they have made sense of the investigation and whether they have focused on the relevant actions and discussions.

At times, students use prepared **notebook sheets** to help organize and think about data. You can note how carefully students are making and organizing observations and how they think about analyzing and interpreting the data. Sometimes students answer a specific question that provides additional insight into understanding. You will find answer sheets for the notebook sheets in the Notebook Answers chapter.

Response sheets provide more formal embedded-assessment data. These are a specific kind of notebook sheet that assesses particular scientific knowledge that students often struggle with, giving you an

additional opportunity to help students untangle concepts that they may be overgeneralizing or have difficulty differentiating.

Students also generate **free-form notebook entries** that can be used for assessing progress. These may occur when you choose to have students organize their own data, or when events in the classroom suggest a new aspect of students' learning that you want to know more about.

A **quick write** (or quick draw) is a question that students answer on a separate sheet of paper before instruction, so you can analyze their prior knowledge and misconceptions. Collect quick writes and quickly sample them for insight into what students think about certain phenomena before you begin formal instruction. Knowing students' intuitive ideas (or prior knowledge) will help you know what parts of the investigations need the most attention. Make sure students date their entries for later reference. Quick writes can be done on a quarter sheet of paper or an index card. You collect them, review them, and return them to students to affix into their notebooks for self-assessment later in the investigation.

Noting students' **science and engineering practices** throughout the course is a way to check their advancement in scientific thinking processes during an investigation. These observations happen during class, as you circulate among student groups. Sometimes you will simply watch what students are doing; at other times prompts or interview questions will be suggested.

Time Management

In order to collect enough data from embedded assessment to adequately inform instruction, plan to spend 15 minutes on each day of instruction, reviewing student learning by examining student work. In middle school, you face the challenge of having a large number of students. This may mean collecting only a portion of students' notebooks at a time to keep your workload manageable. A sample of student notebooks across your classes should represent the general levels of conceptual understanding that students have. In some cases, you may also examine student work during class, while students are actively engaged in the course, and provide verbal feedback. Certain work, such as quick writes and notebook sheets, is first completed on separate sheets of paper. These are easier to collect, read, and later return to be glued into students' notebooks.

Planning for Embedded Assessment

Embedded assessments are suggested for each investigation part. You will find a description of what and when to assess in the Getting Ready section of each part of each investigation. Here is the Getting Ready assessment step for Part 2 of Investigation 3.

8. Plan assessment: notebook entry

Use notebook sheets 15 and 16, *Air in a Syringe A* and *B*, to assess how students are progressing in their understanding of the particulate model as an explanation for the structure and behavior of gas.

Preview the assessment in Step 18 of Guiding the Investigation and consider which one or two concepts you will record on *Embedded Assessment Notes*. Fill in the investigation and part numbers, and write the concept(s) in the next section of the sheet.

As you progress through the lesson, you will find a step in the **Guiding the Investigation** section that reminds you about what to assess. It will also give you a detailed list of what to look for, in terms of how students should be building and communicating their scientific knowledge and practices.

18. Assess progress: notebook entry

After students have finished updating their *Air in a Syringe* notebook sheets, collect a sample from each class, and assess students' progress. The sample you select should give you a snapshot of the range of student understanding at this point in time.

What to look for

- *Students draw 20 particles in each syringe, closer together in syringe D, and farther apart in syringe E.*
- *Students use the particulate model to explain the behavior of air.*
- *Students include the terms* **expansion** *and* **compression** *to explain their drawings.*
- *Students explain that the space between particles expands or compresses, not the particles themselves.*

The Getting Ready section of each investigation part will identify which assessment master will be used as a tool to consider student progress in that part.

Recording Data: Embedded Assessment Notes

Research shows that if you spend time reviewing student work each day, students achieve significantly more. Use the technique described here to make this a quick and easy process. If you have several classes, choose a random sample across the classes and plan 15 minutes to review student work. The important thing is that you are looking at student work on a daily basis as much as possible.

Make copies of ***Embedded Assessment Notes*** to record observations and help assess students' work in the embedded assessments suggested for each part of an investigation.

Embedded Assessment Notes Chemical Interactions, Second Edition

Investigation ___, Part ___	Date ______
Concept:	
Tally: Got it	Doesn't get it
Misconceptions/incomplete ideas:	
Reflections/next steps:	

Investigation ___, Part ___	Date ______
Concept:	
Tally: Got it	Doesn't get it
Misconceptions/incomplete ideas:	
Reflections/next steps:	

Investigation ___, Part ___	Date ______
Concept:	
Tally: Got it	Doesn't get it
Misconceptions/incomplete ideas:	
Reflections/next steps:	

FOSS Chemical Interactions Course, Second Edition

Embedded Assessment Notes
No. 1—Assessment Master

Anticipate. Check the Getting Ready section for the suggested embedded assessment for an investigation part. Before class, fill in the investigation and part numbers and the date on *Embedded Assessment Notes*. Check the assessment step in Guiding the Investigation, and write in the concept(s) that you will be recording on the sheet. Limit your assessment to one or two important ideas.

Teach the lesson. Keep in mind the What to Look For as you teach the investigation. During the investigation, you might circulate among students as they work, reviewing their progress and interviewing them. Pay attention to misconceptions that come across in student activities or discussion, and record notes on *Embedded Assessment Notes*.

Review. At the end of class, have students turn in their notebooks *open to the page that you will be reviewing*. (This will save you a lot of time.) Collect a sample of student notebooks across the classes. Try to represent students of all abilities within the sample, so you can fairly judge whether your classes are mastering the concepts. Check the assessment step in Guiding the Investigation so you know the one or two important ideas that you are looking for and where to find them (focus-question answer, notebook entry, notebook sheet, or response sheet). Make a tally mark for each student who gets it or doesn't get it. Consider misconceptions or incomplete ideas that students are expressing in their language, and record patterns on *Embedded Assessment Notes*.

Reflect. Summarize the trends and patterns you saw in the class's understanding of the concepts in the "Reflections/next steps" section (5 minutes to reflect and plan next steps).

Next steps. Describe the next steps you will take to clear up any problems, or note highlights you saw in students' understanding. This is the key to formative assessment. You must take some action to help students improve their understanding. If you do this process frequently, the next steps should take only a few minutes of class time when the next part begins. A number of next-step strategies are listed later in this chapter.

Science and Engineering Practices Checklist
Chemical Interactions, Second Edition

Start Date ____________
End Date ____________

Class	Asking questions and defining problems	Developing and using models	Planning and carrying out investigations	Analyzing and interpreting data	Using mathematics and computational thinking	Constructing explanations and designing solutions	Engaging in argument from evidence	Obtaining, evaluating, and communicating information

FOSS Chemical Interactions Course, Second Edition

NOTE: See the Assessment chapter for a discussion about how to use this checklist.

Science and Engineering Practices Checklist
No. 2—Assessment Master

Recording Data: Science and Engineering Practices

Assessing science and engineering practices requires you to peek over students' shoulders to make note of what they are doing and discussing or to conduct 30-second interviews. When you are observing, the rich conversation among students and the actions they are taking to investigate phenomena or design solutions to problems will often be all the information you need to assess progress. At times, you might step in with a 30-second interview to ask a few carefully crafted questions to learn more about students' deeper thinking. One part of each investigation is designated specifically for assessing students' science and engineering practices. Throughout the designated parts, carry *Science and Engineering Practices Checklist* with you to record students' progress. Here are the practices to look for. (Quotations are from National Research Council, *A Framework for K–12 Science Education,* 2012.)

TEACHING NOTE

This set of science and engineering practices is not meant to be seen as a linear process or "scientific method." It is more important to think about the purpose of each practice and employ each as needed in an investigation.

Asking questions and defining problems. "Students at any grade level should be able to ask questions of each other about the texts they read, the features of the phenomena they observe, and the conclusions they draw from their models or scientific investigations. For engineering, they should ask questions to define the problem to be solved and to elicit ideas that lead to the constraints and specifications for its solution. As they progress across the grades, their questions should become more relevant, focused, and sophisticated." Assess this practice whenever students have the opportunity to ask questions about objects, organisms, systems, or events (science); or to define a problem, determine criteria for solutions, or identify constraints (engineering).

Developing and using models. "Modeling can begin in the earliest grades, with students' models progressing from concrete 'pictures' and/or physical scale models . . . to more abstract representations of relevant relationships in later grades, such as a diagram representing forces on a particular object in a system. Students should be asked to use diagrams, maps, and other abstract models as tools that enable them to elaborate on their own ideas or findings and present them to others." Assess this

practice when students create models to develop explanations, make predictions, or analyze existing systems. Students should also recognize strengths and limitations of those models.

Planning and carrying out investigations. "Students need opportunities to design investigations so that they may learn the importance of such decisions as what to measure, what to keep constant, and how to select or construct data collection instruments that are appropriate to the needs of the inquiry. They also need experiences that help them recognize that the laboratory is not the sole domain for legitimate scientific inquiry." Assess this practice whenever students are engaged in planning investigations and gathering appropriate data.

Analyzing and interpreting data. "In middle school, students should have opportunities to learn standard techniques for displaying, analyzing, and interpreting data; such techniques include different types of graphs, the identification of outliers in the data set, and averaging to reduce the effects of measurement error. Students should also be asked to explain why these techniques are needed." Assess this practice when students use a range of tools to organize observations (data) in order to identify significant features and patterns (numbers, words, tables, graphs, images, diagrams, and equations).

Using mathematics and computational thinking. "Increasing student familiarity with the role of mathematics in science is central to developing a deeper understanding of how science works. As soon as students learn to count, they can begin using numbers to find or describe patterns in nature. At appropriate grade levels, they should learn to use such instruments as rulers, protractors, and thermometers for the measurement of variables that are best represented by a continuous numerical scale, to apply mathematics to interpolate values, and to identify features . . . of simple data sets." Assess this practice whenever students record measurements or use mathematics to help them analyze data and look for patterns.

Constructing explanations and designing solutions. "Early in their science education, students need opportunities to engage in constructing and critiquing explanations. They should be encouraged to develop explanations of what they observe when conducting their own investigations and to evaluate their own and others' explanations for consistency with the evidence." Assess this practice when students construct explanations (science) or propose solutions (engineering).

TEACHING NOTE

*The word **argument** or **argumentation** in this context means the discourse used by scientists and engineers that is central to constructing deeper understanding (not the everyday meaning that implies a heated disagreement).*

Engaging in argument from evidence. "The study of science and engineering should produce a sense of the process of argument necessary for advancing and defending a new idea or an explanation of a phenomenon and the norms for conducting such arguments. In that spirit, students should argue for the explanations they construct, defend their interpretations of the associated data, and advocate for the designs they propose. . . . Learning to argue scientifically offers students not only an opportunity to use their scientific knowledge in justifying an explanation and in identifying the weaknesses in others' arguments, but also to build their own knowledge and understanding." Assess this practice when students defend explanations, formulate evidence based on data, and examine their own understanding, based on comments from others.

Obtaining, evaluating, and communicating information. "Any education in science and engineering needs to develop students' ability to read and produce domain-specific text. As such, every science or engineering lesson is in part a language lesson, particularly reading and producing the genres of texts that are intrinsic to science and engineering. . . . From the very start of their science education, students should be asked to engage in the communication of science, especially regarding the investigations they are conducting and the observations they are making." Assess this practice when students communicate ideas and results of investigations or engage in discussions with peers.

BENCHMARK ASSESSMENT

I-Checks

At the end of most investigations, you will find a benchmark assessment called an I-Check. In some cases, content from two investigations is combined into one I-Check. This assessment serves as a checkpoint for student learning. To track achievement (a summative use of the I-Checks), use the scoring guides in this chapter to score the items. We recommend that you score one item at a time, that is, score item 1 for all students, then move on to item 2, and so on. Even though you have to shuffle papers more, you will find it actually takes less time overall to score the assessments. Scoring tends to be more consistent across students when you use this method, and it allows you to think about the whole class's performance on an item and the kind of next steps you might take to correct learning weaknesses.

I-Checks can also be used for formative assessment. Research has shown that students learn more when they take part in evaluating their own responses. To do this, score students' tests but *do not write on them.* Learning tends to come to a halt when students see a grade on their work, especially if it is a poor grade. Instead, record marks in a grade book or computer spreadsheet. Use class discussion and **next-step strategies**, such as the line-of-learning strategy, to help students reflect on and refine their thinking. More information about how to scaffold these activities is given in the following pages and in the Science Notebooks in Middle School chapter under "Next-Step Strategies."

Choose three or four items from the I-Check that you want to discuss with students during class time. Determine the next steps you want to take. In the next session, start with these three or four items, using the strategies you chose. Then quickly go over other items, so that students can check the rest of their answers. When students check their own understanding, you are creating a class culture of assessment as a tool in the service of learning.

Here is a summary for using I-Checks.

1. Have students complete an I-Check unassisted.
2. Score I-Checks item by item, but do not make any marks on students' tests. Record scores in a grading program, spreadsheet, or grade book. As you finish scoring each item, note important points to review with students.
3. Return I-Checks to students. Use the self-assessment strategies in this chapter to help students reflect on and clarify their thinking.

Survey/Posttest

The posttest evaluates students' knowledge after they finish all the investigations. You can give it as a survey before instruction starts, to see where students are in their thinking.

Test items are designed in a variety of formats, including multiple choice, short answer, and constructed response. Items require students to draw diagrams, solve problems, and explain their understanding in writing. The scoring guides in this chapter help you evaluate the level of understanding that students have obtained.

NEXT-STEP STRATEGIES

The ASK Project (Assessing Science Knowledge) was funded by the National Science Foundation in 2003. For 6 years, the FOSS development team worked with nine centers using the FOSS Program around the United States, including more than 600 teachers and their students as research partners. Based on the evidence provided by the assessments, we learned very quickly that assessment is worth doing only if follow-up action is taken to enhance understanding. Self-assessment provides students the opportunity to be responsible for their own learning and is a very effective tool for building students' scientific knowledge and practice.

Self-assessments provide students with opportunities to reflect on their thinking and what they have learned from the investigations. Self-assessment usually follows a quick write—after students have completed more activities and have been given more information to help them further their conceptual development. Student work is checked for students' ability to reflect on their thinking and to identify needed changes and additions to their explanations of the science content. Sometimes a next-step strategy can help with self-assessment. More information about next-step strategies is available below and in the Science Notebooks in Middle School chapter.

Self-assessment is more than reading correct answers to the class and having students mark whether they got the right answer. Self-assessment must provide an opportunity for students to reflect on their current thinking and judge whether that thinking needs to change. This kind of reflective process also helps students develop a better understanding of what is expected in terms of well-constructed responses.

The Importance of Feedback

Teacher feedback is an important step for students' understanding of how their conceptual thinking can advance. The science notebook provides an excellent medium for providing feedback to individual students or the class regarding their work. Productive feedback calls for students to listen to or read the teacher comment, think about the issue raised by the comment, and act on it. The feedback may ask for clarification, an example, additional information, precise vocabulary, or review of previous work in the notebook. In this way, you can determine whether the problems with the student work relate to flawed understanding of the science content or a breakdown in communication.

Your feedback will also encourage students to take the notebook more seriously and to write more clearly as they attempt to create a complete record of the course. By writing explanations, students clarify what they know . . . and expose what they don't. And when students use their notebooks as an integral part of their science studies, they think critically about their thinking.

Self-assessment requires deep, thoughtful engagement with complex ideas. It involves students in whole-class or small-group discussion, followed by critical analysis of their own work. For this reason, we suggest that you focus your probing discussions on three or four questions from an I-Check, rather than on the entire assessment. The techniques described here are meant to give you a few strategies for entering the process of self-assessment. There is no single right way to engage students in this process: it works best when you change the process from time to time to keep it fresh. The strategies listed here are sorted into two groups: strategies for whole-class feedback, and strategies for individual-student and small-group feedback.

Strategies for the Whole Class

Key points. Discuss the item in question. After it is clear that students understand what is intended by the item prompt, call on individuals or groups to suggest key points that should be included in a complete answer. Write the key points on the board as phrases or individual words that will scaffold students' revision, rather than complete sentences they might mindlessly copy. When students return to their responses, they can number each of the key points they originally included in their answers, then add anything they missed.

Multiple-choice discussions. Students sit in groups of three or four, depending on how many possible answers there were for a given question. You assign an answer to each student (not necessarily the answer they chose). Each student is responsible for explaining to the group whether the assigned answer is correct and why or why not.

Class debate. A student volunteers an answer to an item on an assessment (usually one that many students are having trouble with, or one that elicits a persistent misconception). That student is in charge of the debate. He or she puts forth an answer or explanation. Other students agree or disagree, but must provide evidence to back up their thinking. Students are allowed to disagree with themselves if they hear an argument during the discussion that leads them to change their thinking. You can ask questions to keep the discussion on track, but otherwise you should stay on the sidelines.

Multiple-choice corners. When the class is equally split on what students have chosen as the correct response or only a few students have gotten the correct answer, have them meet in different corners of the room. Those who chose *A* go to one corner, those who chose *B* go to another corner, and so on. Each corner group needs to come up with an argument to convince the other corners that their answer is correct. As in a class debate, students are allowed to disagree with themselves if they become convinced their position is flawed or the reasoning of another group is more convincing. They then move to that corner and continue by helping their new group shape their arguments. (Don't be surprised if you find all students migrating to one corner before the presentation of arguments even begins!)

Revision with color. Another way that students can revise their answers after a key-points discussion is to use colored pens or pencils and the three Cs. As they read over their responses, they *confirm* correct information by underlining with a green pen; *complete* their responses by adding information that was missing, using a blue pen; and *correct* wrong information, using a red pen.

Review and critique anonymous student work. Use examples of student work from another class, or fabricate student work samples that emulate the problems that students in your class are having. Project the work using an overhead projector, document camera, or interactive whiteboard. Have students discuss the strengths and weaknesses of the responses. This is a good strategy to use when first getting students to write in their notebooks. It helps them understand expectations about what and how much to write.

Line of learning. Many teachers have students use a line of learning to show how their thinking has changed. When students return to original work (embedded or benchmark) to revise their understanding of a concept, they start by drawing and dating a line of learning under the original writing. The line delineates students' original, individual thinking from their thinking after a class or group discussion has helped them reconsider and revise their thoughts.

TEACHING NOTE

You can make inexpensive whiteboards using cardstock paper and plastic sheet protectors. Students use whiteboard marking pens to write answers. Washcloths make great erasers.

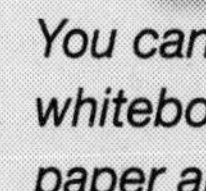

Group consensus/whiteboards. Have students in each group (or pairs in each group) work together to compare their answers on selected I-Check questions during a class review. First, they create a response that the group agrees is the best answer. Groups write their responses on a whiteboard. When you give a signal, everyone holds their whiteboards up and compares answers. The class discusses any discrepant answers.

Critical competitor. Use the critical-competitor strategy when you want students to attend to a specific detail. You need to present students with two things that are similar in all but one or two aspects. You can use any medium: two drawings, two pieces of writing, or a combination (such as a diagram compared to a description). The point is to compare two pieces of communication or representations in some way that will help students focus on an important detail they may be missing.

Sentence frames. After completing other self-assessment activities, have students consider all the items on the assessment and write a short reflection using sentence frames. This strategy directs students to choose one or two items that they would like to tell you more about.

I used to think ____, but now I think ____.

I should have gotten this one right, I just ____.

I know____, but I'm still not sure about ____.

The most important thing to remember about ____ is ____.

Can you help me with ____?

I shouldn't have gotten this one wrong, because I know ____.

I'm still confused about ____.

Next time, I will remember to ____.

Now I know ____.

Strategies for Individual Students and Small Groups

Self-stick-note feedback. As you read through students' notebooks, add self-stick notes with comments or questions that help guide students to reflect on and improve their understanding.

Response log. Set up a response log at the back of students' science notebooks. Fold a notebook page in half, or draw a line down the center of the page. Write "Teacher Feedback" at the top of the left side of the page and "Student Comments" at the top of the right side of the page. When you want a student to think about something in his or her notebook, write your note in the "Teacher Feedback" column (or students can move a self-stick note from another page to the response log). Students then respond in the right-hand column, either addressing your comment there, or telling you which page to turn to in order to see how they have responded.

Response Log

Teacher Feedback	Student Comments
Response Sheet - Inv. 2 1. You told the friend that other elements might be there. Can you think of any ingredients that are not made of elements?	1. Anything that is matter is made of elements, so all the ingredients are made of elements even if I don't know which ones.
Response Sheet - Inv. 6 1. Can you add some labels to your diagram? 2. Can you add what's happening with the kinetic energy to your response?	1 & 2. See page 53.

Conferences. Use silent-reading time, or other times when students work independently, to confer with small groups or individual students.

Centers. Set up a center at which students can continue to explore their ideas and refine their thinking. You might try to pair students so that a student who understands the concept well works with another student who needs some help.

Reteach or clarify a concept. Set up a modified investigation in which a small group of students works with the concept again.

SURVEY/POSTTEST

SURVEY/POSTTEST
CHEMICAL INTERACTIONS

ANSWERS

1. a. A chemical reaction is _____.
   (Mark the one best answer.)

   ● **A** a process in which starting substances change into different substances

   ❍ **B** a form of matter with a unique composition

   ❍ **C** an interaction between two substances in which one breaks apart and intermingles with the other

   ❍ **D** the result of a change of energy in the particles in a substance

   b. Mark an **X** next to each word or phrase that describes evidence that a chemical reaction occurred.

X	bubbles	X	a precipitate forms
X	color change	X	temperature change
___	one substance melts	X	a new substance

   c. What happens to the atoms in substances when a chemical reaction occurs?

   The atoms of the reactants rearrange to form new substances (products). Mass and matter are conserved.

2. When air is heated in a basketball _____.
   *(Mark an **X** next to all correct answers.)*

   X the air particles move faster

   X the air particles hit each other more frequently

   ___ the air particles get larger

   X the air particles get farther apart

   ___ the number of air particles increases

FOSS Chemical Interactions Course, Second Edition

Survey/Posttest
Page 1 of 6

Item 1a

Score	If the student . . .
2	marks A.
1	marks anything else.
0	makes no attempt.

Item 1b

Score	If the student . . .
3	marks all of the choices except "one substance melts."
2	marks all but one correct answer.
1	marks any other way.
0	makes no attempt.

Item 1c

Score	If the student . . .
3	writes that atoms rearrange to form new substances and indicates that mass/matter is conserved.
2	writes that atoms rearrange to form new substances, but does not mention conservation of matter or mass.
1	writes anything else.
0	makes no attempt.

Item 2

Score	If the student . . .
3	marks the first, second, and fourth answers.
2	marks two of the correct answers (no wrong answers).
1	marks any other way.
0	makes no attempt.

SURVEY/POSTTEST
CHEMICAL INTERACTIONS

ANSWERS

3. Which of the following is made up of atoms?
(Mark an **X** *next to all correct answers.)*

X Solids

X Matter

X Gas

___ Heat

X Liquid

4. Two students each conducted an experiment. They measured the amount of gas produced when they mixed different amounts of liquids A and B. Their results are shown below.

Student 1

Liquid A	Liquid B	Gas produced
5 mL	5 mL	8 mL
5 mL	10 mL	12 mL
5 mL	15 mL	16 mL

Student 2

Liquid A	Liquid B	Gas produced
5 mL	5 mL	8 mL
10 mL	5 mL	8 mL
15 mL	5 mL	8 mL

Which liquid limited the amount of gas produced?
(Mark the one best answer.)

○ **A** Liquid A

● **B** Liquid B

○ **C** Neither liquid

5. Explain what happens to the particles in a solid block of gold as it melts.

The kinetic energy of the particles increases until they break away from each other and begin moving around the other particles of gold. The solid gold has changed phase to liquid gold.

FOSS Chemical Interactions Course, Second Edition

Survey/Posttest
Page 2 of 6

Item 3

Score	If the student . . .
2	marks all except heat.
1	marks any other way.
0	makes no attempt.

Item 4

Score	If the student . . .
2	marks B.
1	marks any other answer.
0	makes no attempt.

Item 5

Score	If the student . . .
3	writes that the kinetic energy of the particles increases until they break away from each other and begin sliding around one another.
2	mentions kinetic energy and particle movement, but explanation is incomplete or contains errors.
1	writes anything else.
0	makes no attempt.

SURVEY/POSTTEST

CHEMICAL INTERACTIONS

ANSWERS

6. A student heated 25 mL of water from 10°C to 20°C. How much energy did she use to heat the water? Remember: $cal = m \times \Delta T$

(Use the space below to show your math and your final answer.)

ΔT = 20°C - 10°C
ΔT = 10°C

cal = 25 g x 10°C
cal = 250 cal

7. When water boils, bubbles rise up through the water. What is inside those bubbles?
(Mark the one best answer.)

- ○ **A** Air particles
- ○ **B** Carbon dioxide particles
- ● **C** Water particles
- ○ **D** Oxygen particles and hydrogen particles

8. Look at the list below and mark an **X** to indicate the following.
   a. Which are substances?
   b. Which are particles?
   c. Which are single elements?
   d. Which are compounds?

Chemical formula	a. Substance	b. Particle	c. Element	d. Compound
H_2O	X	X		X
He	X	X	X	
$C_6H_8O_7$	X	X		X
NaCl	X	X		X
O_2	X	X	X	
CO_2	X	X		X

FOSS Chemical Interactions Course, Second Edition

Survey/Posttest
Page 3 of 6

Item 6

Score	If the student . . .
3	writes 250 cal and shows correct math.
2	shows math but makes a minor calculation error.
1	writes any answer without showing math.
0	makes no attempt.

Item 7

Score	If the student . . .
2	marks C.
1	marks any other answer.
0	makes no attempt.

Item 8a and 8b

Score	If the student . . .
2	marks all the choices.
1	marks any other way.
0	makes no attempt.

Item 8c

Score	If the student . . .
2	marks He and O_2.
1	marks any other way.
0	makes no attempt.

Item 8d

Score	If the student . . .
2	marks H_2O, $C_6H_8O_7$, NaCl, and CO_2.
1	marks any other way.
0	makes no attempt.

SURVEY/POSTTEST

CHEMICAL INTERACTIONS

ANSWERS

9. Imagine that you remove all the particles that make up a wooden table. What remains?
(Mark the one best answer.)

- ❍ **A** A table that looks the same, but has less volume
- ❍ **B** A table that weighs less
- ❍ **C** Sawdust
- ● **D** Nothing

10. The diagram below shows a chemical reaction. The different-shaded circles represent different kinds of atoms. When circles are touching, that indicates that those atoms form a molecule.

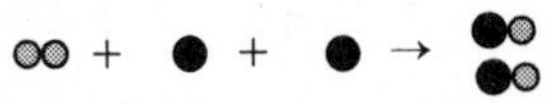

○○ + ● + ● → ●○ ●○

If this reaction occurs in a sealed chamber, what happens to the mass of the matter inside and why?
(Mark the one best answer.)

- ● **A** The mass will stay the same because the number of each kind of atom stays the same.
- ❍ **B** The mass will decrease because two substances combine to form one substance.
- ❍ **C** The mass will increase because a new kind of molecule is formed.
- ❍ **D** More information is needed to tell if the mass will change.

11. Engineers use scientific discoveries to develop solutions to real-life problems. After they discover a good solution, should they consider their work done? Why or why not?

They may have found a solution that works, but there could be something better. Or a new scientific discovery could be made in the future that would allow the engineer to make a better design.

FOSS Chemical Interactions Course, Second Edition

Survey/Posttest
Page 4 of 6

Item 9

Score	If the student . . .
2	marks D.
1	marks any other answer.
0	makes no attempt.

Item 10

Score	If the student . . .
2	marks A.
1	marks any other answer.
0	makes no attempt.

Item 11

Score	If the student . . .
3	explains that even though the solution worked, there could be a better design; mentions that a scientific discovery could provide new information to improve future designs.
2	explains that there could be a better design than the current solution.
1	writes any other answer.
0	makes no attempt.

SURVEY/POSTTEST
CHEMICAL INTERACTIONS

ANSWERS

12. The water and the air in this system are at equilibrium.

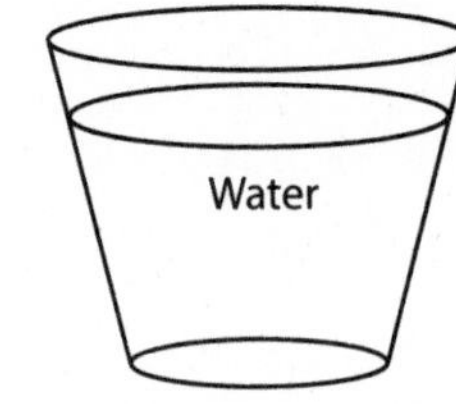

a. Which particles have more average kinetic energy? *(Mark the one best answer.)*

❍ **A** The water particles

❍ **B** The air particles

● **C** They have the same

Why did you choose that answer?

The water and air are the same temperature, so they have the same average kinetic energy.

b. Describe the energy transfer between the water and the air.

The energy transfer is equal in both directions because they are at equilibrium so they have the same average kinetic energy.

13. How do particles of cold air differ from particles of hot air? *(Mark an **X** next to each correct answer.)*

_X_ The particles of cold air are closer together than the particles of hot air.

____ The particles of cold air have less mass than the particles of hot air.

_X_ The particles of cold air have less kinetic energy than the particles of hot air.

____ The particles of cold air are smaller than the particles of hot air.

_X_ The particles of cold air move slower than the particles of hot air.

____ The particles of cold air move at the same speed as the particles of hot air.

Item 12a

Score	If the student . . .
3	marks C; explains that because they are the same temperature, they both have the same average kinetic energy.
2	marks C; give no explanation or an incorrect one.
1	marks any other answer with any explanation.
0	makes no attempt.

Item 12b

Score	If the student . . .
3	writes that the energy transfer is equal in both directions because they are at equilibrium; the average kinetic energy is the same.
2	writes that the energy transfer is the same but gives no further explanation or an incorrect one.
1	writes any other answer.
0	makes no attempt.

Item 13

Score	If the student . . .
3	marks the first, third, and fifth answers.
2	marks one answer incorrectly.
1	marks any other answer.
0	makes no attempt.

SURVEY/POSTTEST
CHEMICAL INTERACTIONS

ANSWERS

14. Sugar can melt, and sugar can dissolve. Mark an **X** next to each statement that explains what happens at the particle level when melting or dissolving occurs.

_____ Sugar melts when its particles get soft enough to turn into liquid.

_____ Sugar melts when a liquid breaks particles away from the solid substance.

__X__ Sugar melts when kinetic energy increases enough for the particles to move past one another.

__X__ Sugar dissolves when a liquid breaks particles away from the solid substance.

_____ Sugar dissolves when its particles get soft enough to turn into liquid.

_____ Sugar dissolves when its particles are heated until the bonds holding them together as a solid break.

15. Solid water (ice) does not flow. Liquid water does flow because the particles of liquid water _____.
(Mark the one best answer.)

❍ **A** are not as hard as the particles of solid ice

❍ **B** weigh less than the particles of solid ice

❍ **C** are moving, but the particles of solid ice are not

● **D** can easily move past one another, but the particles of solid ice cannot

16. When a syringe is filled with air, you can compress the air by pushing the plunger down. If you fill the syringe with water, you cannot compress the water. The difference is because the water particles _____.
(Mark the one best answer.)

❍ **A** are packed less closely together than air particles

● **B** can't be pushed closer using only your hands like air particles can

❍ **C** can no longer move, but air particles can

❍ **D** don't shrink like air particles do when you squeeze the syringe

FOSS Chemical Interactions Course, Second Edition

Survey/Posttest
Page 6 of 6

Item 14

Score	If the student . . .
3	marks the third and fourth statements.
2	marks the third or fourth statement, but not both.
1	marks any other way.
0	makes no attempt.

Item 15

Score	If the student . . .
2	marks D.
1	marks any other answer.
0	makes no attempt.

Item 16

Score	If the student . . .
2	marks B.
1	marks any other answer.
0	makes no attempt.

INVESTIGATIONS 1–2 I-CHECK

INVESTIGATIONS 1–2 I-CHECK
CHEMICAL INTERACTIONS

ANSWERS

Instructions: Use the periodic table of the elements on page 3 to help you answer these questions.

1. What is the difference between the substances represented by the symbols Co and CO?

Co is the symbol for the element cobalt.
CO is the symbol for a substance composed of two elements: carbon and oxygen.

2. What elements are found in the following substances?

Substance	Chemical formula	Names of the elements
Water	H_2O	hydrogen, oxygen
Sodium chloride	NaCl	sodium, chlorine
Carbon dioxide	CO_2	carbon, oxygen

3. Which Venn diagram best represents the relationship between an element and a substance?

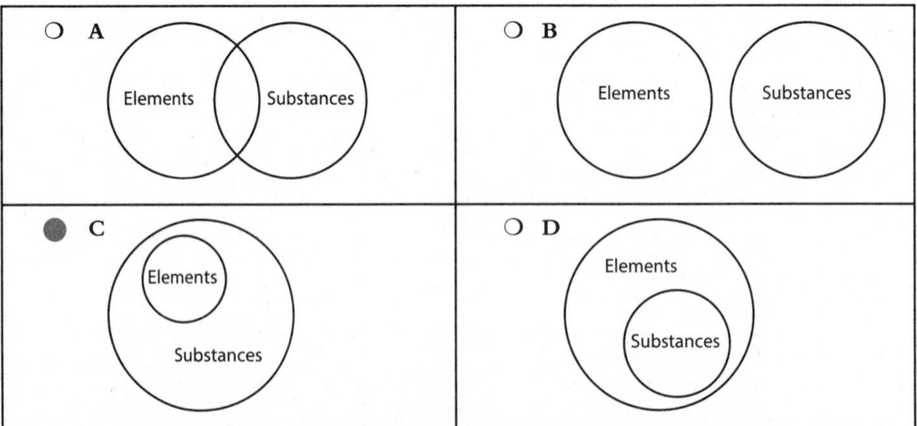

FOSS Chemical Interactions Course, Second Edition

Investigations 1–2 I-Check
Page 1 of 3

Item 1

Score	If the student . . .
3	writes that Co is the symbol for the element cobalt and CO represents two elements, carbon and oxygen.
2	explains what one substance is but not the other, such as Co is an element or CO represents two elements.
1	writes any other answer.
0	makes no attempt.

Item 2

Score	If the student . . .
2	writes the names for the elements in each substance.
1	writes any other answer.
0	makes no attempt.

Item 3

Score	If the student . . .
2	marks C.
1	marks any other answer.
0	makes no attempt.

INVESTIGATIONS 1–2 I-CHECK
CHEMICAL INTERACTIONS

ANSWERS

4. What are three ways that substances can be identified or labeled?

   A substance can be described by chemical formula (or element name), chemical name, and common name.

5. a. What was Mendeleyev's purpose for reorganizing the periodic table? *(Mark the one best answer.)*

   - ❍ **A** He wanted to fit all of the elements on one page instead of in a long line.
   - ● **B** He wanted to put elements with similar characteristics in the same column.
   - ❍ **C** He wanted to order the elements from the lightest to the heaviest.
   - ❍ **D** He wanted to put all the metals on one side of the table and gases on the other.

   b. When Mendeleyev changed the layout, there were gaps (no known element fit in those places). How did the gaps help scientists look for undiscovered elements?

   The gaps in Mendeleyev's table predicted the characteristics of the undiscovered elements.

6. a. What is a chemical reaction?

   A chemical reaction is an interaction in which starting substances change into new (different) substances.

   b. If you mix two substances together, what evidence would tell you a chemical reaction occurred? *(List as many examples as you can.)*

   Answers may include bubbling, color change, temperature change, new substances formed, new gas (smell) formed, new liquid formed, new solid formed.

FOSS Chemical Interactions Course, Second Edition

Investigations 1–2 I-Check
Page 2 of 3

Item 4

Score	If the student . . .
2	writes chemical formula (or element name), chemical name, and common name.
1	writes any other answer.
0	makes no attempt.

Item 5a

Score	If the student . . .
3	marks B.
2	marks C.
1	marks any other answer.
0	makes no attempt.

Item 5b

Score	If the student . . .
3	writes that the gaps allowed scientists to predict the characteristics of undiscovered elements.
2	writes that scientists knew which elements were missing.
1	writes any other answer.
0	makes no attempt.

Item 6a

Score	If the student . . .
2	writes that a chemical reaction occurs when starting substances change into new substances.
1	writes any other answer.
0	makes no attempt.

Item 6b

Score	If the student . . .
3	describes correct evidence of a chemical reaction and does not include any misconceptions.
2	describes at least two correct examples of evidence but also includes incorrect examples.
1	writes any other answer.
0	makes no attempt.

NOTE

Page 3 of this assessment is the periodic table that students use to answer questions on page 1.

INVESTIGATION 3 I-CHECK

INVESTIGATION 3 I-CHECK
CHEMICAL INTERACTIONS

ANSWERS

1. A student trapped air inside a syringe (illustration A). She pushed the plunger down (illustration B) and then pulled the plunger up (illustration C).

   a. Draw the air particles inside the syringes in illustrations B and C.

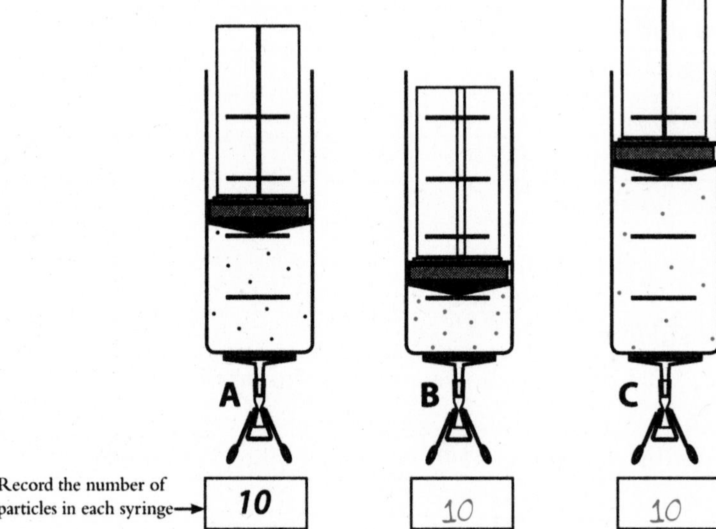

Record the number of particles in each syringe → **10** | 10 | 10

   b. What happens to the particles when you push the plunger down (B)?

   The particles get closer together, but there are still the same number of particles in the syringe.

   c. What happens to the particles when you pull the plunger back up (C)?

   The particles move farther apart, but there are still the same number of particles in the syringe.

   d. Between the air particles in each syringe is _____.
   (Mark the one best answer.)

   ○ **A** Matter ○ **B** More air
   ● **C** Space ○ **D** Atoms

FOSS Diversity of Life Course, Second Edition

Investigation 3 I-Check
Page 1 of 3

Item 1a

Score	If the student . . .
3	draws 10 dots randomly distributed over the entire space in syringes B and C.
2	draws an inconsistent number of dots in syringes B and C or draws dots clustered near the top or bottom.
1	shades in the syringes or any other representation.
0	makes no attempt.

Item 1b–c

Score	If the student . . .
3	writes that the same number of air particles are in both syringes and that they are closer together in B and farther apart in C. (Check the drawing if the number of particles is not mentioned.)
2	writes that the same amount of air is in each syringe. (Check the drawing for same number of particles.)
1	states that the particles themselves contract or expand, or writes any other answer.
0	makes no attempt.

Item 1d

Score	If the student . . .
2	marks C.
1	marks any other answer.
0	makes no attempt.

INVESTIGATION 3 I-CHECK
CHEMICAL INTERACTIONS

ANSWERS

2. a. What is between the helium particles in a helium-filled balloon?

   Nothing

   b. Can helium be compressed? Yes

   Why or why not?

   Helium is a gas, and the particles are far apart. Gases can be compressed by pushing the particles closer together.

3. Mark an **X** next to each statement that describes the particles if a gas is placed in a sealed container.

   _____ The particles are packed closely throughout the container.

   X The particles are spread far apart throughout the container.

   _____ Almost all of the particles are at the top of the container.

   _____ Almost all of the particles are at the bottom of the container.

   X All of the particles are spread evenly throughout the container.

4. Which of the following always results from a chemical reaction?
   (Mark the one best answer.)

   ○ **A** Bubbles

   ○ **B** Fire or smoke

   ○ **C** Temperature change

   ● **D** A new substance

FOSS Chemical Interactions Course, Second Edition

Investigation 3 I-Check
Page 2 of 3

Item 2a

Score	If the student . . .
2	writes that nothing (or empty space) is between the helium particles in the balloon.
1	writes that there is something between the helium particles, such as air, or writes any other answer.
0	makes no attempt.

Item 2b

Score	If the student . . .
3	writes yes; explains that helium is a gas and the particles are far apart, and that gases can be compressed by pushing the particles closer together.
2	writes yes; gives explanation that is incomplete or contains errors.
1	writes no with any explanation, or writes any other answer.
0	makes no attempt.

Item 3

Score	If the student . . .
2	marks the second and last statements.
1	marks any other answer.
0	makes no attempt.

Item 4

Score	If the student . . .
2	marks D.
1	marks any other answer.
0	makes no attempt.

INVESTIGATION 3 I-CHECK

CHEMICAL INTERACTIONS

ANSWERS

5. a. What do we mean when we talk about a particle?

   A particle is the smallest piece of a substance that is still that substance.

   b. Describe the motion of air particles inside a soccer ball.

   The air particles inside a soccer ball are constantly moving and bumping into each other and the inner surface of the ball.

6. A student was investigating air in a closed syringe. He compressed the air by pushing the plunger in as far as he could and then let go. The plunger returned to its original position.

   a. Why did the plunger return to its original position?
   (Mark the one best answer.)

   ○ **A** The air particles outside the syringe pulled the plunger up.

   ● **B** The air particles inside the syringe pushed the plunger up.

   ○ **C** More air particles rushed into the syringe and pushed the plunger up.

   ○ **D** The air pushed the plunger up when it tried to get out.

   b. Explain why you chose that answer.

   When air particles are compressed, they are closer together and hit each other and the sides of the syringe more often. When the student stopped pushing, the particles that hit the plunger pushed the plunger up until the frequency of hits inside and outside the syringe were equal.

Item 5a

Score	If the student...
2	writes that a particle is the smallest piece of any substance that is still that substance.
1	writes any other answer.
0	makes no attempt.

Item 5b

Score	If the student...
3	writes that the air particles inside the ball are in constant motion and bumping into each other and the inside surface of the ball.
2	writes that the air inside the ball is moving, and includes that they bump into each other or they bump into the inside surface of the ball, but not both.
1	writes any other answer.
0	makes no attempt.

Item 6a

Score	If the student...
2	marks B.
1	marks any other answer.
0	makes no attempt.

Item 6b

Score	If the student...
3	writes that the air particles are in constant motion and that when the student stopped pushing, the air particles inside pushed the plunger up until the particles inside and outside were hitting the plunger equally.
2	writes that the air particles inside the plunger pushed it back up, but does not provide any more information.
1	writes any other answer.
0	makes no attempt.

INVESTIGATION 4 I-CHECK

INVESTIGATION 4 I-CHECK
CHEMICAL INTERACTIONS

ANSWERS

1. A student put room-temperature water into a bottle. She pushed a stopper and tube into the bottle until the water came halfway up the tube.

   The student turned the bottle system sideways and put a cold wrap around the bottle for 2 minutes. She then put a hot wrap around the bottle.

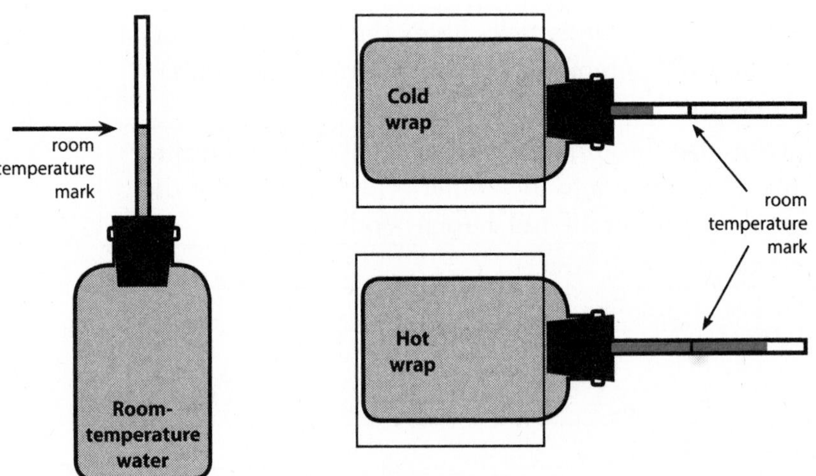

   a. Draw the water level in the tube with the cold wrap and with the hot wrap.

   b. What happened to the kinetic energy of the water particles when the student put the hot wrap on the cold bottle?
   (Mark the one best answer.)

   ● **A** The kinetic energy of the water particles increased.

   ❍ **B** The kinetic energy of the water particles decreased.

   ❍ **C** There was no change in the kinetic energy of the water particles.

   c. What caused the water level in the tube to change when the student put the hot wrap on the bottle?

   As the kinetic energy of the water increased, more collisions happened between the particles that pushed them farther apart. The water expanded, and moved farther out into the tube.

FOSS Chemical Interactions Course, Second Edition

Investigation 4 I-Check
Page 1 of 4

Item 1a

Score	If the student . . .
2	draws the water level in the cold-wrap bottle shorter than the room-temperature mark; draws the water level in the hot-water bottle longer than the room-temperature mark.
1	draws the water level any other way.
0	makes no attempt.

Item 1b

Score	If the student . . .
2	marks A.
1	marks any other answer.
0	makes no attempt.

Item 1c

Score	If the student . . .
3	explains that as kinetic energy increases and the number of collisions increases, the volume increases, which pushes the water into the tube. (Compare to drawing in 1a for consistency.)
2	explains that the volume increases with no explanation why.
1	includes a misconception such as particles get larger or closer together, or writes any other answer.
0	makes no attempt.

INVESTIGATION 4 I-CHECK
CHEMICAL INTERACTIONS

ANSWERS

2. An aluminum nut and bolt are stuck together.

   a. To get them apart, would you put ice on the nut or on the bolt? *(Mark the one best answer.)*

   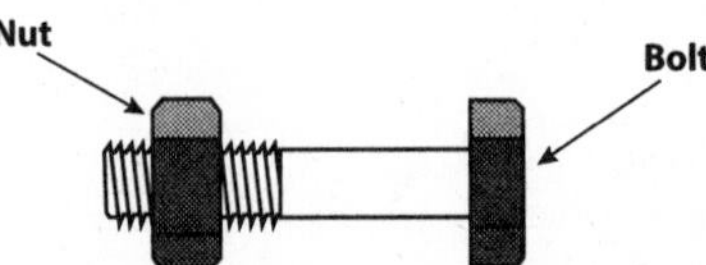

   ○ **A** The nut

   ● **B** The bolt

   Why did you choose that answer?

   Putting ice on the bolt will cause it to cool and contract. The bolt will become smaller, and it will be easier to get the nut and bolt apart.

   b. What role does kinetic energy play in getting the nut and bolt apart?

   When you cool the bolt, it decreases the kinetic energy of the particles, and they slow down. The particles pack closer together, so the bolt gets smaller.

3. What happens to the particles in a cup of cold juice as it warms up to room temperature? *(Mark the one best answer.)*

   ○ **A** The number of juice particles decreases.

   ○ **B** The size of the juice particles increases.

   ○ **C** The motion of the juice particles decreases.

   ● **D** The space between the juice particles increases.

Item 2a

Score	If the student . . .
3	marks B; explains that cooling the bolt will cause it to contract, making it easier to get the nut and bolt apart.
2	marks B; gives explanation with minor errors.
1	marks A with any explanation.
0	makes no attempt.

Item 2b

Score	If the student . . .
2	writes that the kinetic energy of the particles in the bolt decreases as it cools.
1	writes any other answer.
0	makes no attempt.

Item 3

Score	If the student . . .
2	marks D.
1	marks any other answer.
0	makes no attempt.

INVESTIGATION 4 I-CHECK

CHEMICAL INTERACTIONS

ANSWERS

4. A student put a cap on a bottle, trapping room-temperature air inside. He put the bottle in the freezer for 15 minutes, then took it out and saw that the bottle looked different. What caused the bottle to change shape?
(Mark the one best answer.)

- ❍ **A** Some of the air particles got out of the bottle.
- ● **B** The air particles in the bottle got closer together.
- ❍ **C** The air particles settled to the bottom of the bottle.
- ❍ **D** The air particles cooled and became smaller.

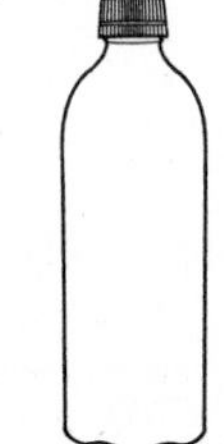
Before freezer

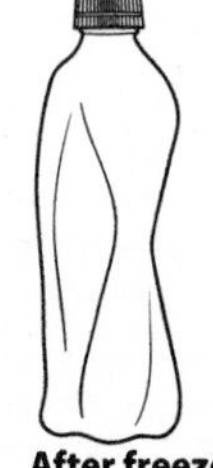
After freezer

5. Compare the particles in a sample of liquid water and the particles in a sample of solid water (ice).
(Mark the one best answer.)

- ❍ **A** Particles in the liquid are smaller than the particles in the solid.
- ● **B** Particles in the liquid move past each other, and particles in the solid cannot.
- ❍ **C** Particles in the liquid are less firm than particles in the solid.
- ❍ **D** Particles in the liquid are moving, and the particles in the solid are not moving.

6. When a piece of solid lead is heated (but not melted), the lead particles _____.
(Mark all that apply.)

_____ move slower

__X__ get farther apart

_____ have fewer collisions

_____ get closer together

__X__ bump into each other more

FOSS Chemical Interactions Course, Second Edition

Investigation 4 I-Check
Page 3 of 4

Item 4

Score	If the student . . .
2	marks B.
1	marks any other answer.
0	makes no attempt.

Item 5

Score	If the student . . .
2	marks B.
1	marks any other answer.
0	makes no attempt.

Item 6

Score	If the student . . .
2	marks the second and last phrases.
1	marks any other way.
0	makes no attempt.

INVESTIGATION 4 I-CHECK
CHEMICAL INTERACTIONS

ANSWERS

7. a. What is the difference between compression and contraction?

   When you compress a substance, the particles are physically pushed into a smaller space. When a substance contracts, the kinetic energy of the particles decreases, and the particles move closer together.

   b. Give an example of compression.

   You can compress air by pushing the plunger down in a closed syringe.

   Give an example of contraction.

   The water in a bottle contracts when cooled, causing the volume to decrease.

8. In what phase of matter are the particles spaced farthest apart?
   (Mark the one best answer.)

   ● **A** A gas
   ❍ **B** A liquid
   ❍ **C** A solid
   ❍ **D** All are equal

9. A jeweler heats a silver strip and bends it into a bracelet. The bracelet cools down when the jeweler is finished. What happens to the kinetic energy of the silver particles as the solid silver cools? The kinetic energy of the particles _____.
   (Mark the one best answer.)

   ❍ **A** increases
   ❍ **B** decreases until the particles stop moving
   ● **C** decreases, but the particles still move
   ❍ **D** does not change

FOSS Chemical Interactions Course, Second Edition

Investigation 4 I-Check
Page 4 of 4

Item 7a

Score	If the student . . .
3	explains that compression is due to pressure applied to an object and contraction is the result of lowering kinetic energy of the object.
2	correctly explains either compression or contraction, but not both.
1	writes any other answer.
0	makes no attempt.

Item 7b

Score	If the student . . .
2	gives appropriate examples that may or may not be from classroom examples.
1	writes any other answer.
0	makes no attempt.

Item 8

Score	If the student . . .
2	marks A.
1	marks any other answer.
0	makes no attempt.

Item 9

Score	If the student . . .
2	marks C.
1	marks any other answer.
0	makes no attempt.

INVESTIGATION 5 I-CHECK

INVESTIGATION 5 I-CHECK
CHEMICAL INTERACTIONS

ANSWERS

1. A student put a vial of plain water into a container of ice. She put the container into a freezer. The starting temperatures are listed below.

   - Water in the vial 22°C
   - Ice 0°C
   - Freezer environment −17°C

   In the diagram, draw arrows in the blank boxes to show the direction of energy transfer between

   - the freezer and the ice (X)
   - the freezer and the water in the vial (Y)
   - the ice and the water in the vial (Z)

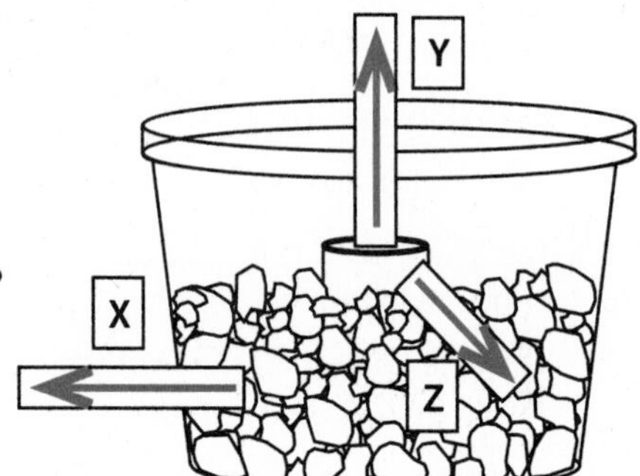

2. A closed container of water is kept at a constant temperature. Which of the following statements about the water particles is true?
   (Mark the one best answer.)

   ● **A** The average kinetic energy of the water particles stays the same.
   ○ **B** The average kinetic energy of the water particles increases a little bit.
   ○ **C** The average kinetic energy of the water particles decreases a little bit.
   ○ **D** The water particles stop moving.

3. A plastic bottle filled with warm air is placed into cold water.

   The temperature of the air gets cooler.

   The temperature of the water gets warmer.

   Describe the energy transfer between the air particles and the water particles.

   Energy transfers from the warmer air to the cooler water, through the plastic bottle.

Item 1

Score	If the student . . .
3	draws arrow X from the ice to the freezer/air, draws arrow Y from the vial to the freezer/air, and draws arrow Z from the vial to the ice.
2	draws the arrows as in score 3, but draws one in the wrong direction.
1	draws more than one arrow incorrectly.
0	makes no attempt.

Item 2

Score	If the student . . .
2	marks A.
1	marks any other answer.
0	makes no attempt.

Item 3

Score	If the student . . .
3	writes the air gets cooler and the water gets warmer; explains that the energy transfers from the warm air to the cold water, through the plastic bottle.
2	writes that the air gets cooler and the water gets warmer; explanation includes minor errors.
1	writes any other answer.
0	makes no attempt.

INVESTIGATION 5 I-CHECK
CHEMICAL INTERACTIONS

ANSWERS

4. What happens when cold milk is poured into hot chocolate?
*(Mark an **X** next to each correct answer.)*

   ____ Energy flows from the milk to the chocolate.

   _X_ Energy flows from the chocolate to the milk.

   _X_ The kinetic energy of the milk increases.

   ____ The kinetic energy of the chocolate increases.

5. A fast-moving particle (A) and a slow-moving particle (B) collide.

   a. Which particle has more kinetic energy before the collision?
   (Mark the one best answer.)

   ● **A** Particle A

   ○ **B** Particle B

   ○ **C** A and B have the same kinetic energy.

   Particle A - fast

   Particle B - slow

   b. What happens to the kinetic energy when the particles collide?

   ○ **A** Energy transfers to particle A.

   ● **B** Energy transfers to particle B.

   ○ **C** Energy transfers to both particles.

   c. Describe the change in speed of each particle after the collision.

   The fast-moving particle (A) slows down, and the slow-moving particle (B) speeds up.

Item 4

Score	If the student . . .
3	marks the second and third answers.
2	marks the second or third answer, but not both.
1	marks any other answer.
0	makes no attempt.

Item 5a

Score	If the student . . .
2	marks A.
1	marks any other answer.
0	makes no attempt.

Item 5b

Score	If the student . . .
2	marks B.
1	marks any other answer.
0	makes no attempt.

Item 5c

Score	If the student . . .
2	writes that the fast particle (A) slows down and the slow particle (B) speeds up.
1	writes any other answer.
0	makes no attempt.

INVESTIGATION 5 I-CHECK
CHEMICAL INTERACTIONS

ANSWERS

6. A baker has two identical cakes except that one cake is hot, and the other cake is room temperature. He places both cakes on a cold plate. What happens?
(Mark the one best answer.)

- ○ **A** Only the hot cake transfers energy to the plate.
- ○ **B** The plate transfers energy to the room-temperature cake.
- ● **C** Both cakes transfer energy to the plate.
- ○ **D** Neither cake transfers energy to the plate.

Why did you choose that answer?

Both cakes transfer energy to the plate because they both have greater average kinetic energy than the plate (they are hotter than the plate).

7. A student heated 50 mL of water from 0°C to 60°C. How much energy did she use to heat the water? Remember: $cal = m \times \Delta T$
(Use the space below to show your math and your final answer.)

$\Delta T = 60°C - 0°C$

$\Delta T = 60°C$

$cal = 50g \times 60°C$

$cal = 3{,}000\ cal$

FOSS Chemical Interactions Course, Second Edition

Investigation 5 I-Check
Page 3 of 4

Item 6

Score	If the student . . .
3	marks C; explains that both cakes will transfer energy to the plate because they are hotter/have more kinetic energy.
2	marks C, but gives explanation with minor errors.
1	marks any other answer.
0	makes no attempt.

Item 7

Score	If the student . . .
3	writes 3,000 cal and shows correct math.
2	shows math; makes minor calculation error.
1	writes any other answer.
0	makes no attempt.

INVESTIGATION 5 I-CHECK
CHEMICAL INTERACTIONS

ANSWERS

8. Things heat up and cool down as a result of energy transfer. Energy flows _____.
(Mark the one best answer.)

- ● **A** from hot materials to cold materials
- ❍ **B** from cold materials to hot materials
- ❍ **C** in both directions
- ❍ **D** only until equilibrium is reached

9. The iron and water in this system are at the same temperature.

a. Which particles have more average kinetic energy?
(Mark the one best answer.)

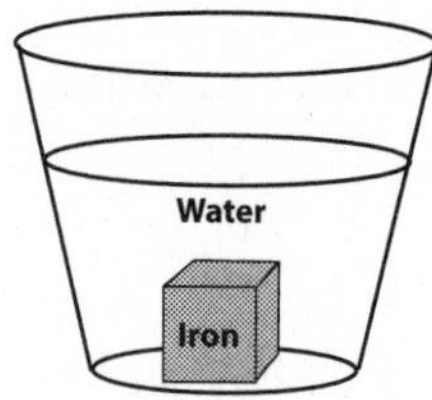

- ❍ **A** The water particles
- ❍ **B** The iron particles
- ● **C** They both have the same

Why did you choose that answer?

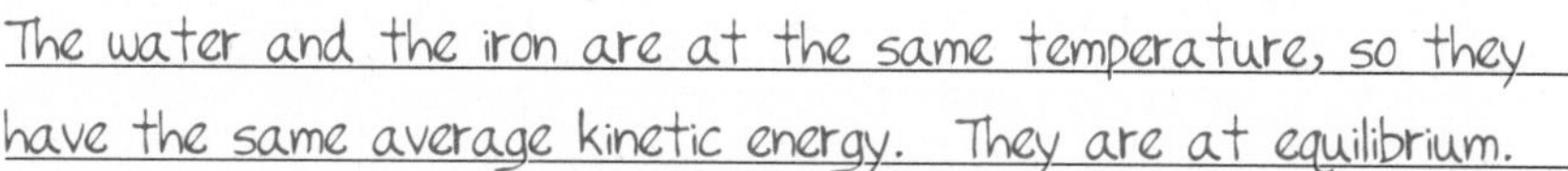

The water and the iron are at the same temperature, so they have the same average kinetic energy. They are at equilibrium.

b. Describe the energy transfer between the water and the iron.

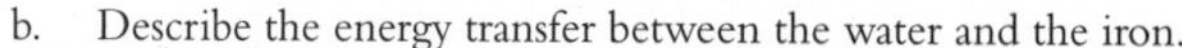

The energy transfer between the water and the iron are equal in both directions because they are the same temperature.

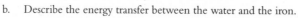

Item 8

Score	If the student . . .
2	marks A.
1	marks any other answer.
0	makes no attempt.

Item 9a

Score	If the student . . .
3	marks C; explains because the water and iron are at the same temperature, they have the same average kinetic energy.
2	marks C; gives explanation with minor errors.
1	marks any other answer with any explanation.
0	makes no attempt.

Item 9b

Score	If the student . . .
3	writes that the energy transfer is equal in both directions because the substances are at the same temperature.
2	writes that there is no energy transfer, or gives explanation with minor errors.
1	writes any other answer.
0	makes no attempt.

INVESTIGATIONS 7–8 I-CHECK

INVESTIGATIONS 7–8 I-CHECK

CHEMICAL INTERACTIONS

ANSWERS

1. The melting/freezing point of mercury is –39°C. A scientist put liquid mercury into a freezer that is kept at a constant temperature of –35°C.

   Will the liquid mercury freeze? No

   Why or why not?

   The mercury will not freeze because the environment (the freezer) is warmer than the freezing point of mercury.

2. What is between the water particles in a glass of pure water?

   Nothing . . . except space

3. When a substance changes from a liquid to a solid, which of the following is true? *(Mark an **X** next to each true statement.)*

   ___ The particles change shape.

   ___ The particles change from soft to hard.

   X The particles are held more strongly to one another.

   ___ The particles have more kinetic energy.

   X The particles have less kinetic energy.

   X The substance is freezing.

   ___ The substance is melting.

Item 1

Score	If the student . . .
3	writes no; explains that the freezer is warmer than the freezing point of mercury.
2	writes no; gives explanation with minor errors.
1	writes yes and gives any explanation, or writes any other answer.
0	makes no attempt.

Item 2

Score	If the student . . .
2	writes that there is nothing between water particles; may include that water particles are touching.
1	writes any other answer.
0	makes no attempt.

Item 3

Score	If the student . . .
3	marks third, fifth, and sixth statements.
2	marks one or two of the correct statements noted in score 3.
1	marks any other answer.
0	makes no attempt.

INVESTIGATIONS 7–8 I-CHECK
CHEMICAL INTERACTIONS

ANSWERS

4. Some people confuse what happens during melting and dissolving.

   a. How would you explain what happens to the particles during each process to someone who is confused?

   When a substance melts, heat causes the particles to move faster changing from a solid to a liquid; when a substance dissolves the particles of a solute (solid) break apart from each other and move among the particles of the solvent.

   b. How would you explain the role of kinetic energy in each process?

   When a substance is heated, it melts because the average kinetic energy has increased; when a substance dissolves the average kinetic energy doesn't change (as long as both substances are the same temperature), the particles of the solid solute are physically broken away from each other by the solvent's particle motion (kinetic energy).

5. You wash a T-shirt. You hang the wet T-shirt on a clothesline. A few hours later, the T-shirt is dry. Mark an **X** next to each statement that explains what happens to the water particles after you hang the shirt up.

   ____ The water particles are absorbed by the T-shirt.

   __X__ The water particles evaporate into the air.

   ____ The water particles disappear and no longer exist.

   ____ The water particles melt into the T-shirt.

   __X__ The water particles moved faster and become part of the air.

   ____ The water particles break down to hydrogen and oxygen particles and move into the air.

FOSS Chemical Interactions Course, Second Edition

Investigations 7–8 I-Check
Page 2 of 3

Item 4a

Score	If the student . . .
3	differentiates between what causes the particles to change configuration: in melting, the particles gain energy and move faster, flowing over and around one another; and in dissolving, the particles of the solute are broken apart from each other by the solvent.
2	writes something relevant about the difference between melting and dissolving, but answer is incomplete or includes errors.
1	writes any other answer.
0	makes no attempt.

Item 4b

Score	If the student . . .
4	writes that the average kinetic energy increases when a substance melts; the average kinetic energy stays the same when a substance dissolves, but the kinetic energy (motion) of the solvent particles break the solute into smaller pieces.
3	writes that the kinetic energy increases when a substance melts; describes that average kinetic energy does not change during dissolving, but does not explain that the kinetic energy of the solvent particles causes the dissolving.
2	describes what happens when a substance melts or when it dissolves; describes only one process or explanations include several errors.
1	writes any other answer.
0	makes no attempt.

Item 5

Score	If the student . . .
2	marks second and fifth statements.
1	marks any other answer.
0	makes no attempt.

INVESTIGATIONS 7–8 I-CHECK

CHEMICAL INTERACTIONS

ANSWERS

6. Explain what happens to the particles in liquid water when it changes to ice.

Water changes from liquid to solid when the particles lose energy, stop moving over and around each other, and take fixed positions in relation to one another.

7. A student dissolved 20 g of salt in a cup of water. She left the cup uncovered in an area where nobody could touch it. When she returned to the cup 10 days later, she found that all the water was gone, and there were crystals in the bottom of the cup. What is the best conclusion, based on her observations?

(Mark the one best answer.)

- ● **A** The water evaporated, and there is 20 g of salt in the cup.
- ❍ **B** The water and some salt evaporated, but some salt is left in the cup.
- ❍ **C** There was a chemical reaction, and a precipitate was left behind.
- ❍ **D** The water and salt separated and then the water evaporated, but there is no way to know what is left in the cup.

8. There are three vials of the same substance in the diagram: one solid, one liquid, and one gas.

In the four boxes above and below the arrows, write the name of the process that results in the phase change.

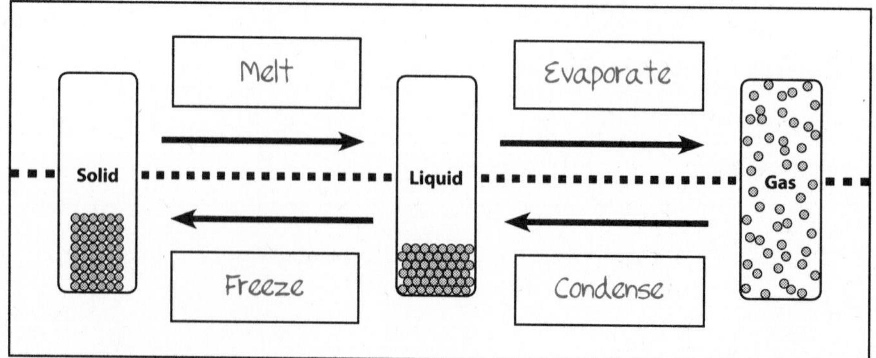

Item 6

Score	If the student . . .
4	writes that the water changes from liquid to solid when (1) the particles lose energy, and (2) they stop moving over and around one another/take fixed positions.
3	writes that the water particles slow down until the water is frozen or has changed to a solid.
2	uses the term freezing; does not mention particles slowing down.
1	writes any other answer.
0	makes no attempt.

Item 7

Score	If the student . . .
2	marks A.
1	marks any other answer.
0	makes no attempt.

Item 8

Score	If the student . . .
2	writes the correct process in each box.
1	writes any other answer.
0	makes no attempt.

INVESTIGATION 9 I-CHECK

INVESTIGATION 9 I-CHECK
CHEMICAL INTERACTIONS

ANSWERS

1. What holds the atoms together in molecules and compounds?
(Mark the one best answer.)

   - ❍ **A** Glue
   - ❍ **B** Freezing
   - ● **C** Bonds
   - ❍ **D** Magnetism

2. Below are the models for four common substances. In the columns, write

   a. the chemical formula.

   b. the total number of atoms present.

   c. the total number of elements present.

   d. the name of each element present.

Model	a. Chemical formula	b. Number of atoms	c. Number of elements	d. Element names
Cl Ca Cl	$CaCl_2$	3	2	calcium chlorine
H Na C O O O	$NaHCO_3$	6	4	sodium hydrogen carbon oxygen
O C O	CO_2	3	2	carbon oxygen
Ca C O O O	$CaCO_3$	5	3	calcium carbon oxygen

FOSS Chemical Interactions Course, Second Edition

Investigation 9 I-Check
Page 1 of 5

Item 1

Score	If the student . . .
2	marks C.
1	marks any other answer.
0	makes no attempt.

Item 2a

Score	If the student . . .
3	writes the correct chemical formula for each model.
2	writes the correct chemical formula for the models with minor errors, such as elements in a different order, e.g., $HNaCO_3$, or writes unconventional representations for the models, such as NaOCOOH or ClCaCl.
1	writes any other answer.
0	makes no attempt.

Item 2b

Score	If the student . . .
2	writes the correct number of atoms for each model.
1	writes any other answer.
0	makes no attempt.

Item 2c

Score	If the student . . .
2	writes the correct number of elements for each model.
1	writes any other answer.
0	makes no attempt.

Item 2d

Score	If the student . . .
2	writes the correct element name for each model.
1	writes any other answer.
0	makes no attempt.

INVESTIGATION 9 I-CHECK
CHEMICAL INTERACTIONS

ANSWERS

3. Which of the following statements about atoms are true?
   (Mark an **X** *next to each correct answer.)*

   ____ Atoms are not matter.

   ____ Atoms are inside matter.

   ____ Atoms make up only living things.

   ____ Atoms make up only nonliving things.

   _X_ Atoms make up all matter.

4. The chemical formula for tin chloride is $SnCl_4$.

   a. Mark the model you think represents tin chloride. *(Mark the one best answer.)*

   ● A　　○ B　　○ C

   b. Why did you select that model?

   The formula for tin chloride shows one tin atom and four chlorine atoms. A is the only model that has the right number of atoms.

5. What happens to the atoms in substances when a chemical reaction occurs?

   They rearrange to form new substances.

FOSS Chemical Interactions Course, Second Edition

Investigation 9 I-Check
Page 2 of 5

Item 3

Score	If the student . . .
2	marks only the last statement.
1	marks any other way.
0	makes no attempt.

Item 4a

Score	If the student . . .
2	marks A.
1	marks any other answer.
0	makes no attempt.

Item 4b

Score	If the student . . .
2	writes that A is the only one that shows the correct number of atoms.
1	writes any other answer.
0	makes no attempt.

Item 5

Score	If the student . . .
3	writes that the atoms rearrange to form new substances; may include that bonds break and re-form.
2	writes that the atoms rearrange or form new substances, but not both.
1	writes any other answer.
0	makes no attempt.

INVESTIGATION 9 I-CHECK
CHEMICAL INTERACTIONS

ANSWERS

6. Which of the following are examples of a chemical reaction? *(Mark an* **X** *next to each correct answer.)*

 X Sugar turning black when heated over a fire

 ___ Water evaporating from a pot on a hot stove

 ___ A snowman melting into a puddle of water

 X The surface of a penny changing color after many years

 ___ Melted butter becoming a solid when placed in the refrigerator

 ___ A white substance left behind after water evaporates from a solution

 ___ A spoonful of sugar dissolving in a glass of water

 X Bubbles forming when substances are mixed together

7. a. The reaction below is shown with atomic models. Write the chemical equation on the line below the model.

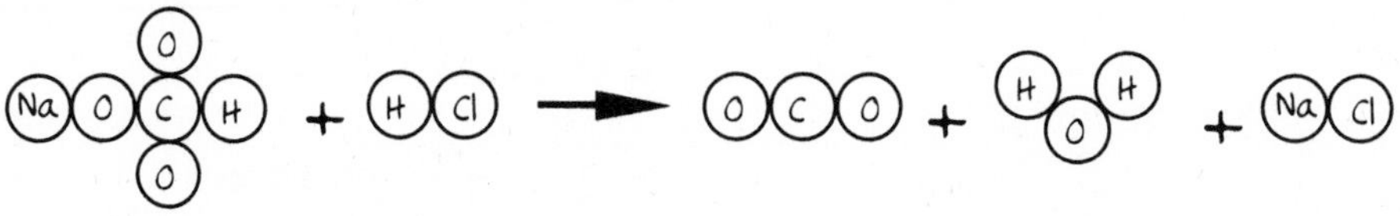

Na O C(O)(O) H + H Cl → O C O + H O H + Na Cl

$NaHCO_3 + HCl \rightarrow CO_2 + H_2O + NaCl$

b. The reaction below is shown using a chemical equation. Draw the atomic model that describes the equation.

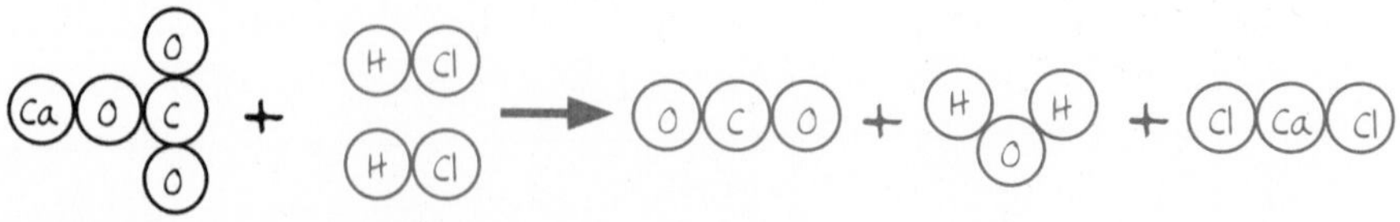

Ca O C(O)(O) + H Cl, H Cl → O C O + H O H + Cl Ca Cl

$CaCO_3 + 2HCl \rightarrow CO_2 + H_2O + CaCl_2$

FOSS Chemical Interactions Course, Second Edition

Investigation 9 I-Check
Page 3 of 5

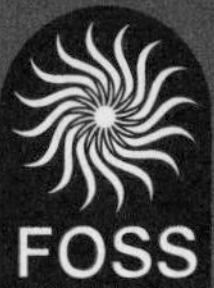

Item 6

Score	If the student . . .
3	marks the first, fourth, and last statements.
2	marks only one or two of the correct answers listed above.
1	marks any other answer.
0	makes no attempt.

Item 7a

Score	If the student . . .
3	writes the correct chemical equation for the reaction.
2	writes the correct reactants and products, but makes errors in form, such as NaCOOOH.
1	writes any other answer.
0	makes no attempt.

Item 7b

Score	If the student . . .
3	draws the correct atomic model for the reaction.
2	draws an atomic model that includes minor errors.
1	draws anything else.
0	makes no attempt.

INVESTIGATION 9 I-CHECK

CHEMICAL INTERACTIONS

ANSWERS

8. A student dropped an eggshell into hydrochloric acid (HCl). An eggshell is made of calcium carbonate ($CaCO_3$). Bubbles formed on the shell.

   a. What gas was in the bubbles?
   (Mark the one best answer.)

   ❍ **A** $CaCl_2$

   ❍ **B** O_2

   ● **C** CO_2

   ❍ **D** H_2

   b. Write the chemical equation that supports your choice.

   $$CaCO_3 + 2HCl \longrightarrow CO_2 + H_2O + CaCl_2$$

   c. What test could you perform to confirm your prediction?

   You could bubble the gas through limewater ($Ca(OH)_2$). If a precipitate forms (the solution gets cloudy), the gas is carbon dioxide (CO_2).

9. The different-shaded circles represent different kinds of atoms. When circles are touching, they indicate that those atoms form a molecule. Which of the following could accurately represent a chemical reaction?
   (Mark the one best answer.)

   ❍ **A** ●● + ○○ → ●○ + ●○

   ❍ **B** ●● + ○○ → ○○○○

   ❍ **C** ●● + ○○ → ○○ + ●●

   ● **D** ●● + ○○ → ○●/○●

Item 8a

Score	If the student . . .
2	marks C.
1	marks any other answer.
0	makes no attempt.

Item 8b

Score	If the student . . .
4	writes the correct chemical formula.
3	writes the correct reactants and products, but the equation is not balanced, such as $CaCO_3 + HCl \rightarrow CO_2 + H_2O + CaCl_2$.
2	writes $CaCO_3$ and HCl as reactants, but has incorrect products.
1	writes any other answer.
0	makes no attempt.

Item 8c

Score	If the student . . .
3	suggests bubbling the gas through limewater or any other reasonable test for carbon dioxide.
2	suggests repeating the same experiment the student did, such as putting the eggshell in HCl and seeing what happens.
1	writes any other answer.
0	makes no attempt.

Item 9

Score	If the student . . .
2	marks D.
1	marks any other answer.
0	makes no attempt.

INVESTIGATION 9 I-CHECK
CHEMICAL INTERACTIONS

ANSWERS

10. A scientist prepares a chamber where a chemical reaction can take place and no matter can escape. During the reaction, bubbles form. What will happen to the mass of the materials in the container?
(Mark the one best answer.)

- ❍ **A** The mass will increase.
- ❍ **B** The mass will decrease.
- ● **C** The mass will stay the same.
- ❍ **D** It will depend on what the chemical reaction was.

11. When a thermometer is heated, the volume of the liquid inside of the thermometer increases, and the level of the liquid rises. As the volume increases, what happens to the mass of the liquid in the thermometer?
(Mark the one best answer.)

- ❍ **A** The mass increases.
- ❍ **B** The mass decreases.
- ● **C** The mass stays the same.
- ❍ **D** The change in mass depends on the type of liquid.

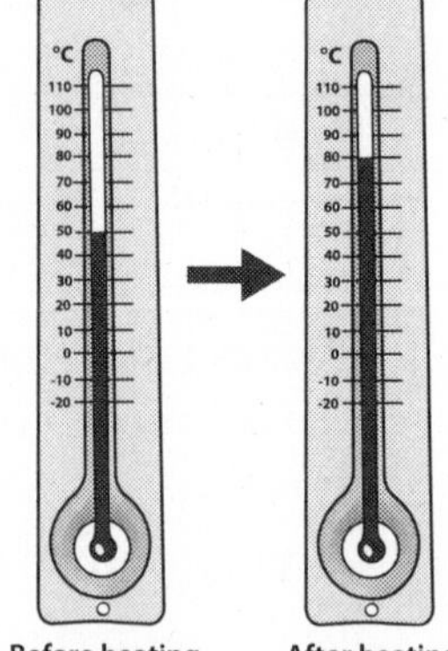

FOSS Chemical Interactions Course, Second Edition

Investigation 9 I-Check
Page 5 of 5

Item 10

Score	If the student . . .
2	marks C.
1	marks any other answer.
0	makes no attempt.

Item 11

Score	If the student . . .
2	marks C.
1	marks any other answer.
0	makes no attempt.

Science Notebooks in Middle School

Science Notebooks in Middle School

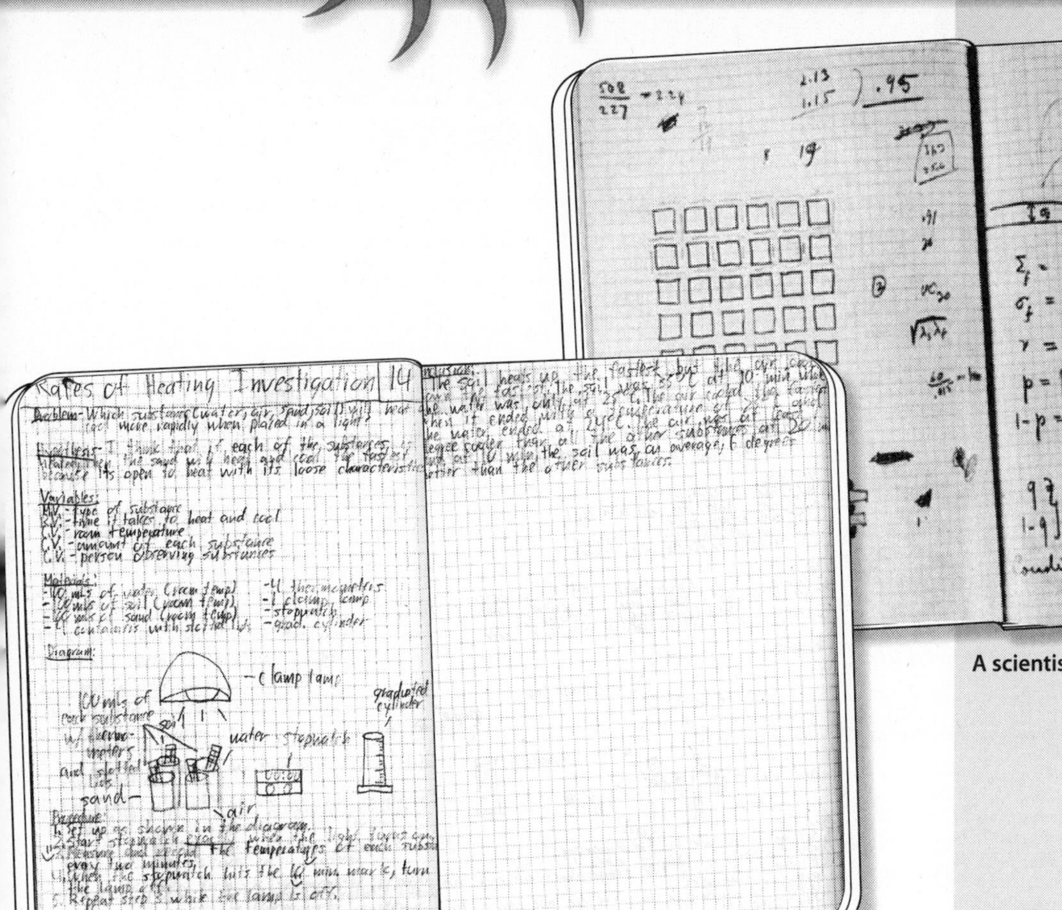

A scientist's notebook

Source: Special Collections Research Center, University of Chicago Library

A student's notebook

Contents

INTRODUCTION

Scientists keep notebooks. The scientist's notebook is a detailed record of his or her engagement with scientific phenomena. It is a personal representation of experiences, observations, and thinking—an integral part of the process of doing scientific work. A scientist's notebook is a continuously updated history of the development of scientific knowledge and reasoning. The notebook organizes the huge body of knowledge and makes it easier for a scientist to work. As developing scientists, FOSS students are encouraged to incorporate notebooks into their science learning. First and foremost, the notebook is a tool for student learning.

From the Human Brain and Senses Course

NOTEBOOK BENEFITS

Engaging in active science is one part experience and two parts making sense of the experience. Science notebooks help students with the sense-making part by providing two major benefits: documentation and cognitive engagement.

Benefits to Students

Science notebooks centralize students' data. When data are displayed in functional ways, students can think about the data more effectively. A well-kept notebook is a useful reference document. When students have forgotten a fact or relationship that they learned earlier in their studies, they can look it up. Learning to reference previous discoveries and knowledge structures is important.

Documentation: an organized record. As students become more accomplished at keeping notebooks, their work will become better organized and efficient. Tables, graphs, charts, drawings, and labeled illustrations will become standard means for representing and displaying data. A complete and accurate record of learning allows students to reconstruct the sequence of learning events and relive the experience. Discussions about science among students, students and teachers, or students, teachers, and families, have more meaning when they are supported by authentic documentation in students' notebooks. Questions and ideas generated by experimentation or discussion can be recorded for future investigation.

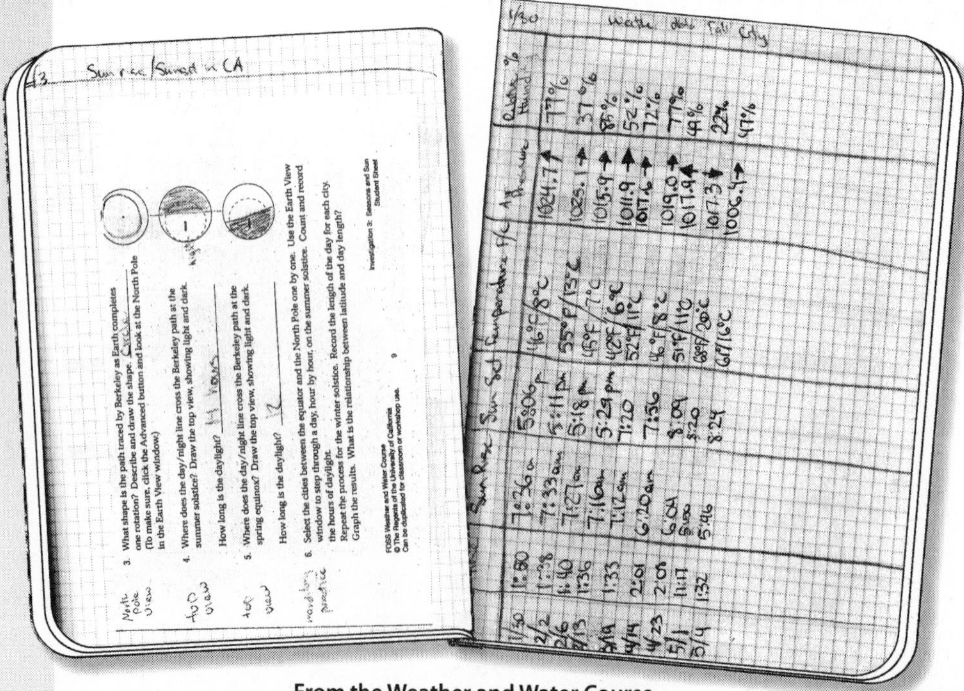

From the Weather and Water Course

Cognitive engagement. Once data are recorded and organized in an efficient manner in science notebooks, students can think about the data and draw conclusions about the way the world works. Their data are the raw materials that students use to forge concepts and relationships from their experiences and observations.

Writing stimulates active reasoning. There is a direct relationship between the formation of concepts and the rigors of expressing them in words. Writing requires students to impose discipline on their thoughts. When you ask students to generate derivative products (summary reports, detailed explanations, posters, oral presentations, etc.) as evidence of learning, the process will be much more efficient and meaningful because they have a coherent, detailed notebook for reference.

When students use notebooks as an integral part of their science studies, they think critically about their thinking. This reflective thinking can be encouraged by notebook entries that present opportunities for self-assessment. Self-assessment motivates students to rethink and restate their scientific understanding. Revising their notebook entries helps students clarify their understanding of the science concepts under investigation. By writing explanations, students clarify what they know and expose what they don't know.

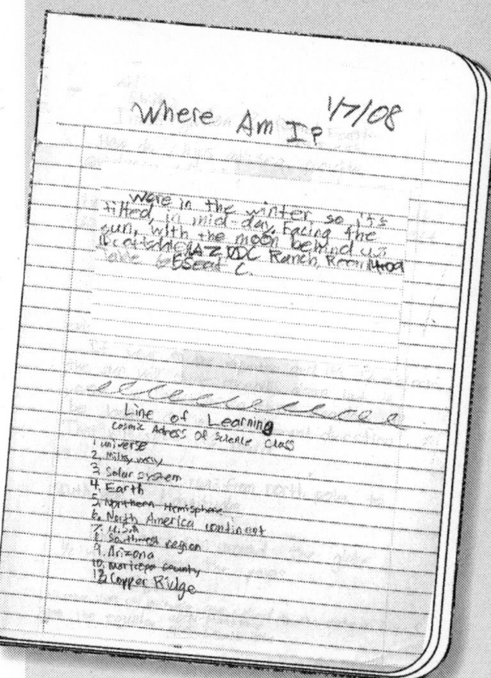

From the Planetary Science Course

11/30/11

Calculating Asteroid Size

Directions:

Use the 20:1 crater-to-asteroid ratio to determine the size of the asteroid that created these Earth craters.

Earth Crater	Diameter (km)	Asteroid Size (km)
Manicouagan (p. 76)	100	5
Chicxulub (p. 33)	300	15
Gosses Bluff (p. 75)	24	1.2
Barringer (p. 74)	1.2	0.06

Lunar Crater	Diameter (km)	Asteroid Size (km)
Archimedes (p. 70)	83	4.1
Aristillus (p. 70)	55	2.5
Clavius (p. 73)	225	11.3
Copernicus (p. 71)	93	4.6
Posidonius (p. 72)	95	4.8
Stofler (p. 73)	126	6.3
Tycho (p. 73)	85	4.2
Sea of Rains (p. 65)	1000	50

Comparing asteroid impacts

Why are there more craters on the Moon than on Earth?

On Earth, craters get covered by plants, buildings, and water. They can also disappear from weather like rain and wind.

From the Planetary Science Course

Benefits to Teachers

In FOSS, the unit of instruction is the course—a sequence of conceptually related learning experiences that leads to a set of learning outcomes. A science notebook helps you think about and communicate the conceptual structure of the course you are teaching.

Assessment. From the assessment point of view, a science notebook is a collection of student-generated artifacts that exhibit learning. You can informally assess student skills, such as using charts to record data, in real time while students are working with materials. At other times, you might collect student work samples and review them for insights or errors in conceptual understanding. This valuable information helps you plan the next steps of instruction. Students' data analysis, sense making, and reflection provide a measure of the quality and quantity of student learning. The notebook itself should not be graded, though certain assignments might be graded and placed in the notebook.

Medium for feedback. The science notebook provides an excellent medium for providing feedback to individual students regarding their work. Productive feedback calls for students to read a teacher comment, think about the issue it raises, and act on it. The comment may ask for clarification, an example, additional information, precise vocabulary, or a review of previous work in the notebook. In this way, you can determine whether a problem with the student work relates to a flawed understanding of the science content or a breakdown in communication skills.

Focus for professional discussions. The student notebook also acts as a focal point for discussion about student learning at several levels. First, a student's work can be the subject of a conversation between you and the student. By acting as a critical mentor, you can call attention to ways a student can improve the notebook, and help him or her learn how to use the notebook as a reference. You can also review and discuss the science notebook during family conferences. Science notebooks shared among teachers in a study group or other professional-development environment can effectively demonstrate recording techniques, individual styles, various levels of work quality, and so on. Just as students can learn notebook strategies from one another, teachers can learn notebook skills from one another.

GETTING STARTED

A middle school science notebook is more than just a collection of science work, notes, field-trip permission slips, and all the other types of documents that tend to accumulate in a student's three-ring binder or backpack. By organizing the science work systematically into a bound composition book, students create a thematic record of their experiences, thoughts, plans, reflections, and questions as they work through a topic in science.

The science notebook is more than just formal lab reports; it is a record of a student's entire journey through a progression of science concepts. Where elementary school students typically need additional help structuring and organizing their written work, middle school students should be encouraged to develop their organizational skills and take some ownership in creating deliberate records of their science learning, even though they may still require some pointers and specific scaffolding from you.

In addition, the science notebook provides a personal space where students can explore their understanding of science concepts by writing down ideas and being allowed to "mess around" with their thinking. Students are encouraged to look back on their ideas throughout the course to self-assess their conceptual development and record new thoughts. With this purpose of the science notebook in mind, you may need to refine your own thinking around what should or should not be included as a part of the science notebook, as well as expectations about grading and analyzing student work.

Rules of Engagement

Teachers and students should be clear about the conventions students will honor in their notebook entries. Typically, the rules of grammar and spelling are fairly relaxed so as not to inhibit the flow of expression during notebook entries. This also helps students develop a sense of ownership in their notebooks, a place where they are free to write in their own style. When students generate derivative products using information in the notebooks, such as reports, you might require students to exercise more rigorous language-arts conventions.

In addition to written entries, students should be encouraged to use a wide range of other means for recording and communicating, including charts, tables, graphs, drawings, graphics, color codes, numbers, and artifacts attached to the notebook pages. By expanding the options for making notebook entries, each student will find his or her most efficient, expressive way to capture and organize information for later retrieval.

Enhanced Classroom Discussion

One of the benefits of using notebooks is that you will elicit responses to key discussion questions from all students, not just the handful of verbally enthusiastic students in the class. When you ask students to write down their thoughts after you pose a question, all students have time to engage deeply with the question and organize their thoughts. When you ask students to share their answers, those who needed more time to process the question and organize their thinking will be ready to verbalize their responses and become involved in a class discussion.

When students can use their notebooks as a reference during the ensuing discussion, they won't feel put on the spot. At some points, you might ask students to share only what they wrote in their notebooks, to remind them to focus their thoughts while writing. As the class shares ideas during discussions, students can add new ideas to their notebooks under a line of learning (see next-step strategies). Even if some students are still reticent, having students write after a question is posed prevents them from automatically disengaging from conversations.

Notebook Structure

FOSS recommends that students keep their notebooks in 8" × 10" bound composition books. At the most advanced level, students are responsible for creating the entire science notebook from blank pages in their composition books. Experienced students determine when to use their notebooks, how to organize space, what methods of documentation to use, and how to flag important information. This level of notebook use will not be realized quickly; it will likely require systematic development by an entire teaching staff over time.

At the beginning, notebook practice is often highly structured, using prepared sheets from the FOSS notebook masters. You can photocopy and distribute these sheets to students as needed during the investigations. Sheets are sized to fit in a standard composition book. Students glue or tape the sheets into their notebooks. This allows some flexibility between glued-in notebook sheets and blank pages where students can do additional writing, drawings, and other documentation. Prepared notebook sheets are helpful organizers for students with challenges such as learning disabilities or with developing English skills. This model is the most efficient means for obtaining the most productive work from inexperienced middle school students.

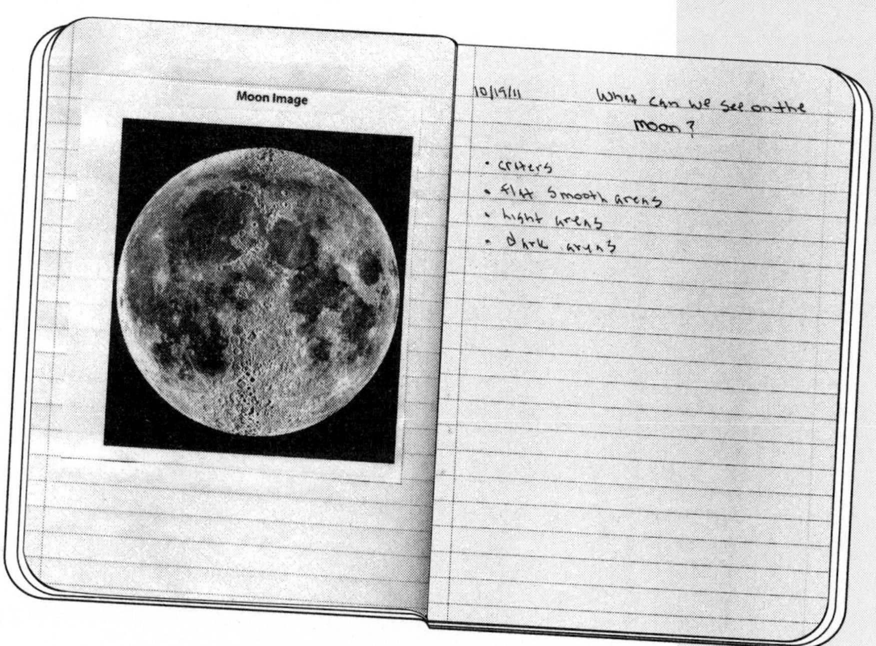

From the Planetary Science Course

Science Notebooks in Middle School

To make it easy for new FOSS teachers to implement a beginning student notebook, Delta Education sells copies of the printed *FOSS Science Notebook* in English for all FOSS middle school courses. Electronic versions of the notebook sheets can be downloaded free of charge at www.FOSSweb.com.

Each *FOSS Science Notebook* is a bound set of the notebook sheets for the course plus extra blank sheets throughout the notebook for students to write focus or inquiry questions, record and organize data, make sense of their thinking, and write summaries. There are also blank pages at the end to develop an index of science vocabulary.

The questions, statements, and graphic organizers on the notebook sheets provide guidance for students and scaffolding for teachers. When the notebook sheets are organized as a series, they constitute a highly structured precursor to an autonomously generated science notebook.

Developing Notebook Skills

Students will initially need more guidance from you. You will need to describe what and when to record, and to model organizational techniques. As the year advances, the notebook work will become increasingly student centered. As the body of work in the notebook grows, students will have more and more examples of useful techniques for reference. This self-sufficiency reduces the amount of guidance you need to provide, and reinforces students' appreciation of their own record of learning.

This gradual shift toward student-centered use of the notebook applies to any number of notebook skills, including developing headers for each page (day, time, date, title, etc.); using space efficiently on the page; preparing graphs, graphic organizers, and labeled illustrations; and attaching artifacts (sand samples, dried flowers, photographs, etc.). For instance, when students first display their data in a two-coordinate graph, the graph might be completely set up for them, so that they simply plot the data. As the year progresses, they will be expected to produce graphs with less and less support, until they are doing so without any assistance from you.

Organizing Science Notebooks

Four organizational components of the notebook should be planned right from the outset: a table of contents, page numbering, entry format, and an index.

Table of contents. Students should reserve the first three to five pages of their notebook for the table of contents. They will add to it systematically as they proceed through the course. The table of contents should include the date, title, and page number for each entry. The title could be based on the names of the investigations in the course, the specific activities undertaken, the concepts learned, a focus question for each investigation, or some other schema that makes sense to everyone.

Page numbering. Each page should have a number. These are referenced in the table of contents as the notebook progresses.

Entry format. During each class session, students will document their learning. Certain information will appear in every record, such as the date and title. Other forms of documentation will vary, including different types of written entries and artifacts, such as a multimedia printout. Some teachers ask their students to start each new entry at the top of the next available page. Others simply leave a modest space before a new entry. Sometimes it is necessary to leave space for work that will be completed on a separate piece of paper and glued or taped in later. Students might also leave space after a response, so that they can add to it at a later time.

Index. Scientific academic language is important. FOSS strives to have students use precise, accurate vocabulary at all times in their writing and conversations. To help them learn scientific vocabulary, students should set up an index at the end of their notebooks. It is not usually possible for students to enter the words in alphabetical order, as they will be acquired as the course advances. Instead, students could use several pages at the end of the notebook blocked out in 24 squares, and assign one or more letters to each square. Students write the new vocabulary word or phrase in the appropriate square and tag it with the page number of the notebook on which the word is defined. By developing vocabulary in context, students construct meaning through the inquiry process, and by organizing the words in an index, they strengthen their science notebooks as a documentary tool of their science learning. As another alternative, students can also define the word within these squares with the page references.

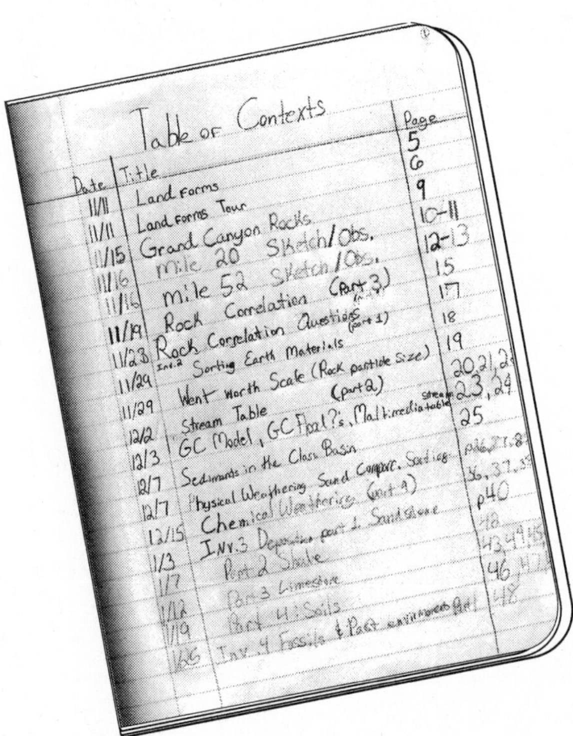

Table of contents

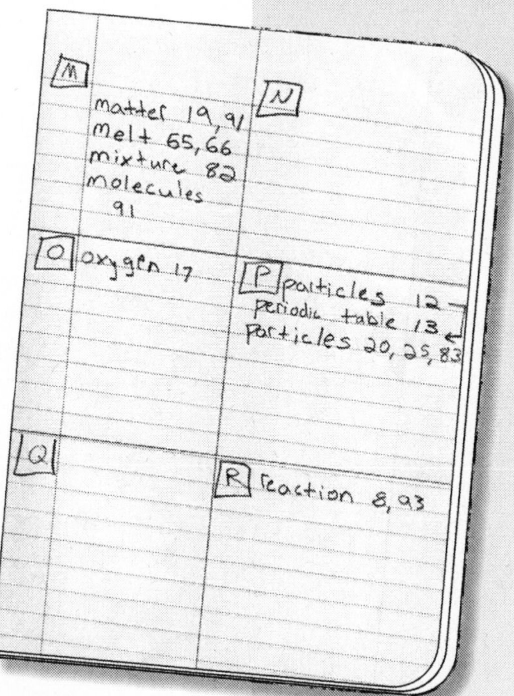

A science notebook index

NOTEBOOK COMPONENTS

Four general types of notebook entries, or components, give the science notebook conceptual shape and direction. These structures don't prescribe a step-by-step procedure for how to prepare the notebook, but they do provide some overall guidance. The general arc of an investigation starts with a question or challenge, proceeds with an activity and data acquisition, continues to sense making, and ends with next steps such as reflection and self-assessment.

All four components are not necessary during each class session, but over the course of an investigation, each component will be visited at least once. It may be useful to keep these four components in mind as you systematically guide students through their notebook entries. The components are overviewed here and described in greater detail on the following pages.

Focusing the investigation. Each part of each FOSS investigation includes a focus question, which students transcribe into their notebooks. Focus questions are embedded in the teacher step-by-step instructions and explicitly labeled. The focus question establishes the direction and conceptual challenge for that part of the investigation. For instance, when students investigate the origins of sand and sandstone in the **Earth History Course**, they start by writing,

➤ *Which came first, sand or sandstone?*

The question focuses both students and you on the learning goals for the activity. Students may start by formulating a plan, formally or informally, for answering the focus question. The goal of the plan is to obtain a satisfactory answer to the focus question, which will be revisited and answered later in the investigation.

Data acquisition and organization. After students have established a plan, they collect data. Students can acquire data from carefully planned experiments, accurate measurements, systematic observations, free explorations, or accidental discoveries. It doesn't matter what process produces the data; the critically important point is that students obtain data and record it. It may be necessary to reorganize and display the data for efficient analysis, often by organizing a data table. The data display is key to making sense of the science inquiry.

Making sense of data. Once students have collected and displayed their data, they need to analyze it to learn something about the natural world. In this component of the notebook, students write explanatory statements that answer the focus question. You can formalize this component by asking students to use an established protocol such as a sentence starter, or the explanation can be purely a thoughtful effort by each student. Explanations may be incorrect or incomplete at this point, but students can remedy this during the final notebook entry, when they have an opportunity to continue processing what they've learned. Unfortunately, this piece is often forgotten in the classroom during the rush to finish the lesson and move on. But without sense making and reflection (the final phase of science inquiry), students might see the lesson as a fun activity without connecting the experience to the big ideas that are being developed in the course.

Next-step strategies. The final component of an investigation brings students back to their notebooks by engaging in a next-step strategy, such as reflection and self-assessment, that moves their understanding forward. This component is the capstone on a purposeful series of experiences designed to guide students to understand the concept originally presented in the focus question. After making sense of the data, and making new claims about the topic at hand, students should go back to their earlier thinking and note their changing ideas and new findings. This reflective process helps students cement their new ideas.

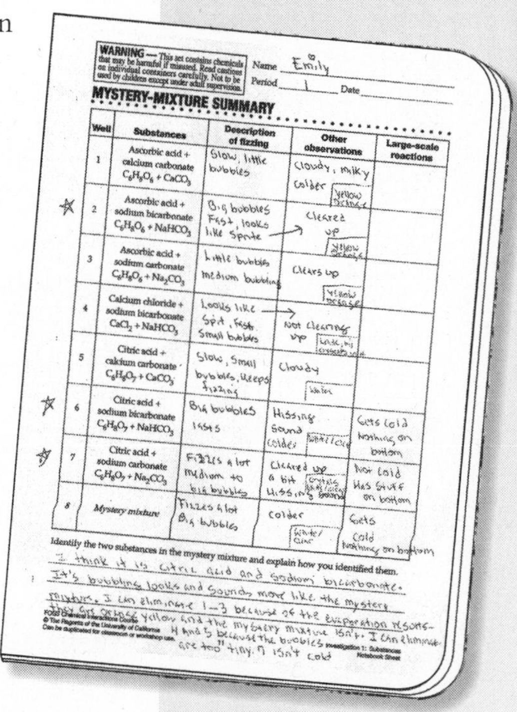

WARNING — This set contains chemicals that may be harmful if misused. Read cautions on individual containers carefully. Not to be used by children except under adult supervision.

Name Emily
Period 1 Date

MYSTERY-MIXTURE SUMMARY

Well	Substances	Description of fizzing	Other observations	Large-scale reactions
1	Ascorbic acid + calcium carbonate $C_6H_8O_6 + CaCO_3$	Slow, little bubbles	Cloudy, milky colder	
2	Ascorbic acid + sodium bicarbonate $C_6H_8O_6 + NaHCO_3$	Big bubbles Fast, looks like Sprite	Cleared up	
3	Ascorbic acid + sodium carbonate $C_6H_8O_6 + Na_2CO_3$	Little bubbles medium bubbling	Clears up	
4	Calcium chloride + sodium bicarbonate $CaCl_2 + NaHCO_3$	Looks like Spit, fast, Small bubbles	Not clearing up	
5	Citric acid + calcium carbonate $C_6H_8O_7 + CaCO_3$	Slow, Small bubbles, keeps fizzing	Cloudy	
6	Citric acid + sodium bicarbonate $C_6H_8O_7 + NaHCO_3$	Big bubbles lasts	Hissing sound colder	Gets cold Nothing on bottom
7	Citric acid + sodium carbonate $C_6H_8O_7 + Na_2CO_3$	Fizzes a lot medium to big bubbles	Cleared up a bit Hissing sound	Not cold Has stuff on bottom
8	Mystery mixture	Fizzes a lot Big bubbles	colder	Gets cold nothing on bottom

Identify the two substances in the mystery mixture and explain how you identified them.

I think it is citric acid and sodium bicarbonate. It's bubbling looks and sounds more like the mystery mixture. I can eliminate 1–3 because of the evaporation results they are orange yellow and the mystery mixture isn't. I can eliminate 4 and 5 because the bubbles are too tiny. 7 isn't cold

FOSS Chemical Interactions Course
© The Regents of the University of California
Can be duplicated for classroom or workshop use.
Investigation 1: Substances
Notebook Sheet

A student organizes and makes sense of data in the Chemical Interactions Course.

Focusing the Investigation

Focus question. The first notebook entry in most investigations is the focus question. Focus questions are embedded in the teacher step-by-step instructions and explicitly labeled. You can write the question on the board or project it for students to transcribe into their notebooks. The focus question serves to focus students and you on the inquiry for the day. It is not always answered immediately, but rather hangs in the air while the investigation goes forward. Students always revisit their initial responses later in the investigation.

Quick write. A quick write (or quick draw) can be used in addition to a focus question. Quick writes can be completed on a quarter sheet of paper or an index card so you can collect, review, and return them to students to be taped or glued into their notebooks and used for self-assessment later in the investigation.

In the **Diversity of Life Course**, you ask,

➤ *What is life?*

For a quick write, students write an answer immediately, before instruction occurs. The quick write provides insight into what students think about certain phenomena before you begin instruction. When responding to the question, students should be encouraged to write down their thoughts, even if they don't feel confident in knowing the answer.

Knowing students' preconceptions will help you know what concepts need the most attention during the investigation. Make sure students date their entries for later reference. Read through students' writing and tally the important points to focus on. Quick writes should not be graded.

Planning. After students enter the focus question or complete a quick write in their notebooks, they plan their investigation. (In some investigations, planning is irrelevant to the task at hand.) Planning may be detailed or intuitive, formal or informal, depending on the requirement of the investigation. Plans might include lists (including materials, things to remember), step-by-step procedures, and experimental design. Some FOSS notebook masters guide students through a planning process specific to the task at hand.

Lists. Science notebooks often include lists of things to think about, materials to get, or words to remember. A materials list is a good organizer that helps students anticipate actions they will take. A list of variables to be controlled clarifies the purpose of an experiment. Simple lists of dates for observations or of the people responsible for completing a task may be useful.

Step-by-step procedures. Middle school students need to develop skills for writing sequential procedures. For example, in the **Chemical Interactions Course**, students write a procedure to answer these questions.

- *Is there a limit to the amount of substance that will dissolve in a certain amount of liquid?*
- *If so, is the amount that will dissolve the same for all substances?*

Students need to recall what they know about the materials, develop a procedure for accurately measuring the amount of a substance that is added to the water, and agree on a definition of "saturated." To check a procedure for errors or omissions, students can trade notebooks and attempt to follow another student's instructions to complete the task.

Experimental design. Some work with materials requires a structured experimental plan. In the **Planetary Science Course**, students pursue this focus question.

- *Are Moon craters the result of volcanoes or impacts?*

Students plan an experiment to determine what affects the size and shape of craters on the Moon. They use information they gathered during the open exploration of craters made in flour to develop a strategy for evaluating the effect of changing the variable of a projectile's height or mass. Each lab group agrees on which variable they will change and then designs a sound experimental procedure that they can refer to during the active investigation.

Data Acquisition and Organization

Because observation is the starting point for answering the focus question, data records should be

- clearly related to the focus question;
- accurate and precise;
- organized for efficient reference.

Data handling can have two subcomponents: data acquisition and data display. Data acquisition is making and recording observations (measurements). The data record can be composed of words, phrases, numbers, and drawings. Data display reorganizes the data in a logical way to facilitate thinking. The display can be a graph, chart, calendar, or other graphic organizer.

Early in a student's experience with notebooks, the record may be disorganized and incomplete, and the display may need guidance. The FOSS notebook masters are designed to help students with data collection and organization. You may initially introduce conventional data-display methods, such as those found in the FOSS notebook masters, but soon students will need opportunities to independently select appropriate data displays. As students become more familiar with collecting and organizing data, you might have them create their own records. With practice, students will become skilled at determining what form of recording to use in various situations, and how best to display the data for analysis.

Narratives. For most students, the most intuitive approach to recording data is narrative—using words, sentence fragments, and numbers in a more or less sequential manner. As students make a new observation, they record it below the previous entry, followed by the next observation, and so on. Some observations, such as a record of weather changes in the **Weather and Water Course** or the interactions of organisms in miniecosystems in the **Populations and Ecosystems Course**, are appropriately recorded in narrative form.

Drawings. A picture is worth a thousand words, and a labeled picture is even more useful. When students use a microscope to discover cells in the *Elodea* leaf and observe and draw structures of microorganisms in the **Diversity of Life Course**, a labeled illustration is the most efficient way to record data.

Charts and tables. An efficient way to record many kinds of data is a chart or table. How do you introduce this skill into the shared knowledge of the classroom? One way is to call for attention during an investigation and demonstrate how to perform the operation. Or you can let students record the data as they like, and observe their methods. There may be one or more groups that invent an appropriate table. During processing time, ask this group to share its method with the class. If no group has spontaneously produced an effective table, you might challenge the class to come up with an easier way to display the data, and turn the skill-development introduction into a problem-solving session.

With experience, students will recognize when a table or chart is appropriate for recording data. When students make similar observations on a series of objects, such as rock samples in the **Earth History Course**, a table with columns is an efficient way to organize observations for easy comparison.

Artifacts. Occasionally an investigation will produce two-dimensional artifacts that students can tape or glue directly into a science notebook. The mounted flower parts in the **Diversity of Life Course** and the sand samples card from the **Earth History Course** can become a permanent part of the record of learning.

Graphs and graphic tools. Reorganizing data into logical, easy-to-use graphic tools is typically necessary for data analysis. Graphs allow easy comparison (bar graph), quick statistical analysis of frequency data (histogram or line plot), and visual confirmation of a relationship between variables (two-coordinate graph). The **Force and Motion Course** offers many opportunities for students to collect data and organize the data into graphs. Students collect data from cars rolling down ramps, graph the data, and use the resulting graph to discuss whether cars traveling downhill maintain a constant velocity or accelerate. Other graphic tools, such as Venn diagrams, pie charts, and concept maps, help students make connections.

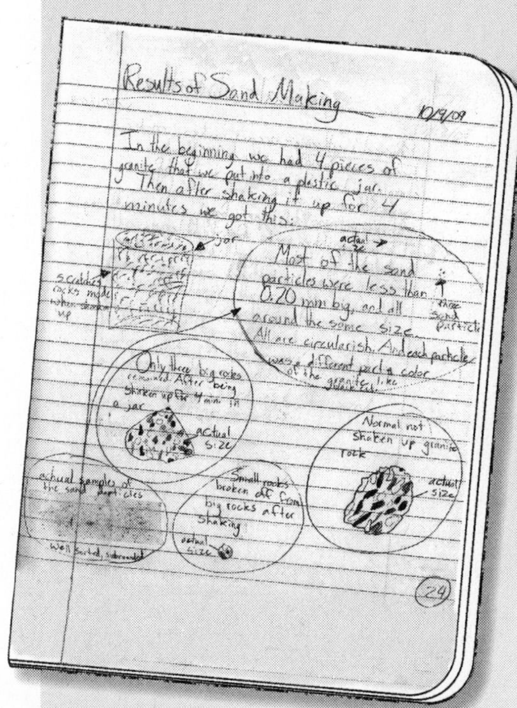

Drawing and artifact from the Earth History Course

Making Sense of Data

After collecting and organizing data, the student's next task is to answer the focus question. Students can generate an explanation as an unassisted narrative, but in many instances you might need to use supports such as the FOSS notebook masters to guide the development of a coherent and complete response to the question. Several other support structures for sense making are described below.

Development of vocabulary. Vocabulary is better introduced after students have experienced the new word(s) in context. This sequence provides a cognitive basis for students to connect accurate and precise language to their real-life experiences. Lists of new vocabulary words in the index reinforce new words and organize them for easy reference.

Data analysis. Interpreting data requires the ability to look for patterns, trends, outliers, and potential causes. Students should be encouraged to develop a habit of looking for patterns and relationships within the data collected. Frequently, this is accomplished by creating a graph with numerical data. In the **Populations and Ecosystems Course**, students review field data acquired by ecologists at Mono Lake to determine how biotic and abiotic factors affect the populations of organisms found in the lake.

Graphic organizers. Students can benefit from organizers that help them look at similarities and differences. A compare-and-contrast chart can help students make a transition from their collected data and experiences to making and writing comparisons. It is sometimes easier for students to use than a Venn diagram, and is commonly referred to as a box-and-T chart (as popularized in *Writing in Science: How to Scaffold Instruction to Support Learning*, listed in the Bibliography section).

In this strategy, students draw a box at the top of the notebook page and label it "similar" or "same." On the bottom of the notebook page, they draw a *T*. At the top of each wing of the *T*, they label the objects being compared. Students look at their data, use the *T* to identify differences for each item, and use the "similar" box to list all the characteristics that the two objects have in common. For example, a box-and-T chart comparing characteristics of extrusive and intrusive igneous rocks in the **Earth History Course** might look like this.

similar

extrusive	intrusive

Students can use the completed box-and-T chart to begin writing comparisons. It is usually easier for students to complete their chart on a separate piece of paper, so they can fill it in as they refer to their data. They affix the completed chart into their notebooks after they have made their comparisons.

Claims and evidence. A claim is an assertion about how the natural world works. Claims should always be supported by evidence—statements that are directly correlated with data. The evidence should refer to specific observations, relationships that are displayed in graphs, tables of data that show trends or patterns, dates, measurements, and so on. A claims-and-evidence construction is a sophisticated, rich display of student learning and thinking. It also shows how the data students collected is directly connected to what they learned.

Frames and prompts. One way to get students to organize their thinking is by providing sentence frames for them to complete.

- *I used to think ______, but now I think ______.*
- *The most important thing to remember about Moon phases is ______.*
- *One new thing I learned about adaptation is ______.*

Prompts also direct students to the content they should be thinking about, but provide more latitude for generating responses. For students who are learning English or who struggle with writing, assistive structures like sentence frames can help them communicate their thinking while they learn the nuances of science writing. The prompts used most often in the FOSS notebook masters take the form of questions for students to answer. In the **Weather and Water Course**, students answer the quick-write question

➤ *What causes seasons?*

After modeling an Earth/Sun system and reviewing solar angle and solar concentration, students revisit their quick write to revise and expand on their original explanations.

- *I used to think seasons were caused by ______, but now I know ______.*

Careful prompts scaffold students by helping them communicate their thinking but do not do the thinking for them. As students progress in communication ability, you might provide frames less frequently.

Conclusions and predictions. At the end of an investigation (major conceptual sequence), it might be appropriate for students to write a summary to succinctly communicate what they have learned. This is where students can make predictions based on their understanding of a principle or relationship. For instance, after completing the investigation of condensation and dew point in the **Weather and Water Course**, a student might predict the altitude at which clouds would form, based on weather-balloon data. Or upon examining the data graphed in the **Force and Motion Course**, students might predict the time it will take a cart to travel 200 centimeters down a slope that is different from the experimental slopes they have tried. The conclusion or prediction will frequently indicate the degree to which a student can apply new knowledge to real-world situations. A prediction can also be the springboard for further inquiry.

Generating new questions. Does the investigation connect to a student's personal interests? Does the outcome suggest a question or pique a student's curiosity? The science classroom is most exciting when students are generating their own questions for further investigation based on class or personal experiences. The notebook is an excellent place to capture students' musings and record thoughts that might otherwise be lost.

Next-Step Strategies

The goal of the FOSS curriculum is for students to develop accurate, durable knowledge of the science content under investigation. Students' initial conceptions are frequently incomplete or confused, requiring additional thought to become fully functional. The science notebook is a useful place to guide reflection and revision. Typically students commit their understanding in writing and reflect in three locations.

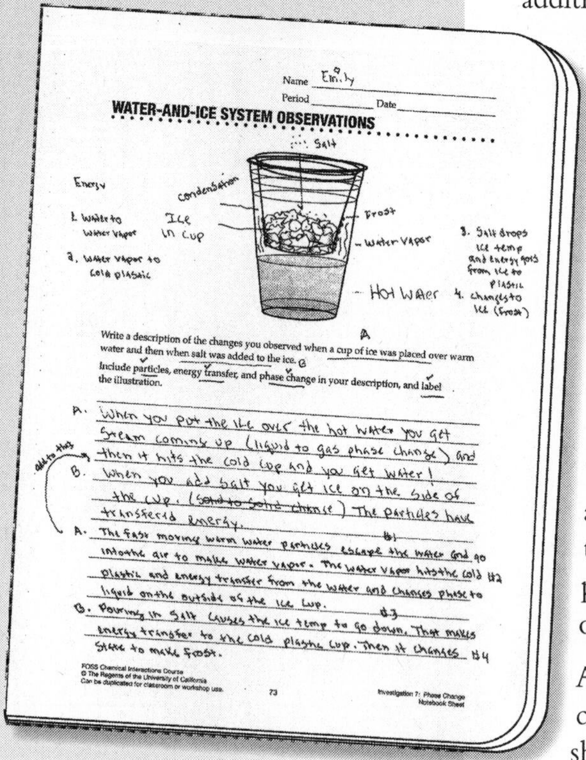

- Explanatory narratives in notebooks
- Response sheets incorporated into the notebook
- Written work on I-Checks

These three categories of written work provide information about student learning for you *and* a record of thinking for students that they can reflect on and revise. Scientists constantly refine and clarify their ideas about how the natural world works. They read scientific articles, consult with other scientists, and attend conferences. They incorporate new information into their thinking about the subject they are researching. This reflective process can result in deeper understanding or a complete revision of thinking.

A student's revised work for the Chemical Interactions Course

After completing one of the expositions of knowledge—a written conclusion, response sheet, or benchmark assessment—students should receive additional instruction or information via a next-step strategy. They will use this information later to complete self-assessment by reviewing their original written work, making judgments about its accuracy and completeness, and writing a revised explanation. You can use any of a number of techniques for providing the additional information to students.

- Group compare-and-share discussion
- Think/pair/share reading
- Whole-class critique of an explanation by an anonymous student
- Identifying key points for a class list
- Whole-class discussion of a presentation by one student

After one of the information-generating processes, students compare the "best answer" to their own answer and rework their explanations if they can no longer defend their original thinking. The revised statement of the science content can take one of several forms.

Students might literally revise the original writing, crossing out extraneous or incorrect bits, inserting new or improved information, and completing the passage. At other times, students might reflect on their original work and, after drawing and dating a line of learning (see below), might redraft their explanation from scratch, producing their best explanation of the concept.

During these self-assessment processes, students have to think actively about every aspect of their understanding of the concept and organize their thoughts into a coherent, logical narrative. The learning that takes place during this process is powerful. The relationships between the several elements of the concept become unified and clarified.

The notebook is the best tool for students when preparing for benchmark assessment, such as an I-Check or posttest. Students don't necessarily have the study skills needed to prepare on their own, but using teacher-guided tasks such as key points and traffic lights will turn the preparation process into a valuable exercise. These same strategies can be used after a benchmark assessment when you identify further areas of confusion or misconceptions you want to address with students. Here are four helpful next-step, or self-assessment, strategies.

Name ______________

Period _____ Date ______________

RESPONSE SHEET—WHERE AM I?

Billy was watching his favorite TV show when the question came up, "Where do you live?" Billy didn't know, so he asked his older sister. She replied, "You live in Birmingham."

Later Billy asked his mom the same question, to which she replied, "Honey, you live in the United States."

Billy was a little confused. He thought, "How can I live in two places at the same time?"

Who was right, Billy's sister? Billy's mom? Explain your answer.

Billy, They are both right. Birmingham is in the united states. its just a different kind of way or saying it frame of refrence

Silly Billy, They both just said a different frame of reference. Your sister said that you live in burmingam. and your mom said you live in the U.S. Its just different frame of reference

A line of learning used with the Planetary Science Course

Line of learning. One technique many teachers find useful in the reflective process is the line of learning. After students have conducted an investigation and entered their initial explanations, they draw and date a line under their original work. As students share ideas and refine their thinking during class discussion, additional experimentation, reading, and teacher feedback, encourage them to make new entries under the line of learning, adding to or revising their original thinking. If the concept is elusive or complex, a second line of learning, followed by more processing and revising, may be appropriate.

The line of learning is a reminder to students that learning is an ongoing process with imperfect products. It points out places in that process where a student made a stride toward full understanding. And the psychological security provided by the line of learning reminds students that they can always draw another line of learning and revise their thinking again. The ability to look back in the science notebook and see concrete evidence of learning gives students confidence and helps them become critical observers of their own learning.

Traffic lights. In the traffic-lights strategy, students use color to self-assess and indicate how well they understand a concept that they are learning. Green means that the student feels that he or she has a good understanding of the concept. Yellow means that the student is still a bit unsure about his or her understanding. Red means that the student needs help; he or she has little or no understanding of the concept. Students can use colored pencils, markers, colored dots, or colored cards to indicate their understanding. They can mark their own work and then indicate their level of understanding by a show of hands or by holding up colored cards. This strategy gives students practice in self-assessment and helps you monitor students' current understanding. You should follow up by looking at student work to ensure that they actually do understand the content that they marked with green.

Three C's. Another approach to revision is to apply the three C's—confirm, correct, complete—to the original work. Students indicate ideas that were correct with a number or a color, code statements needing correction with a second number or color, and assign a third number or color to give additional information that completes the entry.

Key points. Students do not necessarily connect the investigative experience with the key concepts and processes taught in the lesson. It is essential to give students an opportunity to reflect on their experiences and find meaning in those experiences. They should be challenged to use their experiences and data to either confirm or reject their current understanding of the natural world. As students form supportable ideas about a concept, those ideas should be noted as key points, posted in the room, and written in their notebooks. New evidence, to support or clarify an idea, can be added to the chart as the course progresses. If an idea doesn't hold up under further investigation, a line can be drawn through the key point to indicate a change in thinking. A key-points activity is embedded near the end of each investigation to help students organize their thinking and prepare for benchmark assessment.

USING NOTEBOOKS TO IMPROVE STUDENT LEARNING

Notebook entries should not be graded. Research has shown that more learning occurs when students get only comments on written work in their notebooks, not grades or a combination of comments and grades.

If your school district requires a certain number of grades each week, select certain work products that you want to grade and have students turn in that work separate from the notebook. After grading, return the piece to students to insert into their notebooks, so that all their work is in one place.

It may be difficult to stop using grades or a rubric for notebook assessment. But providing feedback that moves learning forward, however difficult, has benefits that make it worth the effort. The key to using written feedback for formative assessment is to make feedback timely and specific, and to provide time for students to act on the feedback by revising or correcting work right in their own notebook.

Teacher Feedback

Student written work often exposes weaknesses in understanding—or so it appears. It is important for you to find out if the flaw results from poor understanding of the science or from imprecise communication. You can use the notebook to provide two types of feedback to the student: to ask for clarification or additional information, and to ask probing questions that will help students move forward in their thinking. Respecting the student's space is important, so rather than writing directly in the notebook, attach a self-stick note, which can be removed after the student has taken appropriate action.

The most effective forms of feedback relate to the content of the work. Here are some examples.

- *You wrote that seasons are caused by Earth's tilt. Does Earth's tilt change during its orbit?*
- *What evidence can you use to support your claim that Moon craters are caused by impacts? Hint: Think of our experiments in class.*

Nonspecific feedback, such as stars, pluses, smiley faces, and "good job!", or ambiguous critiques, such as "try again," "put more thought into this," and "not enough," are less effective and should not be used. Feedback that guides students to think about the content of their work and gives suggestions for how to improve are productive instructional strategies.

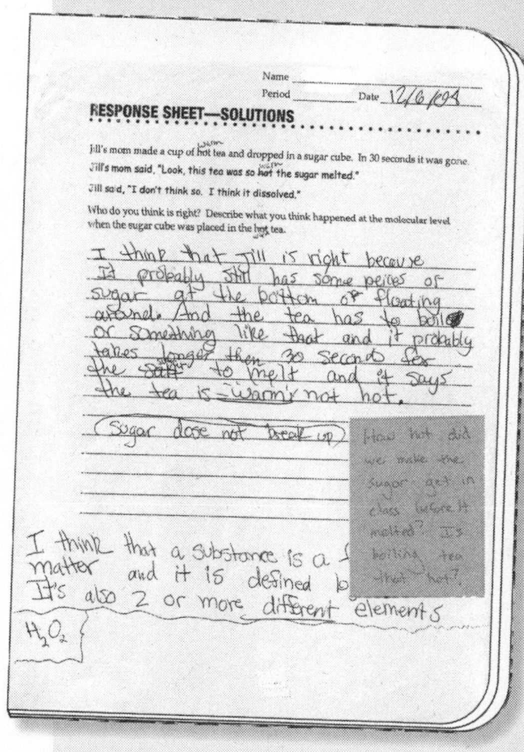

Name ______
Period ______ Date 12/6/09

RESPONSE SHEET—SOLUTIONS

Jill's mom made a cup of ~~hot~~ warm tea and dropped in a sugar cube. In 30 seconds it was gone.

Jill's mom said, "Look, this tea was so ~~hot~~ warm the sugar melted."

Jill said, "I don't think so. I think it dissolved."

Who do you think is right? Describe what you think happened at the molecular level when the sugar cube was placed in the ~~hot~~ warm tea.

I think that Jill is right because It probably still has some peices of sugar at the bottom or floating around. And the tea has to boil or something like that and it probably takes longer then 30 seconds for the sugar to melt and it says the tea is "warm" not hot.

(Sugar dose not break up)

How hot did we make the sugar get in class before it melted? Is boiling tea that hot?

I think that a substance is a matter and it is defined b... It's also 2 or more different elements

H_2O_2

Feedback given during the Chemical Interactions Course

Here are some appropriate generic feedback questions to write or use verbally while you circulate in the class.

- *What vocabulary have you learned that will help you describe ______?*
- *Can you include an example from class to support your ideas?*
- *Include more detail about ______.*
- *Check your data to make sure this is accurate.*
- *What do you mean by ______?*
- *When you record your data, what unit should you use?*

When students return to their notebooks and respond to the feedback, you will have additional information to help you discriminate between learning and communication difficulties. Another critical component of teacher feedback is providing comments to students in a timely manner, so that they can review their work before engaging in benchmark assessment or moving on to other big ideas in the course.

In middle school, you face the challenge of having a large number of students. This may mean collecting a portion of students' notebooks on alternate days. Set a specific focus for your feedback, such as a data table or conclusion, so you aren't trying to look at everything every time.

To help students improve their writing, you might have individuals share notebook entries aloud in their collaborative groups, followed by feedback from a partner or the group. This valuable tool must be very structured to create a safe environment, including ground rules about acceptable feedback and comments.

A good way to develop these skills is to model constructive feedback with the class, using a student-work sample from a notebook. Use a sample from a previous year with the name and any identifying characteristics removed. Project it for the class to practice giving feedback.

Formative Assessment

With students recording more of their thinking in an organized notebook, you have a tool to better understand the progress of students and any misconceptions that are typically not revealed until the benchmark assessment. One way to monitor student progress is during class while they are responding to a prompt. Circulate from group to group, and read notebook entries over students' shoulders. This is a good time to have short conversations with individuals or small groups to gain information about the level of student understanding. Take care to respect the privacy of students who are not comfortable sharing their work during the writing process.

If you want to look at work that is already completed in the notebook, ask students to open their notebooks to the page that you want to review and put them in a designated location. Or consider having students complete the work on a separate piece of paper or an index card. Students can leave a blank page in their notebooks, or label it with a header as a placeholder, until they get the work back and tape it or glue it in place. This makes looking at student work much easier, and the record of learning that the student is creating in the notebook remains intact.

When time is limited, you might select a sample of students from each class, alternating the sample group each time, to get a representative sample of student thinking. This is particularly useful following a quick write.

Once you have some information about student thinking, you can make teaching decisions about moving ahead to a benchmark assessment, going back to a previous concept, or spending more time making sense of a concept. Benchmark assessments can also be used as formative assessment. You might choose to administer an I-Check, score the assessment to find problem areas, and then revisit critical concepts before moving on to the next investigation. Students can use reflection and self-assessment techniques to revisit and build on their original exam responses.

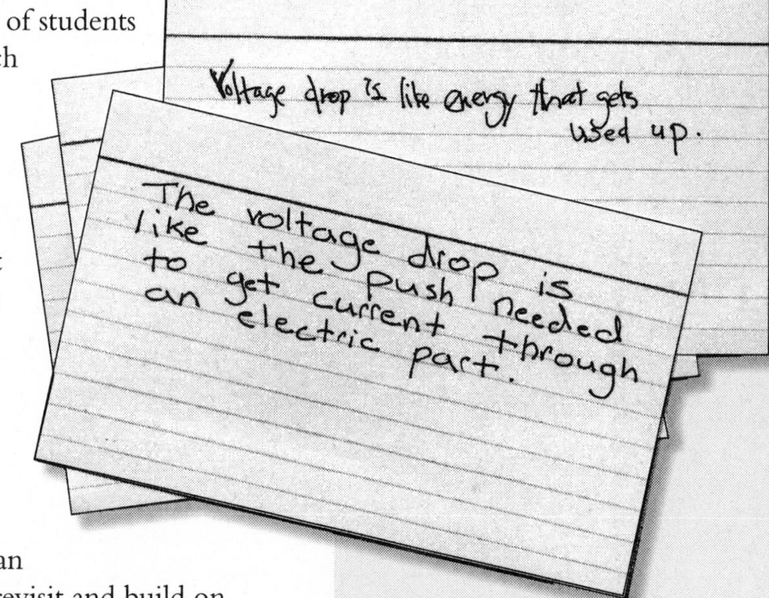

Quick writes for the Electronics Course written on index cards

DERIVATIVE PRODUCTS

On occasion, you might ask students to produce science projects of various kinds: summary reports, detailed explanations, end-of-course projects, oral reports, or posters. Students should use their notebooks as a reference when developing their reports. You could ask them to make a checklist of science concepts and pieces of evidence, with specific page references, extracted from their notebooks. They can then use this checklist to ensure that all important points have been included in the derivative work.

The process of developing a project has feedback benefits, too. While students are developing projects using their notebooks, they have the opportunity to self-monitor the organization and content of the notebook. This offers valuable feedback on locating and extracting useful information. You might want to discuss possible changes students would make next time they start a new science notebook.

Homework is another form of derivative product, as it is an extension of the experimentation started in class. Carefully selected homework assignments enhance students' science learning. Homework suggestions and/or extension activities are included at the end of each investigation. For example, in the **Human Brain and Senses Course**, after being introduced to the properties of lenses and how these properties affect the function of their eyes, students can write about the role of light in vision, considering radiant, transmitted, and reflected light. In the **Electronics Course**, students can calculate the flow of current in home appliances, using the information they have learned in class. Homework should be done on a separate paper, graded, and then inserted into the science notebook.

Science-Centered Language Development in Middle School

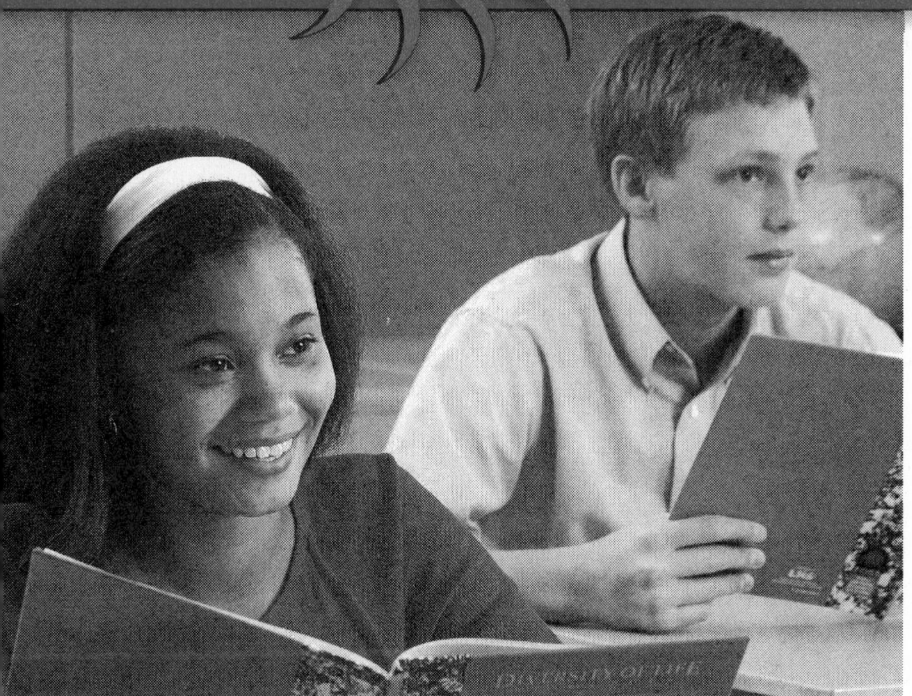

Contents

Reading and writing are inextricably linked to the very nature and fabric of science, and, by extension, to learning science.

Stephen P. Norris and Linda M. Phillips, "How Literacy in Its Fundamental Sense Is Central to Scientific Literacy"

INTRODUCTION

In this chapter, we explore the ways reading, writing, speaking, and listening are interwoven in effective science instruction at the secondary level. To engage fully in the enterprise of science and engineering, students must record and communicate observations and explanations, and read about and discuss the discoveries and ideas of others. This becomes increasingly challenging at the secondary level. Texts become more complex; writing requires fluency of academic language, including domain-specific vocabulary. Here we identify strategies that support sense making. The active investigations, student science notebooks, *FOSS Science Resources* readings, multimedia, and formative assessments provide rich contexts in which students develop and exercise thinking processes and communication skills. Students develop scientific literacy through experiences with the natural world around them in real and authentic ways and use language to inquire, process information, and communicate their thinking about the objects, organisms, and phenomena they are studying. We refer to the acquisition and building of language skills necessary for scientific literacy as science-centered language development.

Language plays two crucial roles in science learning: (1) it facilitates the communication of conceptual and procedural knowledge, questions, and propositions (external; public), and (2) it mediates thinking, a process necessary for understanding (internal; private). These are also the ways scientists use language: to communicate with one another about their inquiries, procedures, and understandings; to transform their observations into ideas; and to create meaning and new ideas from their work and the work of others. For students, language development is intimately involved in their learning about the natural world. Active-learning science provides a real and engaging context for developing literacy; language-arts skills and strategies support conceptual development and scientific and engineering practices. For example, the skills and strategies used for reading comprehension, writing expository text, and oral discourse are applied when students are recording their observations, making sense of science content, and communicating their ideas. Students' use of language improves when they discuss, write, and read about the concepts explored in each investigation.

We begin our exploration of science and language by focusing on language functions and how specific language functions are used in science to facilitate information acquisition and processing (thinking). Then we address issues related to the specific language domains—speaking and listening, writing, and reading. Each section addresses

- how skills in that domain are developed and exercised in FOSS science investigations;
- literacy strategies that are integrated purposefully into the FOSS investigations; and
- suggestions for additional literacy strategies that both enhance student learning in science and develop or exercise academic-language skills.

Following the domain discussions is a section on science-vocabulary development, with scaffolding strategies for supporting all learners. The last section covers language-development strategies specifically for English learners.

NOTE
The term *English learners* refers to students who are learning to understand English. This includes students who speak English as a second language and native English speakers who need additional support to use language effectively.

THE ROLE OF LANGUAGE IN SCIENTIFIC AND ENGINEERING PRACTICES

Language functions are the purpose for which speech or writing is used and involve both vocabulary and grammatical structure. Understanding and using language functions appropriately is important in effective communication. Students use numerous language functions in all disciplines to mediate communication and facilitate thinking (e.g., they plan, compare, discuss, apply, design, draw, and provide evidence).

In science, language functions facilitate scientific and engineering practices. For example, when students are *collecting data*, they are using language functions to identify, label, enumerate, compare, estimate, and measure. When students are *constructing explanations*, they are using language functions to analyze, communicate, discuss, evaluate, and justify.

A Framework for K–12 Science Education (National Research Council 2012) states that "Students cannot comprehend scientific practices, nor fully appreciate the nature of scientific knowledge itself, without directly experiencing the practices for themselves." Each of these scientific and engineering practices uses multiple language functions. Often, these language functions are part of an internal dialogue weighing the merits of various explanations—what we call thinking. The more language functions with which we are facile, the more effective and creative our thinking can be.

The scientific and engineering practices are listed below, along with a sample of the language functions that are exercised when students are effectively engaged in that practice. (Practices are bold; language functions are italic.)

Asking questions and defining problems

- *Ask* questions about objects, organisms, systems, and events in the natural and human-made world (science).
- *Ask* questions to *define* and *clarify* a problem, *determine criteria* for solutions, and *identify* constraints (engineering).

Planning and carrying out investigations

- *Plan* and conduct investigations in the laboratory and in the field to gather appropriate data (*describe* procedures, *determine* observations to *record*, *decide* which variables to control) or to gather data essential for *specifying* and *testing* engineering designs.

Examples of Language Functions

Analyze
Apply
Ask
Clarify
Classify
Communicate
Compare
Conclude
Construct
Critique
Describe
Design
Develop
Discuss
Distinguish
Draw
Enumerate
Estimate
Evaluate
Experiment
Explain
Formulate
Generalize
Group
Identify
Infer
Interpret
Justify
Label
List
Make a claim
Measure
Model
Observe
Organize
Plan
Predict
Provide evidence
Reason
Record
Represent
Revise
Sequence
Solve
Sort
Strategize
Summarize
Synthesize

Analyzing and interpreting data

- Use a range of tools (numbers, words, tables, graphs, images, diagrams, equations) to *organize* observations (data) in order to *identify* significant features and patterns.

Developing and using models

- Use models to help *develop explanations, make predictions*, and *analyze* existing systems, and *recognize* strengths and limitations of the models.

Using mathematics and computational thinking

- Use mathematics and computation to *represent* physical variables and their relationships.

Constructing explanations and designing solutions

- *Construct* logical explanations of phenomena, or *propose solutions* that incorporate current understanding or a model that represents it and is consistent with the available evidence.

Engaging in argument from evidence

- *Defend* explanations, *formulate evidence* based on data, *examine* one's own understanding in light of evidence offered by others, and collaborate with peers in searching for explanations.

Obtaining, evaluating, and communicating information

- *Communicate* ideas and the results of inquiry—orally and in writing—with tables, diagrams, graphs, and equations and in *discussion* with peers.

Research supports the claim that when students are intentionally using language functions in thinking about and communicating in science, they improve not only science content knowledge, but also language-arts and mathematics skills (Ostlund, 1998; Lieberman and Hoody, 1998). Language functions play a central role in science as a key cognitive tool for developing higher-order thinking and problem-solving abilities that, in turn, support academic literacy in all subject areas.

Here is an example of how an experienced teacher can provide an opportunity for students to exercise language functions in FOSS. In the **Planetary Science Course**, one piece of content we expect students to have acquired by the end of the course is

- The lower the angle at which light strikes a surface, the lower the density of the light energy.

The scientific practices the teacher wants the class to focus on are *developing and using models* and *constructing explanations*.

The language functions students will exercise while engaging in these scientific practices include *comparing, modeling, analyzing*, and *explaining*. The teacher understands that these language functions are appropriate to the purpose of the science investigation and support the *Common Core State Standards for English Language Arts and Literacy in Science* (CCSS), in which grades 6–8 students will "write arguments focused on discipline-specific content . . . support claim[s] with logical reasoning and relevant, accurate data and evidence that demonstrate an understanding of the topic" (National Governors Association Center for Best Practices, Council of Chief State School Officers, 2010).

- Students will *compare* the area covered by the same beam of light (from a flashlight) at different angles to *explain* the relationship between the angle and density of light energy.

The teacher can support the use of language functions by providing structures such as sentence frames.

- As ______, then ______.

  As the angle increases, then the light beam becomes smaller and more circular.

- When I changed ______, then ______.

  When I changed the angle of the light beam, then the concentration of light hitting the floor changed.

- The greater/smaller ______, the ______.

  The smaller the angle of the light beam, the more the light beam spread out.

- I think ______, because ______.

  I think the smaller spot of light receives more energy than the larger spot because the light concentration is greatest when light shines directly down on a surface and there is no beam spreading.

CCSS NOTE
This example supports CCSS.ELA-Literacy.WHST.6–8.1.b.

SPEAKING AND LISTENING DOMAIN

The FOSS investigations are designed to engage students in productive oral discourse. Talking requires students to process and organize what they are learning. Listening to and evaluating peers' ideas calls on students to apply their knowledge and to sharpen their reasoning skills. Guiding students in instructive discussions is critical to the development of conceptual understanding of the science content and the ability to think and reason scientifically. It also addresses a key middle school CCSS Speaking and Listening anchor standard that students "engage effectively in a range of collaborative discussions (one-on-one, in groups, and teacher-led) with diverse partners on [grade-level] topics, texts, and issues, building on others' ideas and expressing their own clearly."

CCSS NOTE
This example supports CCSS.ELA-Literacy.SL.6.1, CCSS.ELA-Literacy.SL.7.1, and CCSS.ELA-Literacy.SL.8.1.

FOSS investigations start with a discussion—a review to activate prior knowledge, presentation of a focus question, or a challenge to motivate and engage active thinking. During the active investigation, students talk with one another in small groups, share their observations and discoveries, point out connections, ask questions, and start to build explanations. The discussion icon in the sidebar of the *Investigations Guide* indicates when small-group discussions should take place.

Throughout the activity, the *Investigations Guide* indicates where it is appropriate to pause for whole-class discussions to guide conceptual understanding. The *Investigations Guide* provides you with discussion questions to help stimulate student thinking and support sense making. At times, it may be beneficial to use sentence frames or standard prompts to scaffold the use of effective language functions and structures. Allowing students a few minutes to write in their notebooks prior to sharing their answers also helps those who need more time to process and organize their thoughts.

NOTE
Additional notebook strategies can be found in the Science Notebooks in Middle School chapter in *Teacher Resources* and online at www.FOSSweb.com.

On the following pages are some suggestions for providing structure to those discussions and for scaffolding productive discourse when needed. Using the protocols that follow will ensure inclusion of all students in discussions.

Partner and Small-Group Discussion Protocols

Whenever possible, give students time to talk with a partner or in a small group before conducting a whole-class discussion. This provides all students with a chance to formulate their thinking, express their ideas, practice using the appropriate science vocabulary, and receive input from peers. Listening to others communicate different ways of thinking about the same information from a variety of perspectives helps students negotiate the difficult path of sense making for themselves.

Partner and Small-Group Discussion Protocols
- *Dyads*
- *Partner parade*
- *Put in your two cents*

Dyads. Students pair up and take turns either answering a question or expressing an idea. Each student has 1 minute to talk while the other student listens. While student A is talking, student B practices attentive listening. Student B makes eye contact with student A, but cannot respond verbally. After 1 minute, the roles reverse.

Here's an example from the **Chemical Interactions Course**. After reviewing the results of eight reactions recorded in their notebooks, you ask students to pair up and take turns sharing which two substances they think constitute the mystery mixture and their reasons for selecting those two. The language objective is for students to compare their test results and make inferences based on their observations and what they know about chemical reactions (orally and in writing). These sentence frames can be written on the board to scaffold student thinking and conversation.

- I think the two substances in the mystery mixture are ______ and ______.
- My evidence is ______.

Partner parade. Students form two lines facing each other. Present a question, an idea, an object, or an image as a prompt for students to discuss. Give them 1 minute to greet the person in front of them and discuss the prompt. After 1 minute, call time. Have the first student in one of the lines move to the end of the line, and have the rest of the students in that line shift one step sideways so that everyone has a new partner. (Students in the other line do not move.) Give students a new prompt to discuss for 1 minute with their new partners. This can also be done by having students form two concentric circles. After each prompt, the inner circle rotates.

For example, when students are just beginning the **Earth History Course** investigation on igneous rock, you may want to assess prior knowledge about Earth's layers. Give each student a picture from an assortment of related images such as volcanoes, magma, a diagram of Earth's layers, crystals, and so forth, and have students line up facing each other in two lines or in concentric circles. For the first round, ask, "What do you observe in the image on your card?" For the second round, ask, "What can you infer from the image?" For the third round, ask, "What questions do you have about the image?" The language objective is for students to describe their observations, infer how the landform formed, and reflect upon and relate any experiences they may have had with a similar landform. These sentence frames can be used to scaffold student discussion.

- I observe ______, ______, and ______.
- I think this shows ______ because ______.
- I wonder ______.

Put in your two cents. For small-group discussions, give each student two pennies or similar objects to use as talking tokens. Each student takes a turn putting a penny in the center of the table and sharing his or her idea. Once all have shared, each student takes a turn putting in the other penny and responding to what others in the group have said. For example,

- I agree (or don't agree) with ______ because ______.

Here's an example from the **Diversity of Life Course**. In their notebooks, students have recorded the amount of water lost from their vials containing celery with and without leaves. They discover a discrepancy in the amount of water lost and the mass of the celery. Where did the water go? Students are struggling to form an explanation. The language objective is for students to compare their results and infer that there is a relationship between the amount of water lost and the number of leaves the celery has. You give each student two pennies, and in groups of four, they take turns putting in their two cents. For the first round, each student answers the question "Where did the water go?" They use the frame

- I think the water ______.
- My evidence is ______.

On the second round, each student states whether he or she agrees or disagrees with someone else in the group and why, using the sentence frame.

Whole-Class Discussion Supports

The whole-class discussion is a critical part of sense making. After students have had the active learning experience and have talked with their peers in pairs and/or small groups, sharing their observations with the whole class sets the stage for developing conventional explanatory models. Discrepant events, differing results, and other surprises are discussed, analyzed, and resolved. It is important that students realize that science is a process of finding out about the world around them. This is done through asking questions, testing ideas, forming explanations, and subjecting those explanations to logical scrutiny, that is, argumentation. Leading students through productive discussion helps them connect their observations and the abstract symbols (words) that represent and explain those observations. Whole-class discussion also provides an opportunity for you to interject an accurate and precise verbal summary as a model of the kind of thinking you are seeking. Facilitating effective whole-class discussions takes skill, practice, a shared set of norms, and patience. In the long run, students will have a better grasp of the content and will improve their ability to think independently and communicate effectively.

Norms should be established so that students know what is expected during science discussions.

- Science content and practices are the focus.
- Everyone participates (speaking and listening).
- Ideas and experiences are shared, accepted, and valued. Everyone is respectful of one another.
- Claims are supported by evidence.
- Challenges (debate and argument) are part of the quest for complete understanding.

A variety of whole-class discussion techniques can be introduced and practiced during science instruction that address the CCSS Speaking and Listening standards for students to "present claims and findings [e.g., argument, narrative, informative, summary presentations], emphasizing salient points in a focused, coherent manner with relevant evidence, sound valid reasoning, and well-chosen details; use appropriate eye contact, adequate volume, and clear pronunciation."

For example, during science talk, students are reminded to practice attentive listening, stay focused on the speaker, ask questions, and respond appropriately. In addition, in order for students to develop and practice their reasoning skills, they need to know the language forms

Whole-Class Discussion Supports

- *Sentence frames*
- *Guiding questions*

Let students know that scientists change their minds based on new evidence. It is expected that students will revise their thinking, based on evidence presented in discussions.

CCSS NOTE

This example supports CCSS.ELA-Literacy.SL.6.4, CCSS.ELA-Literacy.SL.7.4, and CCSS.ELA-Literacy.SL.8.4, (grade 8 quoted here).

TEACHING NOTE

Encourage "science talk." Allow time for students to engage in discussions that build on other students' observations and reasoning. After an investigation, use a teacher- or student-generated question, and either just listen or facilitate the interaction with questions to encourage expression of ideas among students.

and structures and the behaviors used in evidence-based debate and argument, such as using data to support claims, disagreeing respectfully, and asking probing questions (Winokur and Worth, 2006).

Explicitly model the language structures appropriate for active discussions, and encourage students to use them when responding to guiding questions and during science talks.

Sentence frames. These samples can be posted as a scaffold as students develop their reasoning and oral participation skills.

- I think ______, because ______.
- I predict ______, because ______.
- I claim ______; my evidence is ______.
- I agree with ______ that ______.
- My idea is similar/related to ______'s idea.
- I learned/discovered/heard that ______.
- <Name> explained ______ to me.
- <Name> shared ______ with me.
- We decided/agreed that ______.
- Our group sees it differently, because ______.
- We have different observations/results. Some of us found that ______. One group member thinks that ______.
- We had a different approach/idea/solution/answer: ______.

Guiding questions. The Investigations Guide provides questions to help concentrate student thinking on the concepts introduced in the investigation. Guiding questions should be used during the whole-class discussion to facilitate sense making. Here are some other open-ended questions that help guide student thinking and promote discussion.

- What did you notice when ______?
- What do you think will happen if ______?
- How might you explain ______? What is your evidence?
- What connections can you make between ______ and ______?

Whole-Class Discussion Protocols

The following tried-and-true participation protocols can be used to enhance whole-class discussions. The purpose of these protocols is to increase meaningful participation by giving all students access to the discussion, allowing students time to think (process), and providing a context for motivation and engagement.

Whole-Class Discussion Protocols
- *Think-pair-share*
- *Pick a stick*
- *Whip around*
- *Commit and toss*
- *Group posters*

Think-pair-share. When asking for a response to a question posed to the class, give students a minute to think silently. Then, have students pair up with a partner to exchange thoughts before you call on a student to share his or her ideas with the whole class.

Pick a stick. Write each student's name on a craft stick, and keep the sticks handy in a cup at the front of the room. When asking for responses, randomly pick a stick, and call on that student to start the discussion. Continue to select sticks as you continue the discussion. Your name can also be on a stick in the cup. To keep students on their toes, put the selected sticks into a smaller cup hidden inside the larger cup out of view of students. That way students think they may be called again.

Cup within a cup pick-a-stick container

Whip around. Each student takes a quick turn sharing a thought or reaction. Questions are phrased to elicit quick responses that can be expressed in one to five words (e.g., "Give an example of a stored-energy source." "What does the word *heat* make you think of?").

Commit and toss. Have students write a response to a question or prompt on a loose piece of paper (Keeley, 2008). Next, tell everyone to crumple up the paper into a ball and toss it to another student. Continue tossing for a few minutes, and then call for students to stop, grab a ball, and read the response silently. Responses can then be shared with partners, small groups, or the whole class. This activity allows students to answer anonymously, so they may be willing to share their thinking more openly.

Group posters. Have small groups design and graphically record their investigation data and conclusions on a quickly generated poster to share with the whole class.

WRITING DOMAIN

Information processing is enhanced when students engage in informal writing. When allowed to write expressively without fear of being scorned for incorrect spelling or grammar, students are more apt to organize and express their thoughts in different ways that support their own sense making. Writing in science promotes use of science and engineering practices, thereby developing a deeper engagement with the science content. This type of informal writing also provides a springboard for more formal derivative science writing (Keys, 1999).

Science Notebooks

The science notebook is an effective tool for enhancing learning in science and exercising various forms of writing. Notebooks provide opportunities both for expressive writing (students craft explanatory narratives that make sense of their science experiences) and for practicing informal technical writing (students use organizational structures and writing conventions). Students learn to communicate their thinking in an organized fashion while engaging in the cognitive processes required to develop concepts and build explanations. Having this developmental record of learning also provides an authentic means for assessing students' progress in both scientific thinking and communication skills.

NOTE
For more information about supporting science-notebook development, see the Science Notebooks in Middle School chapter.

Developing Writing for Literacy in Science

Using student science notebooks in science instruction provides opportunities to address the CCSS for Writing in Science. Grades 6–8 students "write routinely over extended time frames (time for research, reflection, and revision) and shorter time frames (a single sitting or a day or two) for a range of tasks, purposes, and audiences." In addition to providing a structure for recording and analyzing data, notebooks serve as a reference tool from which students can draw information in order to produce derivative products, that is, more formal science writing pieces that have a specific purpose and format. CCSS focus on three text types that students should be writing in science: argument, informational/explanatory writing, and narrative writing. These text types are used in science notebooks and can be developed into derivative products such as reports, articles, brochures, poster boards, electronic presentations, letters, and so forth. Following is a description of these three text types and examples that may be used with FOSS investigations to help students build scientific literacy.

CCSS NOTE
This example supports CCSS.ELA-Literacy.W.10.

Engaging in Argument

In science, middle school students make claims in the form of statements or conclusions that answer questions or address problems. CCSS Appendix A describes that for students to use "data in a scientifically acceptable form, students marshal evidence and draw on their understanding of scientific concepts to argue in support of their claims." Applying the literacy skills necessary for this type of writing concurrently supports the development of critical science and engineering practices—most notably, engaging in argument. According to *A Framework for K–12 Science Education*, upon which the Next Generation Science Standards (NGSS) are based, middle school students are expected to construct a convincing argument that supports or refutes claims for explanations about the natural and designed world in these ways.

In FOSS, this type of writing makes students' thinking visible. Both informally in their notebooks and formally on assessments, students use deductive and inductive reasoning to construct and defend their explanations. In this way, students deepen their science understanding and exercise the language functions necessary for higher-level thinking, for example, comparing, synthesizing, evaluating, and justifying. To support students in both oral and written argumentation, use the questions and prompts in the *Investigations Guide* that encourage students to use evidence, models, and theories to support their arguments. In addition, be prepared for those teachable moments that provide the perfect stage for spontaneous scientific debate. Here are some general questions to help students deepen their writing.

- Why do you agree or disagree with ______?
- How would you prove/disprove ______?
- What data did you use to make that conclusion that ______?
- Why was it better that ______?

Here are the ways engaging in written argument are developed in the FOSS investigations and can be extended through formal writing.

Response sheets. The FOSS response sheets give students practice in constructing arguments by providing hypothetical situations where they have to apply what they have learned in order to evaluate a claim. For example, one of the response sheets in the **Planetary Science Course** asks students to respond to three students' explanations for the seasons. Students write a paragraph to each student with the

Engaging in Argument
- *Response sheets*
- *Think questions*
- *I-Checks and surveys/posttests*
- *Persuasive writing*

CCSS NOTE
This example supports CCSS.ELA-Literacy.W.1.

purpose of changing his or her thinking. In order to refute each claim, students must evaluate the validity of the statements and construct arguments based on evidence from the data they've collected during the investigations and logical reasoning that supports their explanation for what causes seasons.

Think questions. Interactive reading in *FOSS Science Resources* is another opportunity for students to engage in written argumentation. Articles include questions that support reading comprehension and extend student thinking about the science content. Asking students to make a claim and provide evidence to support it encourages the use of language functions necessary for higher-level thinking such as evaluating, applying, and justifying. For example, in *FOSS Science Resources: Planetary Science*, students are asked to respond to the following question: Why do you think there are so few craters on Earth and so many on the Moon? After discussion with their peers, students can hone their argumentation skills by writing an argument that answers the question and is supported by the evidence in the *FOSS Science Resources* book as well as data recorded from their experience making model craters.

I-Checks and surveys/posttests. Like the FOSS response sheets, some test items assess students' ability to make a claim and provide evidence to support it. One way is to provide students with data and have them make a claim based on that data and evidence from their prior investigations. Their argument should use logical reasoning to support their ideas. For example, in **Planetary Science**, students are shown images taken from two different planets. They are told that one has a thick atmosphere and the other has no atmosphere. They are asked which image they think came from a planet with an atmosphere and why. Using the images, they can see evidence of craters, and they can draw on their own experiences as well as knowledge acquired through other sources to piece together a logical argument.

Persuasive writing. Formal writing gives students the opportunity to summarize, explain, apply, and evaluate what they have learned in science. It also provides a purpose and audience that motivate students to produce higher-level writing products. The objective of persuasive writing is to convince the reader that a stated interpretation of data is worthwhile and meaningful. In addition to supporting claims with evidence and using logical argument, the writer also uses persuasive techniques such as a call to action. Students can use their informal notebook entries to form the basis of formal persuasive writing in a variety of formats, such as essays, letters, editorials, advertisements, award nominations, informational pamphlets, and petitions. Animal habitats, energy use, weather patterns, landforms, and water sources are just a few science topics that can generate questions and issues for persuasive writing.

Here is a sample of writing frames that can be used to introduce and scaffold persuasive writing (modified from Gibbons, 2002).

Title: ______

The topic of this discussion is ______.

My opinion (position, conclusion) is ______.

There are <number> reasons why I believe this to be true.

First, ______.

Second, ______.

Finally, ______.

On the other hand, some people think ______.

I have also heard people say ______.

However, my claim is that ______ because ______.

Informational/Explanatory Writing
- *Writing frames*
- *Recursive cycle*

CCSS NOTE
Designing, recording, and following procedures in FOSS courses supports CCSS.ELA-Literacy.RST.6–8.3.

CCSS NOTE
This example supports CCSS.ELA-Literacy.W.2.

Informational/Explanatory Writing

Informational and explanatory writing requires students to examine and convey complex ideas and information clearly and accurately through the effective selection, organization, and analysis of content. In middle school science, this includes writing scientific procedures and experiments. Described in CCSS Appendix A, informational/ explanatory writing answers the questions, What type? What are the components? What are the properties, functions, and behaviors? How does it work? What is happening? Why? In FOSS, this type of writing takes place informally in science notebooks, where students are recording their questions, plans, procedures, data, and answers to the focus questions. It also supports sense making as students attempt to convey what they know in response to questions and prompts, using language functions such as identifying, comparing and contrasting, explaining cause-and-effect relationships, and sequencing.

As an extension of the notebook entries, students can apply their content knowledge to publish formal products such as letters, definitions, procedures, newspaper and magazine articles, posters, pamphlets, and research reports. Strategies such as the writing process (plan, draft, edit, revise, and share) and writing frames (modeling and guiding the use of topic sentences, transition and sequencing words, examples, explanations, and conclusions) can be used to scaffold and help students develop proficiency in science writing.

Writing frames. Here are samples of writing frames (modified from Wellington and Osborne, 2001).

Description

Title: ______

(Identify) The part of the ______ I am describing is the ______.

(Describe) It consists of ______.

(Explain) The function of these parts is ______.

(Example) This drawing shows ______.

Explanation

Title: ______

I want to explain why (how) ______.

An important reason for why (how) this happens is that ______.

Another reason is that ______.

I know this because ______.

Recursive cycle. An effective method for extending students' science learning through writing is the recursive cycle of research (Bereiter, 2002). This strategy emphasizes writing as a process for learning, similar to the way students learn during the active science investigations.

1. Decide on a problem or question to write about.
2. Formulate an idea or a conjecture about the problem or question.
3. Identify a remedy or an answer, and develop a coherent discussion.
4. Gather information (from an experiment, science notebooks, *FOSS Science Resources*, FOSSweb multimedia, books, Internet, interviews, videos, etc.).
5. Reevaluate the problem or question based on what has been learned.
6. Revise the idea or conjecture.
7. Make presentations (reports, posters, electronic presentations, etc.).
8. Identify new needs, and make new plans.

This process can continue for as long as new ideas and questions occur, or students can present a final product in any of the suggested formats.

CCSS NOTE
This example supports CCSS.ELA-Literacy.W.7.

Narrative Writing

Narrative writing conveys an experience to the reader, usually with sensory detail and a sequence of events. In middle school science, students learn the importance of writing narrative descriptions of their procedures with enough detail and precision to allow others to replicate the experiment. Science also provides a broad landscape of stimulating material for stories, songs, biographies, autobiographies, poems, and plays. Students can enrich their science learning by using organisms or objects as characters; describing habitats and environments as settings; and writing scripts portraying various systems, such as weather patterns, states of matter, and the water, rock, or life cycle.

NOTE
Human characteristics should not be given to organisms (anthropomorphism) in science investigations, only in literacy extensions.

CCSS NOTE
This example supports CCSS.ELA-Literacy.W.3.

READING DOMAIN

Reading is an integral part of science learning. Just as scientists spend a significant amount of their time reading each other's published works, students need to learn to read scientific text—to read effectively for understanding, with a critical focus on the ideas being presented.

CCSS NOTE
The use of *FOSS Science Resources* supports CCSS.ELA-Literacy.RST.6–8.10.

The articles in *FOSS Science Resources* facilitate sense making as students make connections to the science concepts introduced and explored during the active investigations. Concept development is most effective when students are allowed to experience organisms, objects, and phenomena firsthand before engaging the concepts in text. The text and illustrations help students make connections between what they have experienced concretely and the abstract ideas that explain their observations.

FOSS Science Resources provides students with clear and coherent explanations, ways of visualizing important information, and different perspectives to examine and question. As students apply these strategies, they are, in effect, using some of the same scientific thinking processes that promote critical thinking and problem solving. In addition, the text provides a level of complexity appropriate for middle schoolers to develop high-level reading comprehension skills. This development requires support and guidance as students grapple with more complex dimensions of language meaning, structure, and conventions. To become proficient readers of scientific and other academic texts, students must be armed with an array of reading comprehension strategies and have ample opportunities to practice and extend their learning by reading texts that offer new language, new knowledge, and new modes of thought.

CCSS NOTE
Reading breakpoints in the *Investigations Guide* support CCSS.ELA-Literacy.RST.6–8.8.

Oral discourse and writing are critical for reading comprehension and for helping students make sense of the active investigations. Use the suggested prompts, questions, and strategies in the *Investigations Guide* to support comprehension as students read from *FOSS Science Resources*. For most of the investigation parts, the articles are designed to follow the active investigation and are interspersed throughout the course. This allows students to acquire the necessary background knowledge in context through active experience before tackling the wider-ranging content and relationships presented in the text. Breakpoints in the readings are suggested in the *Investigations Guide* to support student conceptual development. Some questions make connections between the reading and the student's class experience. Other questions help the students consider the writer's intent. Additional strategies for reading are derived from the seven essential strategies that readers use to help them understand what they read (Keene and Zimmermann, 2007).

- Monitor for meaning: discover when you know and when you don't know.
- Use and create schemata: make connections between the novel and the known; activate and apply background knowledge.
- Ask questions: generate questions before, during, and after reading that reach for deeper engagement with the text.
- Determine importance: decide what matters most, what is worth remembering.
- Infer: combine background knowledge with information from the text to predict, conclude, make judgments, and interpret.
- Use sensory and emotional images: create mental images to deepen and stretch meaning.
- Synthesize: create an evolution of meaning by combining understanding with knowledge from other texts/sources.

Reading Comprehension Strategies

Below are some strategies that enhance the reading of expository texts in general and have proven to be particularly helpful in science. Read and analyze the articles beforehand in order to guide students through the text structures and content more effectively.

Build on background knowledge. Activating prior knowledge is critical for helping students make connections between what they already know and new information. Reading comprehension improves when students have the opportunity to think, discuss, and write about what they know about a topic before reading. Review what students learned from the active investigation, provide prompts for making connections, and ask questions to help students recall past experiences and previous exposure to concepts related to the reading.

Create an anticipation guide. Create true-or-false statements related to the key ideas in the reading selection. Ask students to indicate if they agree or disagree with each statement before reading, then have them read the text, looking for the information that supports their true-or-false claims. Anticipation guides connect students to prior knowledge, engage them with the topic, and encourage them to explore their own thinking. To provide a challenge for advanced students, have them come up with the statements for the class.

Draw attention to vocabulary. Check the article for bold faced words students may not know. Review the science words that are already defined in students' notebooks. For new science and nonscience

Reading Comprehension Strategies
- *Build on background knowledge*
- *Create an anticipation guide*
- *Draw attention to vocabulary*
- *Preview the text*
- *Turn and talk*
- *Jigsaw text reading*
- *Note making*
- *Summarize and synthesize*
- *3-2-1*
- *Write reflections*
- *Preview and predict*
- *SQ3R*

CCSS NOTE

The example of reviewing what students learned from the active investigation supports CCSS.ELA-Literacy.RST.6–8.9.

CCSS NOTE

This example supports CCSS.ELA-Literacy.RST.6–8.4.

vocabulary words that appear in the reading, have students predict their meanings before reading. During the reading, have students use strategies such as context clues and word structure to see if their predictions were correct. This strategy activates prior knowledge and engages students by encouraging analytical participation with the text.

NOTE
Discourse markers are words or phrases that relate one idea to another. Examples are *however, on the other hand,* and *second.*

CCSS NOTE
This example supports CCSS.ELA-Literacy.RST.6-8.5 and CCSS.ELA-Literacy.RST.6-8.6.

Preview the text. Give students time to skim through the selection, noting subheads, before reading thoroughly. Point out the particular structure of the text and what discourse markers to look for. For example, most *FOSS Science Resources* articles are written as cause and effect, problem and solution, question and answer, comparison and contrast, description, or sequence. Students will have an easier time making sense of the text if they know what text structure to look for. Model and have students practice analyzing these different types of expository text structures by looking for examples, patterns, and discourse markers. For example, let's look at a passage from *FOSS Science Resources: Planetary Science.*

> An eclipse of the Moon occurs when Earth passes exactly between the Moon and the Sun. [cause and effect] The Moon moves into Earth's shadow during a lunar eclipse. At the time of a full lunar eclipse, Earth's shadow completely covers the disk of the Moon. [description] This is how Earth, the Moon, and the Sun are aligned for a lunar eclipse to be observed. [photograph] Why don't we see a lunar eclipse every month? [question and answer] Because of the tilt of the Moon's orbit around the Earth, Earth's shadow does not fall on the Moon in most months.

CCSS NOTE
This example supports CCSS.ELA-Literacy.RST.6-8.7.

Point out how the text in *FOSS Science Resources* is organized (titles, headings, subheadings, questions, and summaries) and if necessary, review how to use the table of contents, glossary, and index. Explain how to scan for formatting features that provide key information (such as boldface type and italics, captions, and framed text) and graphic features (such as tables, graphs, photographs, maps, diagrams, and charts) that help clarify, elaborate, and explain important information in the reading.

While students preview the article, have them focus on the questions that appear in the text, as well as questions at the end of the article. Encourage students to write down questions they have that they think the article will answer.

Turn and talk. When reading as a whole class, stop at key points and have students share their thinking about the selection with the student sitting next to them or with their collaborative group. This strategy helps students process the information and allows everyone to participate in the discussion. When reading in pairs, encourage

students to stop and discuss with their partners. One way to encourage engagement and understanding during paired reading is to have students take turns reading aloud a paragraph or section on a certain topic. The one who is listening then summarizes the meaning conveyed in the passage.

Jigsaw text reading. Students work together in small groups (expert teams) to develop a collective understanding of a text. Each expert team is responsible for one portion of the assigned text. The teams read and discuss their portions to gain a solid understanding of the key concepts. They might use graphic organizers to refine and organize the information. Each expert team then presents its piece to the rest of the class. Or form new jigsaw groups that consist of at least one representative from each expert team. Each student shares with the jigsaw group what their team learned from their particular portion of the text. Together, the participants in the jigsaw group fit their individual pieces together to create a complete picture of the content in the article.

Note making. The more students interact with a reading, the better their understanding. Encourage students to become active readers by asking them to make notes as they read. Studies have shown that note making—especially paraphrasing and summarizing—is one of the most effective means for understanding text (Graham and Herbert, 2010; Applebee, 1984). Some investigation parts include notebook sheets that match pages in *FOSS Science Resources*. This allows students to highlight and underline important points, add notes in the margins, and circle words they do not know. Students can also annotate the article by writing thoughts and questions on self-stick notes. Using symbols or codes can help facilitate comprehension monitoring. Here are some possible symbols students can use to communicate their thinking as they interact with text. (Harvey, 1998).

CCSS NOTE
This example supports CCSS.ELA-Literacy.RST.6–8.10.

★	interesting
BK	background knowledge
?	question
C	confusing
I	important
L	learning something new
W	wondering
S	surprising

Students can also use a different set of symbols while making notes about connections: the readings in *FOSS Science Resources* incorporate the active learning that students gain from the investigations, so that they can make authentic text-to-self (T-S) connections. In other words, what they read reminds them of firsthand experiences, making the article more engaging and easier to understand. Text-to-text (T-T) connections are notes students make when they discover a new idea that reminds them of something they've read previously in another text. Text-to-world (T-W) connections involve the text and more global everyday connections to students' lives.

▶ CCSS NOTE

This example supports CCSS.ELA-Literacy.RST.6–8.1 and CCSS.ELA-Literacy.RST.6–8.2.

You can model note-making strategies by displaying a selection of text, using a projection system, a document camera, or an interactive whiteboard. As you read the text aloud, model how to write comments on self-stick notes, and use a graphic organizer in a notebook to enhance understanding.

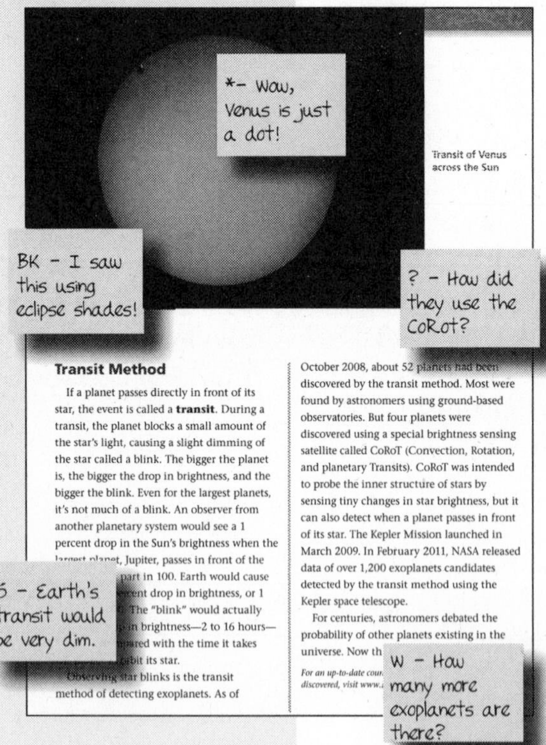

Transit Method

If a planet passes directly in front of its star, the event is called a **transit**. During a transit, the planet blocks a small amount of the star's light, causing a slight dimming of the star called a blink. The bigger the planet is, the bigger the drop in brightness, and the bigger the blink. Even for the largest planets, it's not much of a blink. An observer from another planetary system would see a 1 percent drop in the Sun's brightness when the largest planet, Jupiter, passes in front of the ... part in 100. Earth would cause ... drop in brightness, or 1 ... The "blink" would actually ... in brightness—2 to 16 hours— ... with the time it takes ... its star.

... star blinks is the transit method of detecting exoplanets. As of October 2008, about 52 planets had been discovered by the transit method. Most were found by astronomers using ground-based observatories. But four planets were discovered using a special brightness sensing satellite called CoRoT (Convection, Rotation, and planetary Transits). CoRoT was intended to probe the inner structure of stars by sensing tiny changes in star brightness, but it can also detect when a planet passes in front of its star. The Kepler Mission launched in March 2009. In February 2011, NASA released data of over 1,200 exoplanets candidates detected by the transit method using the Kepler space telescope.

For centuries, astronomers debated the probability of other planets existing in the universe. Now th...

For an up-to-date cou... discovered, visit www...

FACTS	QUESTIONS
L - When a planet crosses in front of a star, it causes a dimming of the star called a "blink." I - Exoplanets can be detected by observing star blinks. C - Earth's transit would cause a very small dimming, but it would be long in brightness.	Can we observe any other transits in our life time? How many more exoplanets are there? What does a "long drop in brightness" mean?

An example of annotated text from *FOSS Science Resources: Planetary Science*

Graphic organizers help students focus on extracting the important information from the reading and analyzing relationships between concepts. This can be done by simply having students make columns in their notebooks to record information and their thinking (Harvey and Goudvis, 2007). Here are two examples.

Notes	Thinking

Facts	Questions	Responses

▶ CCSS NOTE
This example supports CCSS.ELA-Literacy.RST.6–8.1 and CCSS.ELA-Literacy.RST.6–8.2.

Summarize and synthesize. Model how to pick out the important parts of the reading selection. Paraphrasing is one way to summarize. Have students write summaries of the reading, using their own words. To scaffold the learning, use graphic organizers to compare and contrast, group, sequence, and show cause and effect. Another method is to have students make two columns in their notebooks. In one column, they record what is important, and in the other, they record their personal responses (what the reading makes them think about). When writing summaries, tell students,

- *Pick out the important ideas.*
- *Restate the main ideas in your own words.*
- *Keep it brief.*

3-2-1. This graphic-organizer strategy gives students the opportunity to synthesize information and formulate questions they still have regarding the concepts covered in an article. In their notebooks, students write three new things they learned, two interesting things worth remembering and sharing, and one question that occurred to them while reading the article. Other options might include three facts, two interesting ideas, and one insight about themselves as learners; three key words, two new ideas, and one thing to think about (modified from Black Hills Special Services Cooperative, 2006).

Write reflections. After reading, ask students to review their notes in their notebooks to make any additions, revisions, or corrections to what they recorded during the reading. This review can be facilitated by using a line of learning. Students draw a line under their original conclusion or under their answer to a question posed at the end of an article. They add any new information as a new narrative entry. The line of learning indicates that what follows represents a change of thinking.

Preview and predict. Instruct students to independently preview the article, directing attention to the illustrations, photos, boldfaced words, captions, and anything else that draws their attention. Working with a partner, students discuss and write three things they think they will learn from the article. Have partners verbally share their list with another pair of students. The group of four can collaborate to generate one list. Groups report their ideas, and together you create a class list on chart paper.

Read the article aloud, or have students read with a partner aloud or silently. Referring to the preview/prediction list, discuss what students learned. Have them record the most important thing they learned from the reading for comparison with the predictions.

SQ3R. Survey, Question, Read, Recall, Reflect strategy provides an overall structure for before, during, and after reading. Students begin by surveying or previewing the text, looking for features that will help them make predictions about the content. Based on their surveys, students develop questions to answer as they read. They read the selections looking for answers to their questions. Next, they recall what they have learned by retelling a partner and/or recording what they've learned. Finally, they reflect on what they have learned, check to see that they've answered their questions sufficiently, and add any new ideas. Below is a chart students can use to record the SQ3R process in their notebooks.

S Survey	Q Question	R Read	R Recall	R Reflect
Scan the text and record important information.	Ask questions about the subject and what you already know.	Record answers to your questions after you read.	Retell what you learned in your own words.	Did you answer your questions? Record new ideas and comments.

Struggling Readers

For students reading below grade level, the strategies listed on the previous pages can be modified to support reading comprehension by integrating scaffolding strategies such as read-alouds and guided reading. Breaking the reading down into smaller chunks, providing graphic organizers, and modeling reading comprehension strategies can also help students who may be struggling with the text. For additional strategies for English learners, see the supported-reading strategy in the English-Language Development section of this chapter.

Interactive reading aloud. Reading aloud is an effective strategy for enhancing text comprehension. It offers opportunities to model specific reading comprehension strategies and allows students to concentrate on making sense of the content. When modeling, share the thinking processes used to understand the reading (questioning, visualizing, comparing, inferring, summarizing, etc.), then have students share what they observed you thinking about as an active reader.

Guided reading. While the rest of the class is reading independently or in small groups, pull a group aside for a guided reading session. Before reading, review vocabulary words from the investigation and ask questions to activate prior knowledge. Have students preview the text to make predictions, ask questions, and think about text structure. Review reading comprehension strategies they will need to use (monitoring for understanding, asking questions, summarizing, synthesizing, etc.). As students read independently, provide support where needed. Ask questions and provide prompts to guide comprehension. (See the list below for additional strategies.) After reading, have students reflect on what strategies they used to help them understand the text and make connections to the investigation.

- While reading, look for answers to questions and confirm predictions.
- Study graphics, such as pictures, graphs, and tables.
- Reread captions associated with pictures, graphs, and tables.
- Note all italicized and boldfaced words or phrases.
- Reduce reading speed for difficult passages.
- Stop and reread parts that are not clear.
- Read only a section at a time, and summarize after each section.

Struggling Readers
- *Interactive reading aloud*
- *Guided reading*

SCIENCE-VOCABULARY DEVELOPMENT

Words play two critically important functions in science. First and most important, we play with ideas in our minds, using words. We present ourselves with propositions—possibilities, questions, potential relationships, implications for action, and so on. The process of sorting out these thoughts involves a lot of internal conversation, internal argument, weighing options, and complex linguistic decisions. Once our minds are made up, communicating that decision, conclusion, or explanation in writing or through verbal discourse requires the same command of the vocabulary. Words represent intelligence; acquiring the precise vocabulary and the associated meanings is key to successful scientific thinking and communication.

The words introduced in FOSS investigations represent or relate to fundamental science concepts and should be taught in the context of the investigation. Many of the terms are abstract and are critical to developing science content knowledge and scientific and engineering practices. The goal is for students to use science vocabulary in ways that demonstrate understanding of the concepts the words represent—not to merely recite scripted definitions. The most effective strategies for science-vocabulary development help students make connections to what they already know. These strategies focus on giving new words conceptual meaning through experience; distinguishing between informal, everyday language and academic language; and using the words in meaningful contexts.

Building Conceptual Meaning through Experience

In most instances, students should be presented with new words when they need to know them in the context of the active experience. Words such as *kinetic energy, atmospheric pressure, chemical reaction, photosynthesis*, and *transpiration* are abstract and conceptually loaded. Students will have a much better chance of understanding, assimilating, and remembering the new word (or new meaning) if they can connect it with a concrete experience.

The vocabulary icon appears in the sidebar when students are prompted to record new words in their notebook. The words that appear in bold are critical to understanding the concepts or scientific practices students are learning and applying in the investigation.

When you introduce a new word, students should

- Hear it: students listen as you model the correct contextual use and pronunciation of the word;
- See it: students see the new word written out;
- Say it: students use the new word when discussing their observations and inferences; and
- Write it: students use the new words in context when they write in their notebooks.

Bridging Informal Language to Science Vocabulary

FOSS investigations are designed to tap into students' inquisitive nature and their excitement of discovery in order to encourage lively discussions as they explore materials in creative ways. There should be a lot of talking during the investigations! Your role is to help students connect informal language to the vocabulary used to express specific science concepts. As you circulate during active investigations, you continually model the use of science vocabulary. For example, as students are examining a leaf under the microscope, they will say, "I can see little mouths." You might respond, "Yes, those mouthlike openings are called stomates. They are pores that open and close." Below are some strategies for validating students' conversational language while developing their familiarity with and appreciation for science vocabulary.

Bridging Informal Language to Science Vocabulary

- *Cognitive-content dictionaries*
- *Concept maps*
- *Semantic webs*
- *Word associations*
- *Word sorts*

Cognitive-content dictionaries. Choose a term that is critical for conceptual understanding of the science investigation. Have students write the term, predict its meaning, write the final meaning after class discussion (using primary language or an illustration), and use the term in a sentence.

Cognitive-Content Dictionary	
New term	kinetic energy
Prediction (clues)	something that moves a lot
Final meaning	motion energy
How I would use it in a sentence	Fast-moving particles have more kinetic energy than slow-moving particles.

Concept maps. Select six to ten related science words. Have students write them on self-stick notes or cards. Have small groups discuss how the words are related. Students organize words in groups and glue them down or copy them on a sheet of paper. Students draw lines between the related words. On the lines, they write words describing or explaining how the concept words are related.

Semantic webs. Select a vocabulary word, and write it in the center of a piece of paper (or on the board for the whole class). Brainstorm a list of words or ideas that are related to the first word. Group the words and concepts into several categories, and attach them to the central word with lines, forming a web (modified from Hamilton, 2002).

Word associations. In this brainstorming activity, you say a word, and students respond by writing the first word that comes to mind. Then students share their words with the class. This activity builds connections to students' prior frames of reference.

Word sorts. Have students work with a partner to make a set of word cards using new words from the investigation. Have them group the words in different ways, for example, synonyms, root words, and conceptual connections.

Science Vocabulary Strategies

- *Word wall*
- *Drawings and diagrams*
- *Cloze activity*
- *Word wizard*
- *Word analysis/word parts*
- *Breaking apart words*
- *Possible sentences*
- *Reading*
- *Glossary*
- *Index*
- *Poems, chants, and songs*

Using Science Vocabulary in Context

For a new vocabulary word to become part of a student's functional vocabulary, he or she must have ample opportunities to hear and use it. Vocabulary terms are used in the activities through teacher talk, whole-class and small-group discussions, writing in science notebooks, readings, and assessments. Other methods can also be used to reinforce important vocabulary words and phrases.

Word wall. Use chart paper to record science content and procedural words as they come up during and after the investigations. Students will use this word wall as a reference.

Drawings and diagrams. For English learners and visual learners, use a diagram to review and explain abstract content. Ahead of time, draw an illustration lightly, almost invisibly, with pencil on chart paper. You can do this easily by projecting the image onto the paper. When it's time for the investigation, trace the illustration with markers as you introduce the words and phrases to students. Students will be amazed by your artistic ability.

Cloze activity. Structure sentences for students to complete, leaving out the vocabulary words. This can be done as a warm-up with the words from the previous day's lesson. Here's an example from the **Earth History Course**.

Teacher: *The removal and transportation of loose earth materials is called ______.*

Students: *Erosion.*

Word wizard. Tell students that you are going to lead a word activity. You will be thinking of a science vocabulary word. The goal is to figure out the word. Provide hints that have to do with parts of a definition, root word, prefix, suffix, and other relevant components. Students work in teams of two to four. Provide one hint, and give teams 1 minute to discuss. One team member writes the word on a piece of paper or on the whiteboard, using dark marking pens. Each team holds up its word for only you to see. After the third clue, reveal the word, and move on to the next word. Here's an example.

1. *Part of the word means green.*
2. *They are found in plant cells.*
3. *They look like tiny green spheres or ovals.*

*The word is **chloroplasts**.*

Word analysis/word parts. Learning clusters of words that share a common origin can help students understand content-area texts and connect new words to familiar ones. Here's an example: *geology, geologist, geological, geography, geometry, geophysical.* This type of contextualized teaching meets the immediate need of understanding an unknown word while building generative knowledge that supports students in figuring out difficult words for future reading.

Breaking apart words. Have teams of two to four students break a word into prefix, root word, and suffix. Give each team different words, and have each team share the parsed elements of the word with the whole class. Here's an example.

photosynthesis

Prefix = *photo*: meaning light

Root = *synthesis*: meaning to put together

NOTE
See the Science Notebooks in Middle School chapter for an example of an index.

Possible sentences. Here is a simple strategy for teaching word meanings and generating class discussion.

1. Choose six to eight key concept words from the text of an article in *FOSS Science Resources*.
2. Choose four to six additional words that students are more likely to know something about.
3. Put the list of ten to fourteen words on the board or project it. Provide brief definitions as needed.
4. Ask students to devise sentences that include two or more words from the list.
5. On chart paper, write all sentences that students generate, both coherent and otherwise.
6. Have students read the article from which the words were extracted.
7. Revisit students' sentences, and discuss whether the sentences are sensible based on the passage or how they could be modified to be more coherent.

Reading. After the active investigation, students continue to develop their understanding of the vocabulary words and the concepts those words represent by listening to you read aloud, reading with a partner, or reading independently. Use strategies discussed in the Reading Domain section to encourage students to articulate their thoughts and practice the new vocabulary.

Glossary. Emphasize the vocabulary words students should be using when they answer the focus question in their science notebooks. The glossary in *FOSS Science Resources* or on FOSSweb can be used as a reference.

Index. Have students create an index at the back of their notebooks. There they can record new vocabulary words and the notebook page where they defined and used the new words for the first time in the context of the investigation.

Poems, chants, and songs. As extensions or homework assignments, ask students to create poems, raps, chants, or songs, using vocabulary words from the investigation.

ENGLISH-LANGUAGE DEVELOPMENT

Active investigations, together with ample opportunities to develop and use language, provide an optimal learning environment for English learners. This section highlights opportunities for English-language development (ELD) in FOSS investigations and suggests other best practices for facilitating both the learning of new science concepts and the development of academic literacy. For example, the hands-on structure of FOSS investigations is essential for the conceptual development of science content knowledge and the habits of mind that guide and define scientific and engineering practices. Students are engaged in concrete experiences that are meaningful and that provide a shared context for developing understanding—critical components for language acquisition.

When getting ready for an investigation, review the steps and determine the points where English learners may require scaffolds and where the whole class might benefit from additional language-development supports. One way to plan for ELD integration in science is to keep in mind four key areas: prior knowledge, comprehensible input, academic language development, and oral practice. The ELD chart lists examples of universal strategies for each of these components that work particularly well in teaching science.

NOTE
English-language development refers to the advancement of students' ability to read, write, and speak English.

English-Language Development (ELD)	
Activating prior knowledge • Inquiry chart • Circle map • Observation poster • Quick write • Kit inventory	**Using comprehensible input** • Content objectives • Multiple exposures • Visual aids • Supported reading • Procedural vocabulary
Developing academic language • Language objectives • Sentence frames • Word wall, word cards, drawings • Concept maps • Cognitive content dictionaries	**Providing oral practice** • Small-group discussions • Science talk • Oral presentations • Poems, chants, and songs • Teacher feedback

NOTE
Language forms and structures are the internal grammatical structure of words and how those words go together to make sentences.

Students acquiring English benefit from scaffolds that support the language forms and functions necessary for the academic demands of the science course, that is, accessing science text, participating in productive oral discourse, and engaging in science writing. The table at the end of this section (starting on page 38) provides a resource to help students organize their thinking and structure their speaking and writing in the context of the science and engineering practices. The table identifies key language functions exercised during FOSS investigations and provides examples of sentence frames students can use as scaffolds.

For example, if students are planning an investigation to learn more about insect structures and behaviors, the language objective might be "Students plan and design an investigation that answers a question about the hissing cockroach's behavior." For students who need support, a sentence frame that prompts them to identify the variables in the investigation would provide language forms and structures appropriate for planning their investigation. As a scaffold, sentence frames can also help them write detailed narratives of their procedure. Here's an example from the table.

NOTE
The complete table appears at the end of the English-Language Development section starting on page 38.

Language functions	Language objectives	Sentence frames
Planning and carrying out investigations		
Design Sequence Strategize Evaluate	Plan controlled experiments with multiple trials. Identify independent variable and dependent variable. Discuss, describe, and evaluate the methods for collecting data.	To find out ______, I will change ______. I will not change ______. I will measure ______. I will observe ______. I will record the data by ______. First, I will ______, and then I will ______. To learn more about ______, I will need ______ to ______.

Activating Prior Knowledge

When an investigation engages a new concept, students first recall and discuss familiar situations, objects, or experiences that relate to and establish a foundation for building new knowledge and conceptual understanding. Eliciting prior knowledge also supports learning by motivating interest, acknowledging culture and values, and checking for misconceptions and prerequisite knowledge. This is usually done in the first steps of Guiding the Investigation in the form of a discussion, presentation of new materials, or a written response to a prompt. The tools outlined below can also be used before beginning an investigation to establish a familiar context for launching into new material.

Circle maps. Draw two concentric circles on chart paper. In the smaller circle, write the topic to be explored. In the larger circle, record what students already know about the subject. Ask students to think about how they know or learned what they already know about the topic. Record the responses outside the circles. Students can also do this independently in their science notebooks.

An example of a circle map

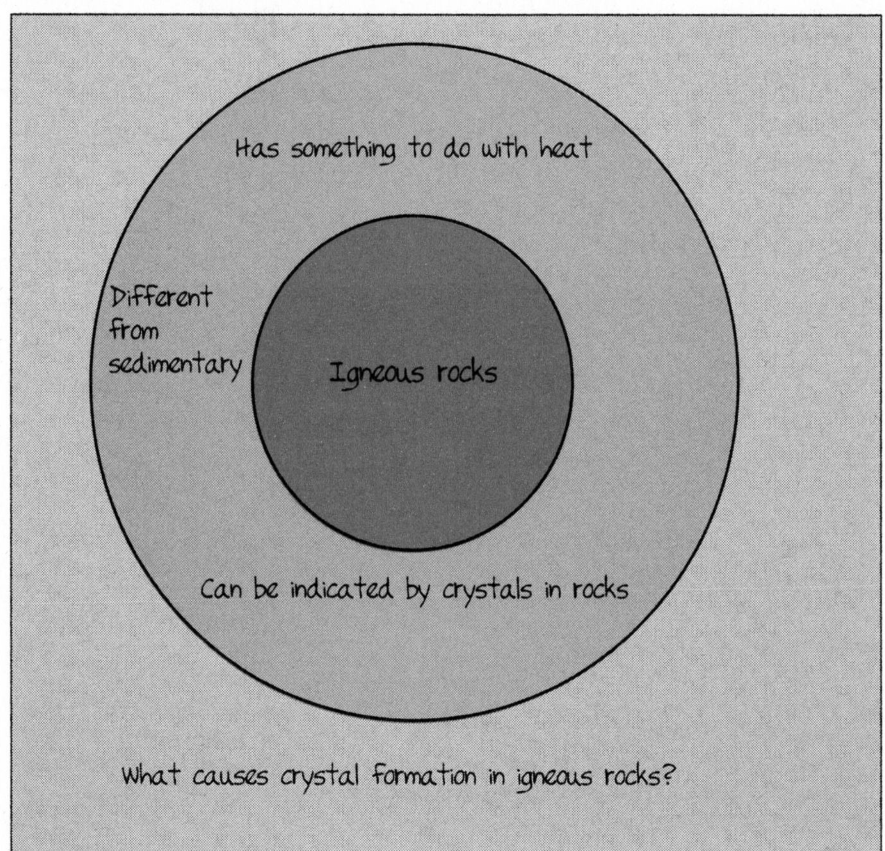

Activating Prior Knowledge
- *Circle maps*
- *Observation posters*
- *Quick writes*
- *Kit inventories*

Observation posters. Make observation posters by gluing or taping pictures and artifacts relevant to the module or a particular investigation onto pieces of blank chart paper or poster paper. Hang them on the wall in the classroom, and have students rotate in small groups to each poster. At each poster, students discuss their observations with their partners or small groups and then record (write or draw) an observation, a question, a prediction, or an inference about the pictures as a contribution to the commentary on the poster.

As a variation on this strategy, give a set of pictures to each group to pass around. Have them choose one and write what they notice, what they infer, and questions they have in their notebooks.

Quick writes. Ask students what they know about the topic of the investigation. Responses can be recorded independently as a quick write in notebooks and then shared collaboratively. Do not correct misconceptions initially. Periodically revisit the quick-write ideas as a whole class, or have students review their notebook entries to correct, confirm, or complete their original thoughts as they acquire new information (possibly using a line of learning). At the conclusion of the investigation, students should be able to express mastery of the new conceptual material.

Kit inventories. Introduce each item from the FOSS kit used in the investigation, and ask students questions to get them thinking about what each item is and where they may have seen it before. Have them describe the objects and predict how they will be used in the investigation.

Comprehending Input

To initiate their own sense making, students must be able to access the information presented to them. We refer to this ability as comprehending input. Students must understand the essence of new ideas and concepts before beginning to construct new scientific meaning. The strategies for comprehensible input used in FOSS ensure that the instruction is understandable while providing students with the opportunity to grapple with new ideas and the critically important relationships between concepts. Additional tools such as repetition, visual aids, emphasis on procedural vocabulary, and auditory reinforcement can also be used to enhance comprehensible input for English learners.

Content objectives. The focus question for each investigation part frames the activity objectives—what students should know or be able to do at the end of the part. Making the learning objectives clear and explicit prepares English learners to process the delivery of new information, and helps you maintain the focus of the investigation. Write the focus question on the board, have students read it aloud and transcribe it into their science notebooks, and have students answer the focus question at the end of the investigation part. You then check their responses for understanding.

Multiple exposures. Repeat an activity in an analogous but slightly different context, ideally one that incorporates elements that are culturally relevant to students. For example, as a homework assignment for landforms, have students interview their parents about landforms common in the area of their ancestry.

Visual aids. On the board or chart paper, write out the steps for conducting the investigation. This provides a visual reference. Include illustrations if necessary. Use graphic representations (illustrations drawn and labeled in front of students) to review the concepts explored in the active investigations. In addition to the concrete objects in the kit, use realia to augment the activity, to help English learners build understanding and make cultural connections. Graphic organizers (webs, Venn diagrams, T-tables, flowcharts, etc.) aid comprehension by helping students see how concepts are related.

Supported reading. In addition to the reading comprehension strategies suggested in the Reading Domain section of this chapter, English learners can also benefit from methods such as front-loading key words, phrases, and complex text structures before reading; using

Comprehending Input

- *Content objectives*
- *Multiple exposures*
- *Visual aids*
- *Supported reading*
- *Procedural vocabulary*

Procedural Vocabulary
Add
Analyze
Assemble
Attach
Calculate
Change
Classify
Collect
Communicate
Compare
Connect
Construct
Contrast
Demonstrate
Describe
Determine
Draw
Evaluate
Examine
Explain
Explore
Fill
Graph
Identify
Illustrate
Immerse
Investigate
Label
List
Measure
Mix
Observe
Open
Order
Organize
Pour
Predict
Prepare
Record
Represent
Scratch
Separate
Sort
Stir
Subtract
Summarize
Test
Weigh

preview-review (main ideas are previewed in the primary language, read in English, and reviewed in the primary language); and having students use sentence frames specifically tailored to record key information and/or graphic organizers that make the content and the relationship between concepts visually explicit from the text as they read.

Procedural vocabulary. Make sure students understand the meaning of the words used in the directions for an investigation. These may or may not be science-specific words. Use techniques such as modeling, demonstrating, and body language (gestures) to explain procedural meaning in the context of the investigation. The words students will encounter in FOSS include those listed in the sidebar. To build academic literacy, English learners need to learn the multiple meanings of these words and their specific meanings in the context of science.

Developing Academic Language

As students learn the nuances of the English language, it is critical that they build proficiency in academic language in order to participate fully in the cognitive demands of school. *Academic language* refers to the more abstract, complex, and specific aspects of language, such as the words, grammatical structure, and discourse markers that are needed for higher cognitive learning. FOSS investigations introduce and provide opportunities for students to practice using the academic vocabulary needed to access and engage with science ideas.

Language objectives. Consider the language needs of English learners and incorporate specific language-development objectives that will support learning the science content of the investigation, such as a specific way to expand use of vocabulary by looking at root words, prefixes, and suffixes; a linguistic pattern or structure for oral discussion and writing; or a reading comprehension strategy. Recording in science notebooks is a productive way to optimize science learning and language objectives. For example, in the **Earth History Course**, one language objective might be "Students will apply techniques for rock observations to compare and contrast sedimentary and igneous rocks. They will discuss and record their observations in their notebooks in an organized manner."

Vocabulary development. The Science-Vocabulary Development section in this chapter describes the ways science vocabulary is introduced and developed in the context of an active investigation and suggests methods and strategies that can be used to support vocabulary development during science instruction. In addition to science vocabulary, students need to learn the nonscience vocabulary that facilitates deeper understanding and communication skills. Words such as *release*, *convert*, *beneficial*, *produce*, *receive*, *source*, and *reflect* are used in the investigations and *FOSS Science Resources* and are frequently used in other content areas. Learning these academic-vocabulary words gives students a more precise and complex way of practicing and communicating productive thinking. Consider using the strategies described in the Science-Vocabulary Development section to explicitly teach targeted, high-leverage words that can be used in multiple ways and that can help students make connections to other words and concepts. Sentence frames, word walls, concept maps, and cognitive-content dictionaries are strategies that have been found to be effective with academic-vocabulary development.

Scaffolds That Support Science and Engineering Practices

Language functions	Language objectives	Sentence frames
Asking questions and defining problems		
Inquire Define a problem	Ask questions to solicit information about phenomena, models, or unexpected results; determine the constraints and criteria of a problem.	I wonder why ____ . What happens when ____? What if ____? What does ____? What can ____? What would happen if ____? How does ____ affect ____? How can I find out if ____? Which ____ is better for ____?
Planning and carrying out investigations		
Design Sequence Strategize Evaluate	Plan controlled experiments with multiple trials. Identify independent variable and dependent variable. Discuss, describe, and evaluate the methods for collecting data.	To find out ____, I will change ____. I will not change ____. I will measure ____. I will observe ____. I will record the data by ____. First, I will ____, and then I will ____. To learn more about ____, I will need ____ to ____.

Language functions	Language objectives	Sentence frames
Planning and carrying out investigations *(continued)*		
Describe	Write narratives using details to record sensory observations and connections to prior knowledge.	I observed/noticed ____. When I touch the ____, I feel ____. It smells ____. It sounds ____. It reminds me of ____, because ____.
Organize Compare Classify	Make charts and tables: use a T-table or chart for recording and displaying data.	The table compares ____ and ____
Sequence Compare	Record changes over time, and describe cause-and-effect relationships.	At first, ____, but now ____. We saw that first ____, then ____, and finally ____. When I ____, it ____. After I ____, it ____.
Draw Label Identify	Draw accurate and detailed representations; identify and label parts of a system using science vocabulary, with attention to form, location, color, size, and scale.	The diagram shows ____. ____ is shown here. ____ is ____ times bigger than ____. ____ is ____ times smaller than ____ .
Analyzing and interpreting data		
Enumerate Compare Represent	Use measures of variability to analyze and characterize data; decide when and how to use bar graphs, line plots, and two-coordinate graphs to organize data.	The mean is ____. The median is ____. The mode is ____. The range is ____. The x-axis represents ____ and the y-axis represents ____. The units are expressed in ____.

Language functions	Language objectives	Sentence frames
Analyzing and interpreting data *(continued)*		
Compare Classify Sequence	Use graphic organizers and narratives to express similarities and differences, to assign an object or action to the category or type to which it belongs, and to show sequencing and order.	This ____ is similar to ____ because ____. This ____ is different from ____ because ____. All these are ____ because ____. ____, ____, and ____ all have/are ____.
Analyze	Use graphic organizers, narratives, or concept maps to identify part/whole or cause–and–effect relationships. Express data in qualitative terms such as more/fewer, higher/lower, nearer/farther, longer/shorter, and increase/decrease; and quantitatively in actual numbers or percentages.	The ____ consists of ____. The ____ contains ____. As ____, then ____. When I changed ____, then ____ happened. The more/less ____, then ____.
Developing and using models		
Represent Predict Explain	Construct and revise models to predict, represent, and explain.	If ____, then ____, therefore ____. The ____ represents ____ . ____ shows how ____. You can explain ____ by ____.

Language functions	Language objectives	Sentence frames
Using mathematics and computational thinking		
Symbolize Measure Enumerate Estimate	Use mathematical concepts to analyze data.	The ratio of ____ is ____ to ____. The average is ____. Looking at ____, I think there are ____. My prediction is ____.
Constructing explanations and designing solutions		
Infer Explain	Construct explanations based on evidence from investigations, knowledge, and models; use reasoning to show why the data are adequate for the explanation or conclusion.	I claim that ____. I know this because ____. Based on ____, I think ____. As a result of ____, I think ____. The data show ____, therefore, ____. I think ____ means ____ because ____. I think ____ happened because ____.
Provide evidence	Use qualitative and quantitative data from the investigation as evidence to support claims. Use quantitative expressions using standard metric units of measurement such as cm, mL, °C.	My data show ____. My evidence is ____. The relationship between the variables is ____. The model of ____ shows that ____.

<table>
<tr><th>Language functions</th><th>Language objectives</th><th>Sentence frames</th></tr>
<tr><th colspan="3">Engaging in argument from evidence</th></tr>
<tr><td>Discuss
Persuade
Synthesize
Negotiate
Suggest</td><td>Use oral and written arguments supported by evidence and reasoning to support or refute an argument for a phenomenon or a solution to a problem.</td><td>I think ___ because___.
I agree/disagree with ___ because__________.
What you are saying is ______. What do you think about _____?
What if ______?
I think you should try ___.
Another way to interpret the data is ______.</td></tr>
<tr><td>Critique
Evaluate
Reflect</td><td>Evaluate competing design solutions based on criteria; compare two arguments from evidence to identify which is better.</td><td>____ makes more sense because ____.
____ is a better design _____ because it ____.
Comparing ___ to ___ shows that ______.
One discrepancy is ____.
____ is inconsistent with _____.
Another way to determine ______ is to _______.
I used to think ____, but now I think ____. I have changed my thinking about ____.
I am confused about ____ because ____.
I wonder ____.</td></tr>
<tr><th colspan="3">Obtaining, evaluating, and communicating information</th></tr>
<tr><td colspan="3">(This practice includes all functions described in the other practices above.)</td></tr>
</table>

REFERENCES

Applebee, A. 1984. "Writing and Reasoning." *Review of Educational Research* 54 (Winter): 577–596.

Bereiter, C. 2002. *Education and Mind in the Knowledge Age.* Hillsdale, NJ: Erlbaum.

Black Hills Special Services Cooperative. 2006. "3-2-1 Strategy." In *On Target: More Strategies to Guide Learning.* Rapid City, SD: South Dakota Department of Education.

Gibbons, P. 2002. *Scaffolding Language, Scaffolding Learning.* Portsmouth, NH: Heinemann.

Graham, S., and M. Herbert. 2010. *Writing to Read: Evidence for How Writing Can Improve Reading.* New York: Carnegie.

Hamilton, G. 2002. *Content-Area Reading Strategies: Science.* Portland, ME: Walch Publishing.

Harvey, S. 1998. *Nonfiction Matters: Reading, Writing, and Research in Grades 3–8.* Portland, ME: Stenhouse.

Harvey, S., and A. Goudvis. 2007. *Strategies That Work: Teaching Comprehension for Understanding and Engagement.* Portland, ME: Stenhouse.

Keeley, P. 2008. *Science Formative Assessment: 75 Practical Strategies for Linking Assessment, Instruction, and Learning.* Thousand Oaks, CA: Corwin Press.

Keene, E., and S. Zimmermann. 2007. *Mosaic of Thought: The Power of Comprehension Strategies.* 2nd ed. Portsmouth, NH: Heinemann.

Keys, C. 1999. *Revitalizing Instruction in Scientific Genres: Connecting Knowledge Production with Writing to Learn in Science.* Athens: University of Georgia.

Lieberman, G. A., and L. L. Hoody. 1998. *Closing the Achievement Gap: Using the Environment as an Integrating Context for Learning.* San Diego, CA: State Education and Environment Roundtable.

National Governors Association Center for Best Practices, Council of Chief State School Officers. 2010. *Common Core State Standards for English Language Arts & Literacy in History/Social Studies, Science, and Technical Subjects.* Washington, DC: National Governors Association Center for Best Practices, Council of Chief State School Officers.

National Research Council. 2012. *A Framework for K–12 Science Education: Practices, Crosscutting Concepts, and Core Ideas.* Committee on a Conceptual Framework for New K–12 Science Education Standards. Board on Science Education, Division of Behavioral and Social Sciences and Education. Washington, DC: The National Academies Press.

NOTE
For additional resources and updated references, go to FOSSweb.

Norris, S. P., and L. M. Phillips. 2003. "How Literacy in Its Fundamental Sense Is Central to Scientific Literacy." *Science Education* 87 (2).

Ostlund, K. 1998. "What the Research Says about Science Process Skills: How Can Teaching Science Process Skills Improve Student Performance in Reading, Language Arts, and Mathematics?" *Electronic Journal of Science Education* 2 (4).

Wellington, J., and J. Osborne. 2001. *Language and Literacy in Science Education*. Buckingham, UK: Open University Press.

Winokur, J., and K. Worth. 2006. "Talk in the Science Classroom: Looking at What Students and Teachers Need to Know and Be Able to Do." In *Linking Science and Literacy in the K–8 Classroom*, ed. R. Douglas, K. Worth, and W. Binder. Arlington, VA: NSTA Press.

FOSSweb and Technology

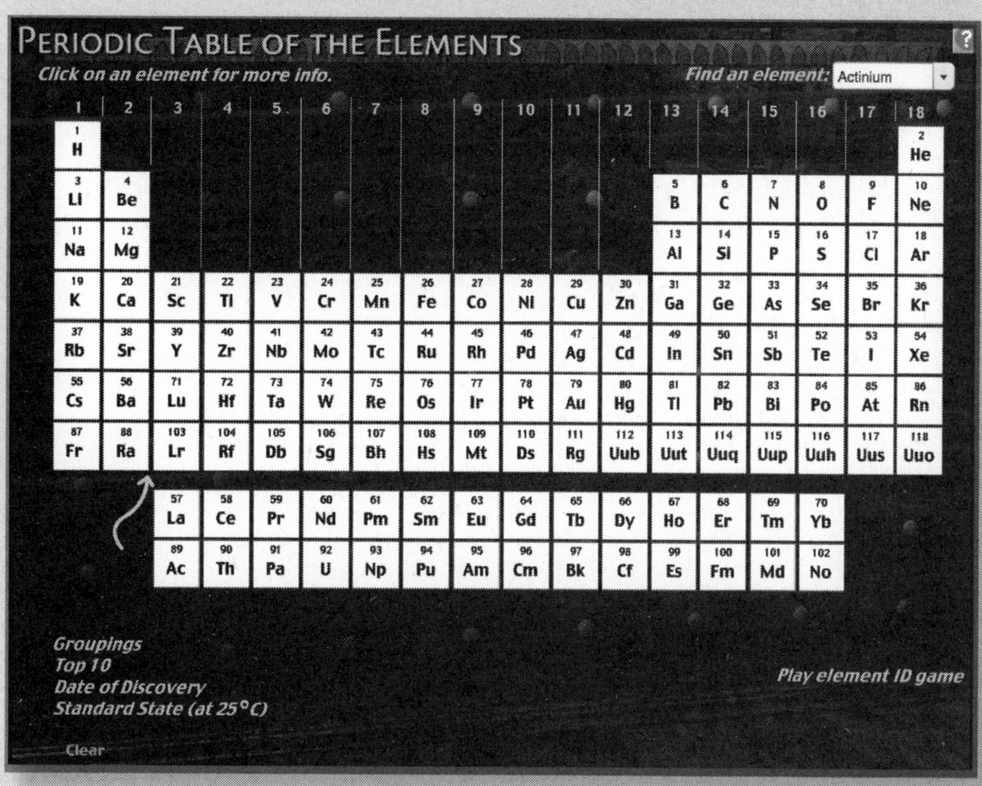

FOSSweb and Technology

Contents

INTRODUCTION

FOSSweb technology is an integral part of the **Chemical Interactions Course**. It provides students with the opportunity to access and interact with simulations, images, video, and text—digital resources that can enhance their understanding of life science concepts. Different sections of digital resources are incorporated into each investigation during the course. Each use is marked with the technology icon in the *Investigations Guide*. You will sometimes use the digital resources to make presentations to the class. At other times, individuals or small groups of students will work with the digital resources to review concepts or reinforce their understanding.

The FOSSweb components are not optional. To prepare to use these digital resources, you should have at a minimum one computer with Internet access that can be displayed to the class by an LCD projector with an interactive whiteboard or a large screen arranged for class viewing. Access to a computer lab or to enough computers in your classroom for students to work in small groups is also required during one investigation, and recommended during others.

The digital resources are available online at www.FOSSweb.com for teachers and students. We recommend you access FOSSweb well in advance of starting the course to set up your teacher-user account and become familiar with the resources.

REQUIREMENTS FOR ACCESSING FOSSWEB

You'll need to have a few things in place on your computer before accessing FOSSweb. Once you're online, you'll create a FOSSweb account. All information in this section is updated as needed on FOSSweb.

Creating a FOSSweb Teacher Account

By creating a FOSSweb teacher account, you can personalize FOSSweb for easy access to the courses you are teaching. When you log in, you will be able to add courses to your "My FOSS Modules" area and access Resources by Investigation for the **Chemical Interactions Course.** This makes it simple to select the investigation and part you are teaching and view all the digital resources connected to that part.

Students and families can also access course resources through FOSSweb. You can set up a class account and class pages where students will be able to access notes from you about assignments and digital resources.

Setting up an account. Set up an account on FOSSweb so you can access the site when you begin teaching a course. Go to FOSSweb to register for an account—complete registration instructions are available online.

Entering your access code. Once your account is set up, go to FOSSweb and log in. The first time you log in, you will need to enter your access code. Your access code should be printed on the inside cover of your *Investigations Guide*. If you cannot find your FOSSweb access code, contact your school administrator, your district science coordinator, or the purchasing agent for your school or district.

Familiarize yourself with the layout of the site and the additional resources available by using your account login. From your course page, you will be able to access teacher masters, assessment masters, notebook sheets, and other digital resources. Explore the Resources by Investigation section, as this will help you plan. It lists the digital resources, notebook sheets, teacher masters, and readings for each investigation part. There are also a variety of beneficial resources on FOSSweb that can be used to assist with teacher preparation and materials management.

Setting up class pages and student accounts. To enable your students to log in to FOSSweb to access the digital resources and see class assignments, set up a class page and generate a user name and password for the class. To do so, log in to FOSSweb and go to your teacher homepage. Under My Class Pages, follow the instructions to create a new class page and to leave notes for students.

If a class page and student accounts are not set up, students can always access digital resources by visiting FOSSweb.com and choosing to visit the site as a guest.

FOSSweb Technical Requirements

To use FOSSweb, your computer must meet minimum system requirements and have a compatible browser and recent versions of Flash® Player, QuickTime™, and Adobe® Reader. The system requirements are subject to change. It is strongly recommended that you visit FOSSweb to review the most recent minimum system requirements.

When using FOSSweb, you can test your browser to confirm that it has the minimum requirements to support the multimedia. You can do so by accessing the Technical Requirements section on FOSSweb.

Preparing your browser. FOSSweb requires a supported browser for Windows or Mac OS with a current version of the Flash Player plug-in, the QuickTime plug-in, and Adobe Reader, or an equivalent PDF reader program. You may need administrator privileges on your computer in order to install the required programs and/or help from your school's technology coordinator.

By accessing the Technical Requirements page on FOSSweb, you can check compatibility for each computer you will use to access FOSSweb, including your classroom computer, computers in a school computer lab, and a home computer. The information at FOSSweb contains the most up-to-date technical requirements.

Support for plug-ins and reader. The Flash Player and Adobe Reader are available on www.Adobe.com as free downloads. QuickTime is available free of charge from www.Apple.com. FOSS does not support these programs. Please go to the program's website for troubleshooting information.

Accessing FOSS Chemical Interactions Digital Resources

When you log in to FOSSweb, the most useful way to access course materials on a daily basis is the Resources by Investigation section of the **Chemical Interactions Course** page. This section lists the digital resources, student and teacher sheets, readings, and focus questions for each investigation part. Each of these items is linked so you can click and go directly to that item.

Students will access digital resources from the Resource Room, accessible from the class page you've set up. Explore where the activities reside in the Resource Room. At various points in the course, students will access interactive simulations, images, videos, and animations from FOSSweb.

Other Technology Considerations

Firewall or proxy settings. If your school has a firewall or proxy server, contact your IT administrator to add explicit exceptions in your proxy server and firewall for these servers:

- fossweb.com
- streamingmediahosting.com

Classroom technology setup. FOSS has a number of digital resources and makes every effort to accommodate users with different levels of access to technology. The digital resources can be used in a variety of ways and can be adapted to a number of classroom setups.

Teachers with classroom computers and an LCD projector, an interactive whiteboard, or a large screen will be able to show multimedia to the class. If you have access to a computer lab, or enough computers in your classroom for students to work in small groups, you can set up time for students to use the FOSSweb digital resources during the school day.

Displaying digital content. You might want to digitally display the notebook and teacher masters during class. In the Resources by Investigation section of FOSSweb, you'll have the option of downloading the masters "to project" or "to copy." Choose "to project" if you plan on projecting the masters to the class. These masters are optimized for a projection system and allow you to type into them while they are displayed. The "to copy" versions are sized to minimize paper use when photocopying for the class, and to fit optimally into student notebooks.

If this projection technology is not available to you, consider making transparencies of the notebook and teacher masters for use with an overhead projector when the Getting Ready section indicates a need to project these sheets.

NOTE

FOSSweb activities are designed for a minimum screen size of 1024 × 768. It is recommended that you adjust your screen resolution to 1024 × 768 or higher.

TROUBLESHOOTING AND TECHNICAL SUPPORT

If you experience trouble with FOSSweb, you can troubleshoot in a variety of ways.

1. First, test your browser to make sure you have the correct plug-in and browser versions. Go to FOSSweb and select the "Technical Requirements" page to review the most recent system requirements and test your browser.
2. Check the FAQs on FOSSweb for additional information that may help resolve the problem.
3. Try emptying the cache from your browser and/or quitting and relaunching it.
4. Restart your computer, and make sure all computer hardware turns on and is connected correctly.

If you are still experiencing problems after taking these steps, send FOSS Technical Support an e-mail at support@FOSSweb.com. In addition to describing the problem, include the following information about your computer: Mac or PC, operating system, browser and version, plug-ins and versions. This will help us troubleshoot the problem.

Science Notebook Masters

Mystery Mixture

WARNING — This set contains chemicals that may be harmful if misused. Read cautions on individual containers carefully. Not to be used by children except under adult supervision.

Part 1. Observe the unknown mixture.

1. Put on your safety goggles.
2. Put one 5 mL spoon of the mystery mixture into a cup.
3. Observe the mixture. (Do not touch or taste the mixture.)
4. Record your observations.

Part 2. Add water.

1. Add one pipette of water to the mystery mixture in the cup. Do not use the pipette to stir the mixture.
2. Observe. Take turns putting additional pipettes of water into the cup. Observe after each pipette of water.
3. Record your observations.

Mystery Mixture

WARNING — This set contains chemicals that may be harmful if misused. Read cautions on individual containers carefully. Not to be used by children except under adult supervision.

Part 1. Observe the unknown mixture.

1. Put on your safety goggles.
2. Put one 5 mL spoon of the mystery mixture into a cup.
3. Observe the mixture. (Do not touch or taste the mixture.)
4. Record your observations.

Part 2. Add water.

1. Add one pipette of water to the mystery mixture in the cup. Do not use the pipette to stir the mixture.
2. Observe. Take turns putting additional pipettes of water into the cup. Observe after each pipette of water.
3. Record your observations.

FOSS Chemical Interactions Course, Second Edition
© The Regents of the University of California
Can be duplicated for classroom or workshop use.
Investigation 1: Substances
No. 1—Notebook Master

White-Substances Information A

WARNING — This set contains chemicals that may be harmful if misused. Read cautions on individual containers carefully. Not to be used by children except under adult supervision.

Fill in the chart with the information for each white substance.

Chemical name	Chemical formula	Common name	Observations	Uses

Investigation 1: Substances
No. 2—Notebook Master

FOSS Chemical Interactions Course, Second Edition

White-Substances Information A

WARNING — This set contains chemicals that may be harmful if misused. Read cautions on individual containers carefully. Not to be used by children except under adult supervision.

Fill in the chart with the information for each white substance.

Chemical name	Chemical formula	Common name	Observations	Uses

Investigation 1: Substances
No. 2—Notebook Master

FOSS Chemical Interactions Course, Second Edition
© The Regents of the University of California
Can be duplicated for classroom or workshop use.

White-Substances Information B

Fill in the chart with the information for each white substance.

Chemical name	Chemical formula	Common name	Observations	Uses

Look for patterns in the chemical names and chemical formulas for the substances. What do you see?

FOSS Chemical Interactions Course, Second Edition
© The Regents of the University of California
Can be duplicated for classroom or workshop use.

White-Substances Information B

WARNING — This set contains chemicals that may be harmful if misused. Read cautions on individual containers carefully. Not to be used by children except under adult supervision.

Fill in the chart with the information for each white substance.

Chemical name	Chemical formula	Common name	Observations	Uses

Look for patterns in the chemical names and chemical formulas for the substances. What do you see?

Investigation 1: Substances
No. 3—Notebook Master

Mystery-Mixture Analysis

WARNING — This set contains chemicals that may be harmful if misused. Read cautions on individual containers carefully. Not to be used by children except under adult supervision.

Challenge. Find out which two substances are in the mystery mixture.

Procedure

1. Put one level minispoon of two different substances (or two minispoons of one substance) in a well. Note the number of the well.
2. Add 10 drops of water. Observe and record.

Well	Substance 1	Substance 2	Results
1	Mystery mixture	+ Mystery mixture	
2		+	
3		+	
4		+	
5		+	
6		+	
7		+	
8		+	
9		+	
10		+	
11		+	
12		+	

Mystery-Mixture Analysis

WARNING — This set contains chemicals that may be harmful if misused. Read cautions on individual containers carefully. Not to be used by children except under adult supervision.

Challenge. Find out which two substances are in the mystery mixture.

Procedure

1. Put one level minispoon of two different substances (or two minispoons of one substance) in a well. Note the number of the well.
2. Add 10 drops of water. Observe and record.

Well	Substance 1	Substance 2	Results
1	Mystery mixture	+ Mystery mixture	
2		+	
3		+	
4		+	
5		+	
6		+	
7		+	
8		+	
9		+	
10		+	
11		+	
12		+	

FOSS Chemical Interactions Course, Second Edition
© The Regents of the University of California
Can be duplicated for classroom or workshop use.
Investigation 1: Substances
No. 4—Notebook Master

WARNING — This set contains chemicals that may be harmful if misused. Read cautions on individual containers carefully. Not to be used by children except under adult supervision.

Mystery-Mixture Summary A

Well	Substances	Description of fizzing	Other observations	Large-scale observations
1	Ascorbic acid + calcium carbonate $C_6H_8O_6 + CaCO_3$			
2	Ascorbic acid + sodium bicarbonate $C_6H_8O_6 + NaHCO_3$			
3	Ascorbic acid + sodium carbonate $C_6H_8O_6 + Na_2CO_3$			
4	Calcium chloride + sodium bicarbonate $CaCl_2 + NaHCO_3$			
5	Citric acid + calcium carbonate $C_6H_8O_7 + CaCO_3$			

FOSS Chemical Interactions Course, Second Edition
© The Regents of the University of California
Can be duplicated for classroom or workshop use.

Investigation 1: Substances
No. 5—Notebook Master

WARNING — This set contains chemicals that may be harmful if misused. Read cautions on individual containers carefully. Not to be used by children except under adult supervision.

Mystery-Mixture Summary A

Well	Substances	Description of fizzing	Other observations	Large-scale observations
1	Ascorbic acid + calcium carbonate $C_6H_8O_6 + CaCO_3$			
2	Ascorbic acid + sodium bicarbonate $C_6H_8O_6 + NaHCO_3$			
3	Ascorbic acid + sodium carbonate $C_6H_8O_6 + Na_2CO_3$			
4	Calcium chloride + sodium bicarbonate $CaCl_2 + NaHCO_3$			
5	Citric acid + calcium carbonate $C_6H_8O_7 + CaCO_3$			

Mystery-Mixture Summary B

WARNING — This set contains chemicals that may be harmful if misused. Read cautions on individual containers carefully. Not to be used by children except under adult supervision.

Well	Substances	Description of fizzing	Other observations	Large-scale observations
6	Citric acid + sodium bicarbonate $C_6H_8O_7 + NaHCO_3$			
7	Citric acid + sodium carbonate $C_6H_8O_7 + Na_2CO_3$			
8	Mystery mixture			

Identify the two substances in the mystery mixture and explain how you identified them.

Mystery-Mixture Summary B

WARNING — This set contains chemicals that may be harmful if misused. Read cautions on individual containers carefully. Not to be used by children except under adult supervision.

Well	Substances	Description of fizzing	Other observations	Large-scale observations
6	Citric acid + sodium bicarbonate $C_6H_8O_7 + NaHCO_3$			
7	Citric acid + sodium carbonate $C_6H_8O_7 + Na_2CO_3$			
8	Mystery mixture			

Identify the two substances in the mystery mixture and explain how you identified them.

Investigation 1: Substances
No. 6—Notebook Master

FOSS Chemical Interactions Course, Second Edition
© The Regents of the University of California
Can be duplicated for classroom or workshop use.

Mystery-Mixture Elements

Chemical name	Chemical formula	Elements
Calcium carbonate	$CaCO_3$	
Sodium carbonate	Na_2CO_3	
Sodium bicarbonate	$NaHCO_3$	
Magnesium sulfate	$MgSO_4$	
Calcium chloride	$CaCl_2$	
Sodium chloride	$NaCl$	
Ascorbic acid	$C_6H_8O_6$	
Citric acid	$C_6H_8O_7$	
Sucrose	$C_{12}H_{22}O_{11}$	

Mystery-Mixture Elements

Chemical name	Chemical formula	Elements
Calcium carbonate	$CaCO_3$	
Sodium carbonate	Na_2CO_3	
Sodium bicarbonate	$NaHCO_3$	
Magnesium sulfate	$MgSO_4$	
Calcium chloride	$CaCl_2$	
Sodium chloride	$NaCl$	
Ascorbic acid	$C_6H_8O_6$	
Citric acid	$C_6H_8O_7$	
Sucrose	$C_{12}H_{22}O_{11}$	

FOSS Chemical Interactions Course, Second Edition
© The Regents of the University of California
Can be duplicated for classroom or workshop use.

Investigation 2: Elements
No. 7—Notebook Master

Mystery-Mixture Element Questions

1. Which substance has the greatest number of elements?

2. Altogether, how many different elements are in the nine substances?

3. Which element is found in the greatest number of substances?

4. How many elements are in the substance carbon dioxide (CO_2)?

5. How many elements are in the substance water (H_2O)?

6. Which of the nine substances are made of two elements?

7. Which of the nine substances are made of three elements?

8. Which of the nine substances are made of four elements?

Mystery-Mixture Element Questions

1. Which substance has the greatest number of elements?

2. Altogether, how many different elements are in the nine substances?

3. Which element is found in the greatest number of substances?

4. How many elements are in the substance carbon dioxide (CO_2)?

5. How many elements are in the substance water (H_2O)?

6. Which of the nine substances are made of two elements?

7. Which of the nine substances are made of three elements?

8. Which of the nine substances are made of four elements?

FOSS Chemical Interactions Course, Second Edition
© The Regents of the University of California
Can be duplicated for classroom or workshop use.

Investigation 2: Elements
No. 8—Notebook Master

Elements in Products

Part 1. List the elements found in several products.

Product	Elements

Part 2. Analyze the elements in the products.

1. How many different elements did you find in all the products you investigated?

2. What is the most common element in the products you investigated?

3. How many metals did you find in the products you investigated? List them.

Elements in Products

Part 1. List the elements found in several products.

Product	Elements

Part 2. Analyze the elements in the products.

1. How many different elements did you find in all the products you investigated?

2. What is the most common element in the products you investigated?

3. How many metals did you find in the products you investigated? List them.

FOSS Chemical Interactions Course, Second Edition
© The Regents of the University of California
Can be duplicated for classroom or workshop use.
Investigation 2: Elements
No. 9—Notebook Master

The Periodic Table of the Elements

1 H Hydrogen																	2 He Helium
3 Li Lithium	4 Be Beryllium											5 B Boron	6 C Carbon	7 N Nitrogen	8 O Oxygen	9 F Fluorine	10 Ne Neon
11 Na Sodium	12 Mg Magnesium											13 Al Aluminum	14 Si Silicon	15 P Phosphorus	16 S Sulfur	17 Cl Chlorine	18 Ar Argon
19 K Potassium	20 Ca Calcium	21 Sc Scandium	22 Ti Titanium	23 V Vanadium	24 Cr Chromium	25 Mn Manganese	26 Fe Iron	27 Co Cobalt	28 Ni Nickel	29 Cu Copper	30 Zn Zinc	31 Ga Gallium	32 Ge Germanium	33 As Arsenic	34 Se Selenium	35 Br Bromine	36 Kr Krypton
37 Rb Rubidium	38 Sr Strontium	39 Y Yttrium	40 Zr Zirconium	41 Nb Niobium	42 Mo Molybdenum	43 Tc Technetium	44 Ru Ruthenium	45 Rh Rhodium	46 Pd Palladium	47 Ag Silver	48 Cd Cadmium	49 In Indium	50 Sn Tin	51 Sb Antimony	52 Te Tellurium	53 I Iodine	54 Xe Xenon
55 Cs Cesium	56 Ba Barium	71 Lu Lutetium	72 Hf Hafnium	73 Ta Tantalum	74 W Tungsten	75 Re Rhenium	76 Os Osmium	77 Ir Iridium	78 Pt Platinum	79 Au Gold	80 Hg Mercury	81 Tl Thallium	82 Pb Lead	83 Bi Bismuth	84 Po Polonium	85 At Astatine	86 Rn Radon
87 Fr Francium	88 Ra Radium	103 Lr Lawrencium	104 Rf Rutherfordium	105 Db Dubnium	106 Sg Seaborgium	107 Bh Bohrium	108 Hs Hassium	109 Mt Meitnerium	110 Ds Darmstadtium	111 Rg Roentgenium	112 Cn Copernicium	113 Nh Nihonium	114 Fl Flerovium	115 Mc Moscovium	116 Lv Livermorium	117 Ts Tennessine	118 Og Oganesson

57 La Lanthanum	58 Ce Cerium	59 Pr Praseodymium	60 Nd Neodymium	61 Pm Promethium	62 Sm Samarium	63 Eu Europium	64 Gd Gadolinium	65 Tb Terbium	66 Dy Dysprosium	67 Ho Holmium	68 Er Erbium	69 Tm Thulium	70 Yb Ytterbium
89 Ac Actinium	90 Th Thorium	91 Pa Protactinium	92 U Uranium	93 Np Neptunium	94 Pu Plutonium	95 Am Americium	96 Cm Curium	97 Bk Berkelium	98 Cf Californium	99 Es Einsteinium	100 Fm Fermium	101 Md Mendelevium	102 No Nobelium

Investigation 2: Elements
No. 10—Notebook Master

The Periodic Table of the Elements

1 H Hydrogen																	2 He Helium
3 Li Lithium	4 Be Beryllium											5 B Boron	6 C Carbon	7 N Nitrogen	8 O Oxygen	9 F Fluorine	10 Ne Neon
11 Na Sodium	12 Mg Magnesium											13 Al Aluminum	14 Si Silicon	15 P Phosphorus	16 S Sulfur	17 Cl Chlorine	18 Ar Argon
19 K Potassium	20 Ca Calcium	21 Sc Scandium	22 Ti Titanium	23 V Vanadium	24 Cr Chromium	25 Mn Manganese	26 Fe Iron	27 Co Cobalt	28 Ni Nickel	29 Cu Copper	30 Zn Zinc	31 Ga Gallium	32 Ge Germanium	33 As Arsenic	34 Se Selenium	35 Br Bromine	36 Kr Krypton
37 Rb Rubidium	38 Sr Strontium	39 Y Yttrium	40 Zr Zirconium	41 Nb Niobium	42 Mo Molybdenum	43 Tc Technetium	44 Ru Ruthenium	45 Rh Rhodium	46 Pd Palladium	47 Ag Silver	48 Cd Cadmium	49 In Indium	50 Sn Tin	51 Sb Antimony	52 Te Tellurium	53 I Iodine	54 Xe Xenon
55 Cs Cesium	56 Ba Barium	71 Lu Lutetium	72 Hf Hafnium	73 Ta Tantalum	74 W Tungsten	75 Re Rhenium	76 Os Osmium	77 Ir Iridium	78 Pt Platinum	79 Au Gold	80 Hg Mercury	81 Tl Thallium	82 Pb Lead	83 Bi Bismuth	84 Po Polonium	85 At Astatine	86 Rn Radon
87 Fr Francium	88 Ra Radium	103 Lr Lawrencium	104 Rf Rutherfordium	105 Db Dubnium	106 Sg Seaborgium	107 Bh Bohrium	108 Hs Hassium	109 Mt Meitnerium	110 Ds Darmstadtium	111 Rg Roentgenium	112 Cn Copernicium	113 Nh Nihonium	114 Fl Flerovium	115 Mc Moscovium	116 Lv Livermorium	117 Ts Tennessine	118 Og Oganesson

57 La Lanthanum	58 Ce Cerium	59 Pr Praseodymium	60 Nd Neodymium	61 Pm Promethium	62 Sm Samarium	63 Eu Europium	64 Gd Gadolinium	65 Tb Terbium	66 Dy Dysprosium	67 Ho Holmium	68 Er Erbium	69 Tm Thulium	70 Yb Ytterbium
89 Ac Actinium	90 Th Thorium	91 Pa Protactinium	92 U Uranium	93 Np Neptunium	94 Pu Plutonium	95 Am Americium	96 Cm Curium	97 Bk Berkelium	98 Cf Californium	99 Es Einsteinium	100 Fm Fermium	101 Md Mendelevium	102 No Nobelium

Investigation 2: Elements
No. 10—Notebook Master

FOSS Chemical Interactions Course, Second Edition
© The Regents of the University of California
Can be duplicated for classroom or workshop use.

Response Sheet—Investigation 2

A student studied the ingredients on a box of cereal. She made a list of the elements she found. She told her friend,

This cereal contains eight different elements. I wonder what the rest of the cereal is made of.

If you were the student's friend, what would you tell her?

Response Sheet—Investigation 2

A student studied the ingredients on a box of cereal. She made a list of the elements she found. She told her friend,

This cereal contains eight different elements. I wonder what the rest of the cereal is made of.

If you were the student's friend, what would you tell her?

FOSS Chemical Interactions Course, Second Edition
© The Regents of the University of California
Can be duplicated for classroom or workshop use.
Investigation 2: Elements
No. 11—Notebook Master

WARNING — This set contains chemicals that may be harmful if misused. Read cautions on individual containers carefully. Not to be used by children except under adult supervision.

How Much Gas?

Challenge. Determine how much gas is produced in a citric acid and sodium bicarbonate reaction.

Record results.

Volume of gas produced (mL)			
Trial 1	**Trial 2**	**Trial 3**	**Average**

My group's average volume of gas ______________

Class average volume of gas ______________

Answer the questions on the next page in your notebook.

1. What happened to the syringe plunger during the reaction between citric acid and sodium bicarbonate?
2. What caused that to happen?
3. Why is a syringe more useful than a balloon to conduct this experiment?
4. What errors might have occurred while gathering data?
5. What do you think might happen if you doubled the amount of either the citric acid solution or the sodium bicarbonate powder? Why do you think so?

WARNING — This set contains chemicals that may be harmful if misused. Read cautions on individual containers carefully. Not to be used by children except under adult supervision.

How Much Gas?

Challenge. Determine how much gas is produced in a citric acid and sodium bicarbonate reaction.

Record results.

Volume of gas produced (mL)			
Trial 1	**Trial 2**	**Trial 3**	**Average**

My group's average volume of gas ______________

Class average volume of gas ______________

Answer the questions on the next page in your notebook.

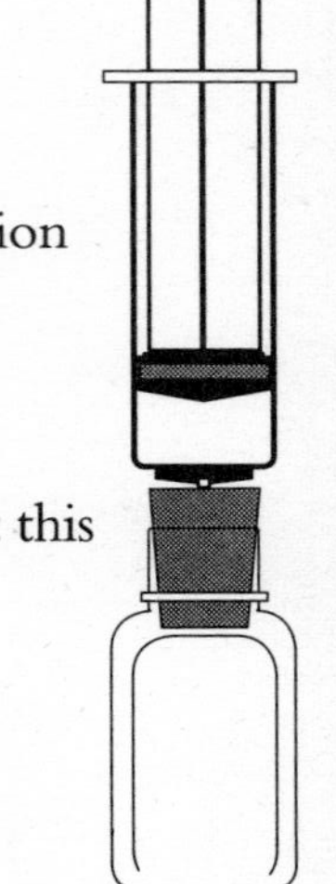

1. What happened to the syringe plunger during the reaction between citric acid and sodium bicarbonate?
2. What caused that to happen?
3. Why is a syringe more useful than a balloon to conduct this experiment?
4. What errors might have occurred while gathering data?
5. What do you think might happen if you doubled the amount of either the citric acid solution or the sodium bicarbonate powder? Why do you think so?

FOSS Chemical Interactions Course, Second Edition
© The Regents of the University of California
Can be duplicated for classroom or workshop use.
Investigation 3: Particles
No. 12—Notebook Master

What's in the Bubbles?

1. Make a list of the gases you know about or have heard about.

2. How would you define *gas*?

3. Everything is made of elements. What elements could be in the gas that forms when sodium bicarbonate ($NaHCO_3$) and citric acid ($C_6H_8O_7$) react?

4. What gas do you think is in the bubbles that form when $NaHCO_3$ and $C_6H_8O_7$ react?

What's in the Bubbles?

1. Make a list of the gases you know about or have heard about.

2. How would you define *gas*?

3. Everything is made of elements. What elements could be in the gas that forms when sodium bicarbonate ($NaHCO_3$) and citric acid ($C_6H_8O_7$) react?

4. What gas do you think is in the bubbles that form when $NaHCO_3$ and $C_6H_8O_7$ react?

FOSS Chemical Interactions Course, Second Edition
© The Regents of the University of California
Can be duplicated for classroom or workshop use.
Investigation 3: Particles
No. 13—Notebook Master

Discuss Air as Particles

1. What is the air in the syringe and the air in the bubble made of?

2. What happens to the air particles in the syringe when you push on the plunger?

3. What happens to the air particles in the bubble when you pull up on the plunger?

4. Are there more air particles in the bubble when it is compressed or when it is expanded?

5. When you push on the plunger, are the air particles closer together in the syringe or in the bubble?

6. What is between air particles?

7. What happens to air particles when a volume of air is compressed?

   When a volume of air expands?

Discuss Air as Particles

1. What is the air in the syringe and the air in the bubble made of?

2. What happens to the air particles in the syringe when you push on the plunger?

3. What happens to the air particles in the bubble when you pull up on the plunger?

4. Are there more air particles in the bubble when it is compressed or when it is expanded?

5. When you push on the plunger, are the air particles closer together in the syringe or in the bubble?

6. What is between air particles?

7. What happens to air particles when a volume of air is compressed?

   When a volume of air expands?

FOSS Chemical Interactions Course, Second Edition
© The Regents of the University of California
Can be duplicated for classroom or workshop use.
Investigation 3: Particles
No. 14—Notebook Master

Air in a Syringe A

A student had a syringe barrel. She drew a picture (A) of her idea of how air filled the room and the syringe.

She put the plunger into the barrel (B) and then clamped the syringe shut (C).

She pushed the plunger down (D) and pulled the plunger up (E).

Draw air particles in syringes B–E.

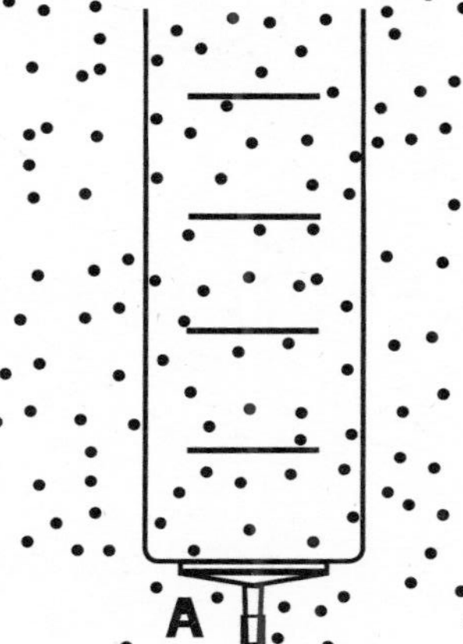

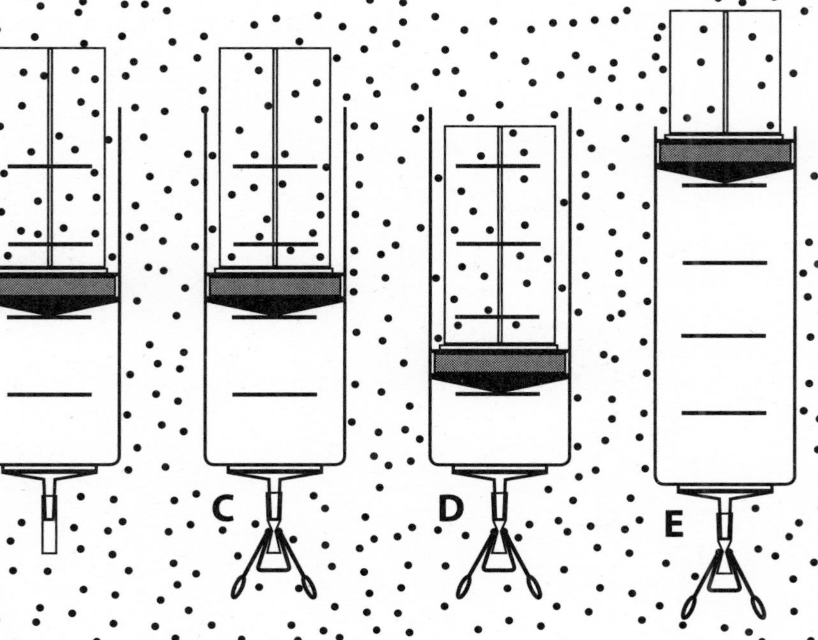

Air in a Syringe A

A student had a syringe barrel. She drew a picture (A) of her idea of how air filled the room and the syringe.

She put the plunger into the barrel (B) and then clamped the syringe shut (C).

She pushed the plunger down (D) and pulled the plunger up (E).

Draw air particles in syringes B–E.

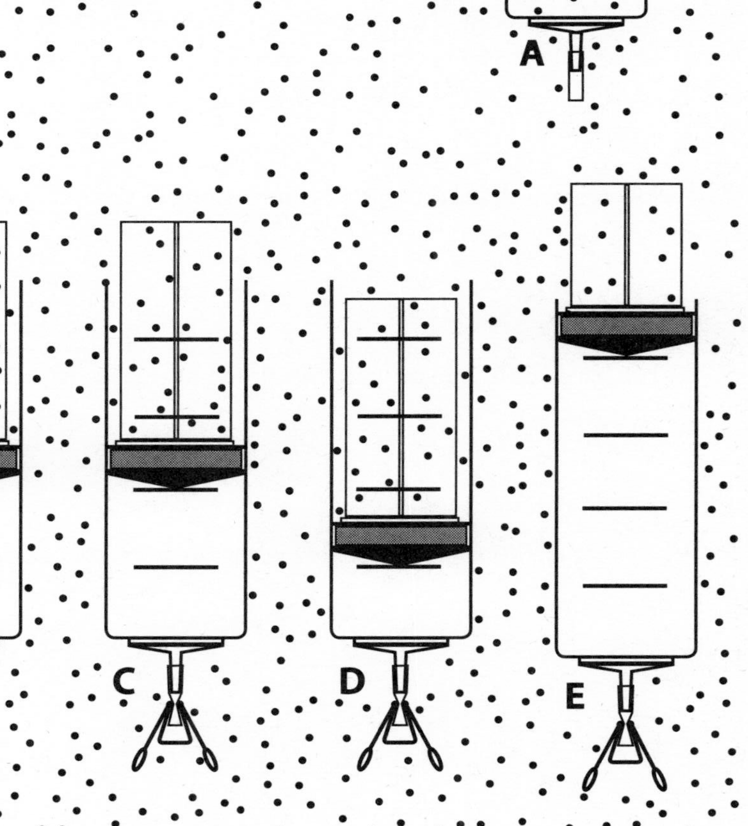

Air in a Syringe B

1. Why did you draw the particles in syringe B the way you did?

2. Why did you draw the particles in syringe C the way you did?

3. Why did you draw the particles in syringe D the way you did?

4. Why did you draw the particles in syringe E the way you did?

5. What happens to the air particles when air expands?

6. What happens to the air particles when air is compressed?

Air in a Syringe B

1. Why did you draw the particles in syringe B the way you did?

2. Why did you draw the particles in syringe C the way you did?

3. Why did you draw the particles in syringe D the way you did?

4. Why did you draw the particles in syringe E the way you did?

5. What happens to the air particles when air expands?

6. What happens to the air particles when air is compressed?

FOSS Chemical Interactions Course, Second Edition
© The Regents of the University of California
Can be duplicated for classroom or workshop use.
Investigation 3: Particles
No. 16—Notebook Master

Heating and Cooling Air

Investigation Question

What happens to a volume of air when it is heated? When it is cooled?

Part 1

Work with the materials to explore what happens to the air when it is heated and when it is cooled.

Part 2

Choose one demonstration to show fourth graders. Draw and label your setup.

Part 3

In your science notebook, describe what happens to air when it gets hot and when it gets cold. Use drawings and labels to help you explain. Make sure it can be understood by fourth graders. Use the words *expand*, *expansion*, *contract*, and *contraction* in your explanation.

Heating and Cooling Air

Investigation Question

What happens to a volume of air when it is heated? When it is cooled?

Part 1

Work with the materials to explore what happens to the air when it is heated and when it is cooled.

Part 2

Choose one demonstration to show fourth graders. Draw and label your setup.

Part 3

In your science notebook, describe what happens to air when it gets hot and when it gets cold. Use drawings and labels to help you explain. Make sure it can be understood by fourth graders. Use the words *expand*, *expansion*, *contract*, and *contraction* in your explanation.

FOSS Chemical Interactions Course, Second Edition
© The Regents of the University of California
Can be duplicated for classroom or workshop use.
Investigation 4: Kinetic Energy
No. 17—Notebook Master

Heating and Cooling Water

Think about the bottle system

1. What happened when you placed your bottle system in cold water?
   Draw and explain.

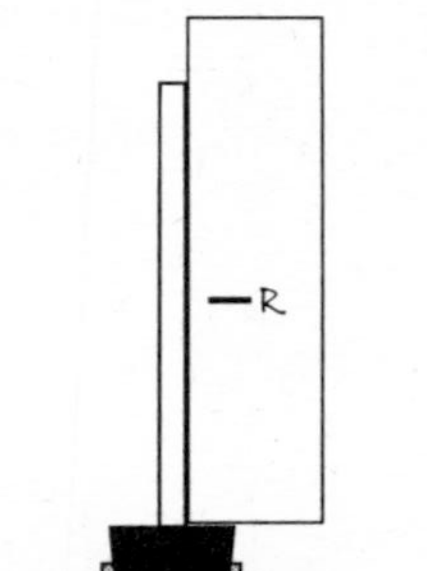

2. What happened when you placed your bottle system in hot water?
   Draw and explain.

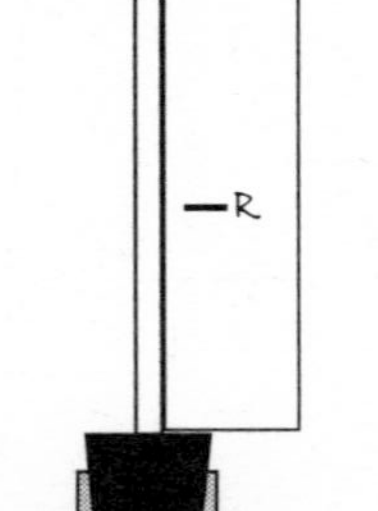

3. What caused the water level in the pipe to change when you put the bottle in cold water?

4. What caused the water level in the pipe to change when you put the bottle in hot water?

5. In your science notebook, describe what you think happened to the water *particles* in the bottle system when it was placed in hot water. Discuss *kinetic energy* and *expansion* in your explanation.

Heating and Cooling Water

Think about the bottle system

1. What happened when you placed your bottle system in cold water?
   Draw and explain.

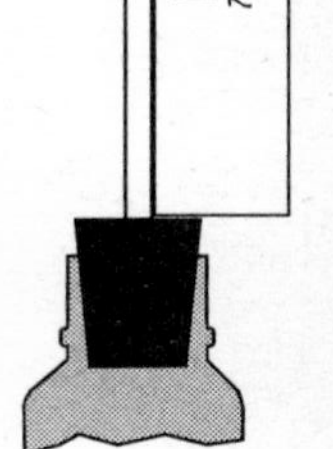

2. What happened when you placed your bottle system in hot water?
   Draw and explain.

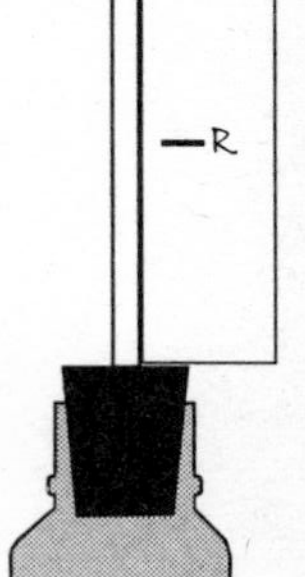

3. What caused the water level in the pipe to change when you put the bottle in cold water?

4. What caused the water level in the pipe to change when you put the bottle in hot water?

5. In your science notebook, describe what you think happened to the water *particles* in the bottle system when it was placed in hot water. Discuss *kinetic energy* and *expansion* in your explanation.

FOSS Chemical Interactions Course, Second Edition
© The Regents of the University of California
Can be duplicated for classroom or workshop use.
Investigation 4: Kinetic Energy
No. 18—Notebook Master

Particles in Motion

Air is matter. It has mass and occupies space. Air is a **mixture** of many gases. It is made of approximately four-fifths nitrogen and one-fifth oxygen. All the other gases, including carbon dioxide (CO_2) and **water vapor** (H_2O), make up only a little more than 1 percent of the mass of a sample of air.

Air is an example of matter in its gas phase. The nitrogen and oxygen particles in air are not bonded to other gas particles. Gas particles fly through space as individuals.

After you drink a bottle of spring water, you have an excellent container for an air investigation. The bottle looks empty, but it is full of air. Because air particles are flying all around, they are going into and out of the open bottle all the time. The **density**

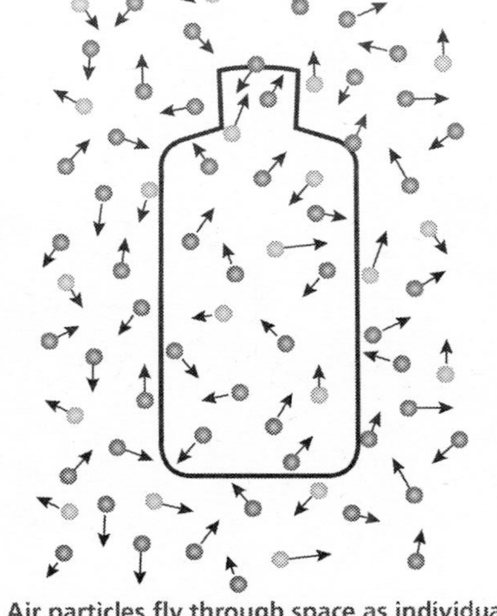

Air particles fly through space as individual particles. Air particles fill an open bottle.

Particles in Motion

Air is matter. It has mass and occupies space. Air is a **mixture** of many gases. It is made of approximately four-fifths nitrogen and one-fifth oxygen. All the other gases, including carbon dioxide (CO_2) and **water vapor** (H_2O), make up only a little more than 1 percent of the mass of a sample of air.

Air is an example of matter in its gas phase. The nitrogen and oxygen particles in air are not bonded to other gas particles. Gas particles fly through space as individuals.

After you drink a bottle of spring water, you have an excellent container for an air investigation. The bottle looks empty, but it is full of air. Because air particles are flying all around, they are going into and out of the open bottle all the time. The **density**

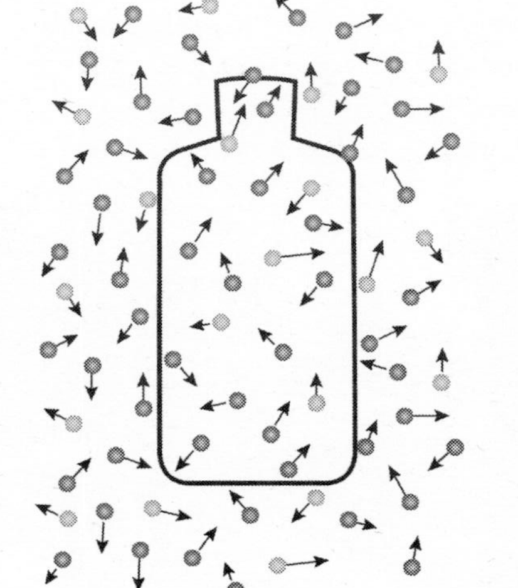

Air particles fly through space as individual particles. Air particles fill an open bottle.

Investigation 4: Kinetic Energy **21**

FOSS Chemical Interactions Course, Second Edition
© The Regents of the University of California
Can be duplicated for classroom or workshop use.

Investigation 4: Kinetic Energy
No. 19—Notebook Master

of air in the bottle is exactly the same as the density of the air outside the bottle. That means that every cubic centimeter of air in the bottle has the same number of particles as every cubic centimeter of air outside the bottle.

Remember that we are using a model to understand particles. Air particles are millions of times smaller than the representations in the illustrations. A cubic centimeter of air actually has about one quintillion air particles! A quintillion is a one followed by 18 zeroes (1,000,000,000,000,000,000). The illustrations are therefore not accurate, but they are a good model for thinking about what is going on at the particle level.

Particles Have Kinetic Energy

Not only are air particles incredibly small, they are always moving. And they move fast. At **room temperature** they move at about 300 meters (m) per second.

All moving objects have energy. This kind of energy is called **kinetic energy**. Anything that is in motion has kinetic energy, whether it is a bicycle, a fly, a snail, you walking to class, water falling down a

A moving bicycle has kinetic energy.

waterfall, or an oxygen particle in the air. They all have kinetic energy.

Kinetic energy, like all forms of energy, can do work. Air particles do work when they crash into things. Air particles push on each other, on you, on the walls of containers, and on everything else around them. Every air particle crashes into another particle about 10 billion times every second!

The amount of kinetic energy an object has depends on the mass of the object and its speed. You can't change the mass of an air particle, but you can change its speed. You can make air particles move faster by heating a sample of air. Heating particles increases their kinetic energy by increasing their speed.

of air in the bottle is exactly the same as the density of the air outside the bottle. That means that every cubic centimeter of air in the bottle has the same number of particles as every cubic centimeter of air outside the bottle.

Remember that we are using a model to understand particles. Air particles are millions of times smaller than the representations in the illustrations. A cubic centimeter of air actually has about one quintillion air particles! A quintillion is a one followed by 18 zeroes (1,000,000,000,000,000,000). The illustrations are therefore not accurate, but they are a good model for thinking about what is going on at the particle level.

Particles Have Kinetic Energy

Not only are air particles incredibly small, they are always moving. And they move fast. At room temperature they move at about 300 meters (m) per second.

All moving objects have energy. This kind of energy is called kinetic energy. Anything that is in motion has kinetic energy, whether it is a bicycle, a fly, a snail, you walking to class, water falling down a

A moving bicycle has kinetic energy.

waterfall, or an oxygen particle in the air. They all have kinetic energy.

Kinetic energy, like all forms of energy, can do work. Air particles do work when they crash into things. Air particles push on each other, on you, on the walls of containers, and on everything else around them. Every air particle crashes into another particle about 10 billion times every second!

The amount of kinetic energy an object has depends on the mass of the object and its speed. You can't change the mass of an air particle, but you can change its speed. You can make air particles move faster by heating a sample of air. Heating particles increases their kinetic energy by increasing their speed.

22

FOSS Chemical Interactions Course, Second Edition
© The Regents of the University of California
Can be duplicated for classroom or workshop use.

Investigation 4: Kinetic Energy
No. 20—Notebook Master

Back to the air investigation. Stretch a balloon over the top of the bottle full of air. Now the air is trapped inside the bottle-and-balloon system. No particles can get in or out.

The density of air particles is the same in the bottle, in the balloon, and in the air surrounding the bottle-and-balloon system.

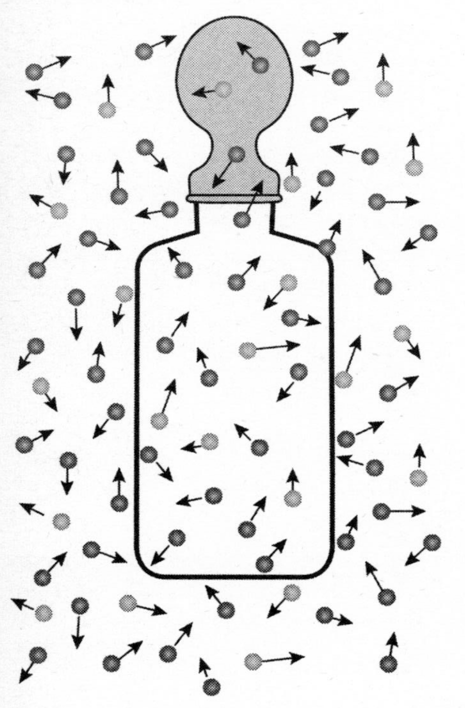

A balloon can trap the air inside a bottle.

Now place the bottle-and-balloon system in a cup of hot water. The hot water warms the air inside the bottle. Particles in the warm air start to move faster. After a few minutes, the bottle-and-balloon system looks like this.

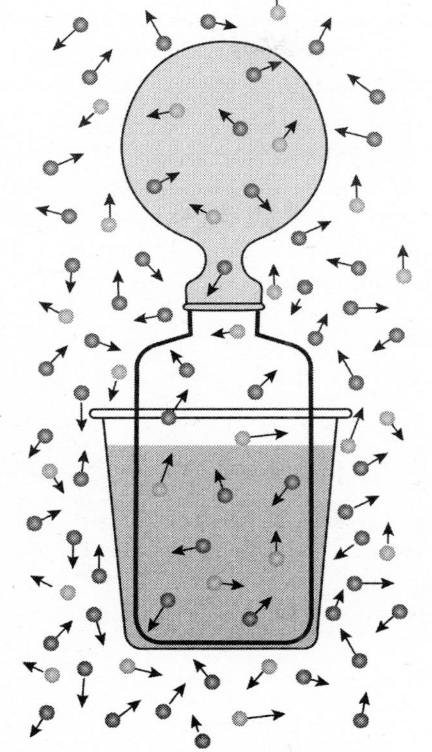

Hot water increases the kinetic energy of the air particles inside the bottle-and-balloon system. The particles fly faster and hit each other harder. The particles push farther apart, causing the gas to expand.

Why did the balloon inflate? The hot water heated the air in the bottle. As a result, the air particles began moving faster. Faster-moving particles have more kinetic energy. Faster-moving particles hit each other harder, which pushes them farther apart. You can see in the illustration that the particles of warm air inside the bottle-and-balloon system are farther apart.

Back to the air investigation. Stretch a balloon over the top of the bottle full of air. Now the air is trapped inside the bottle-and-balloon system. No particles can get in or out.

The density of air particles is the same in the bottle, in the balloon, and in the air surrounding the bottle-and-balloon system.

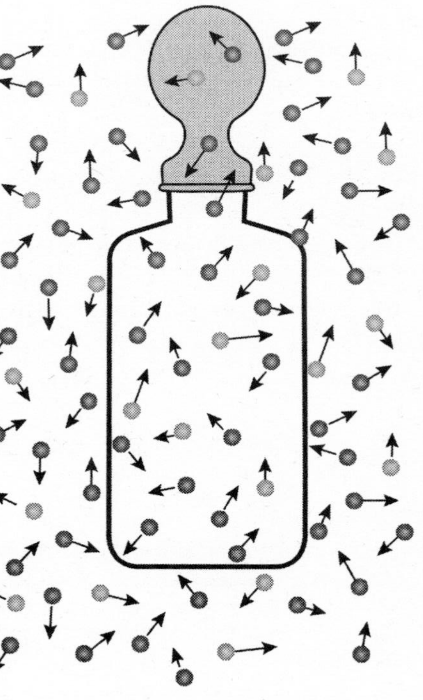

A balloon can trap the air inside a bottle.

Now place the bottle-and-balloon system in a cup of hot water. The hot water warms the air inside the bottle. Particles in the warm air start to move faster. After a few minutes, the bottle-and-balloon system looks like this.

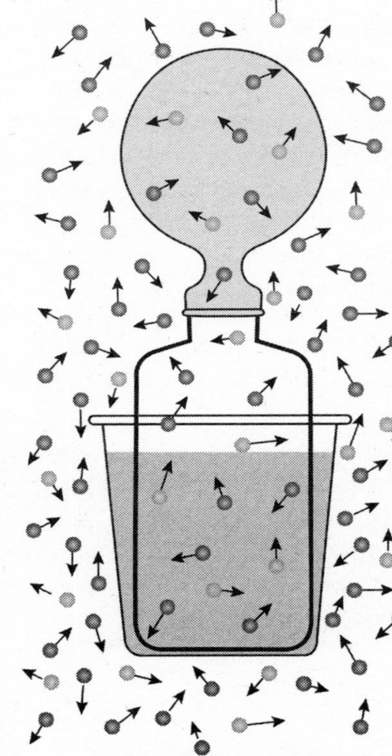

Hot water increases the kinetic energy of the air particles inside the bottle-and-balloon system. The particles fly faster and hit each other harder. The particles push farther apart, causing the gas to expand.

Why did the balloon inflate? The hot water heated the air in the bottle. As a result, the air particles began moving faster. Faster-moving particles have more kinetic energy. Faster-moving particles hit each other harder, which pushes them farther apart. You can see in the illustration that the particles of warm air inside the bottle-and-balloon system are farther apart.

Investigation 4: Kinetic Energy **23**

FOSS Chemical Interactions Course, Second Edition
© The Regents of the University of California
Can be duplicated for classroom or workshop use.

Investigation 4: Kinetic Energy
No. 21—Notebook Master

The faster-moving particles also push harder on the balloon. The force that the particles apply to the balloon is enough to stretch the balloon membrane. The increased kinetic energy of the particles pushes them farther apart (the air expands), and the balloon stretches to hold the increased volume of air. Note that the particles themselves do not become larger or smaller! The relationship between particles changes, making the sample expand or contract, but the particles stay the same size.

What Happens When Gases, Liquids, and Solids Heat Up?

Gas. Remember that the particles in a gas are not bonded (attached) to other particles. Each particle moves freely through space. When a sample of air heats up, the particles move faster and hit each other harder. The result is that the particles push each other farther apart.

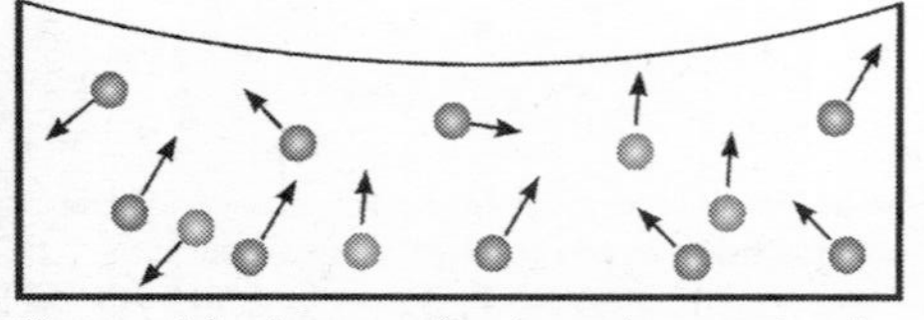

The particles in gases fly through space in all directions as individuals.

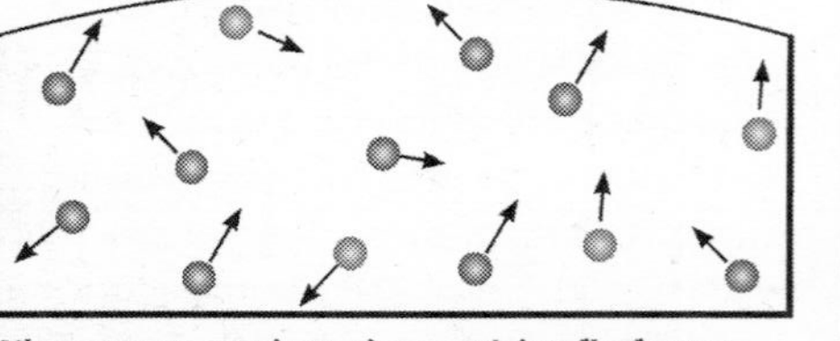

When gases get hot, the particles fly faster. Faster particles hit other particles harder, pushing the particles farther apart. This causes the gas to expand.

In the previous illustrations, a container of gas has a flexible membrane across the top. When the gas gets warm, the kinetic energy of the particles increases, particles hit each other harder, and the gas expands. As the gas expands, it pushes the membrane upward.

Liquid. Particles in liquids are in close contact with one another. Attractions between the particles keep them from flying freely through space. The particles in liquids can, however, move over, around, and past one another. Individual particles in liquids are able to move all through the sample of liquid.

The motion of particles in a liquid is kinetic energy. When a liquid gets warm, the particles move faster. The particles have more kinetic energy. As a result, they hit other particles more often and hit harder. This pushes the particles farther apart. When particles are pushed farther apart, the liquid expands.

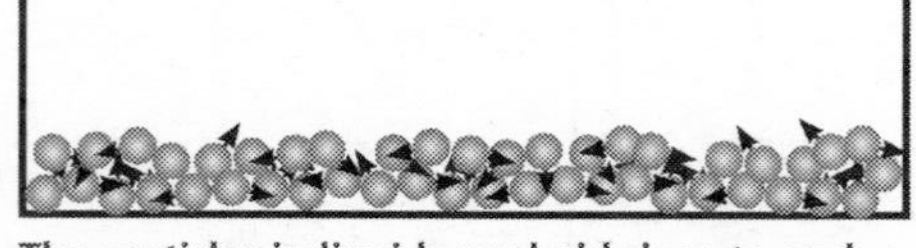

The particles in liquids are held close to each other. Particles bump and slide around and past each other.

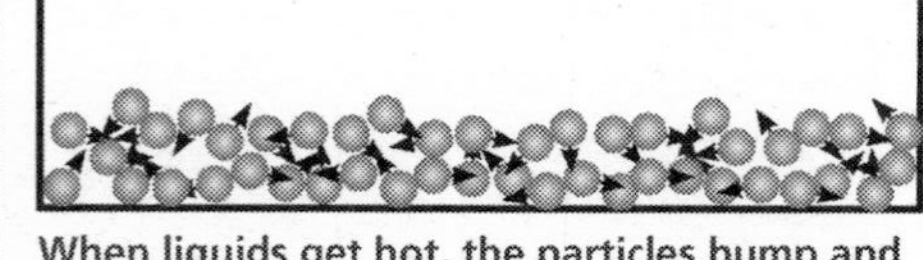

When liquids get hot, the particles bump and push each other more. This causes the liquid to expand.

The faster-moving particles also push harder on the balloon. The force that the particles apply to the balloon is enough to stretch the balloon membrane. The increased kinetic energy of the particles pushes them farther apart (the air expands), and the balloon stretches to hold the increased volume of air. Note that the particles themselves do not become larger or smaller! The relationship between particles changes, making the sample expand or contract, but the particles stay the same size.

What Happens When Gases, Liquids, and Solids Heat Up?

Gas. Remember that the particles in a gas are not bonded (attached) to other particles. Each particle moves freely through space. When a sample of air heats up, the particles move faster and hit each other harder. The result is that the particles push each other farther apart.

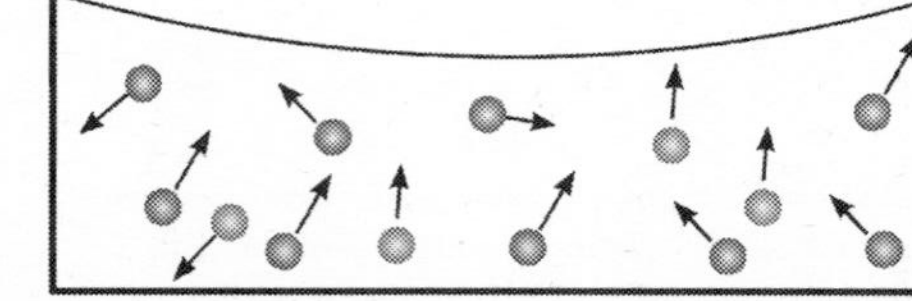

The particles in gases fly through space in all directions as individuals.

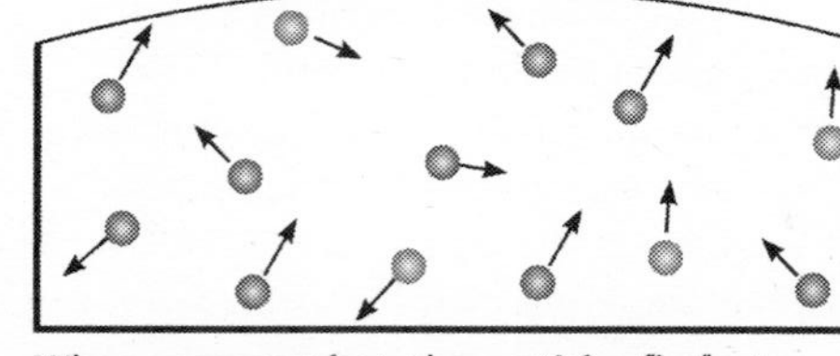

When gases get hot, the particles fly faster. Faster particles hit other particles harder, pushing the particles farther apart. This causes the gas to expand.

In the previous illustrations, a container of gas has a flexible membrane across the top. When the gas gets warm, the kinetic energy of the particles increases, particles hit each other harder, and the gas expands. As the gas expands, it pushes the membrane upward.

Liquid. Particles in liquids are in close contact with one another. Attractions between the particles keep them from flying freely through space. The particles in liquids can, however, move over, around, and past one another. Individual particles in liquids are able to move all through the sample of liquid.

The motion of particles in a liquid is kinetic energy. When a liquid gets warm, the particles move faster. The particles have more kinetic energy. As a result, they hit other particles more often and hit harder. This pushes the particles farther apart. When particles are pushed farther apart, the liquid expands.

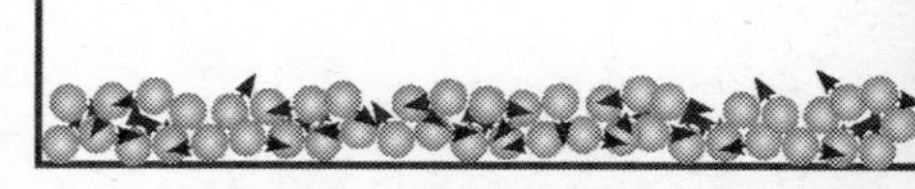

The particles in liquids are held close to each other. Particles bump and slide around and past each other.

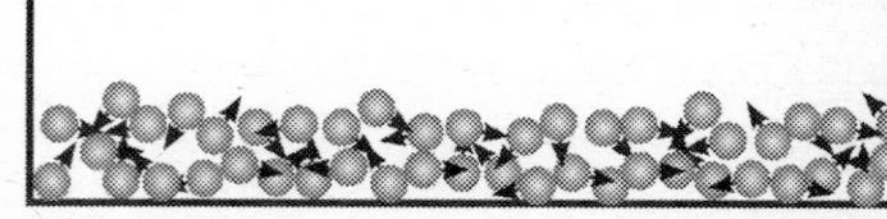

When liquids get hot, the particles bump and push each other more. This causes the liquid to expand.

24

FOSS Chemical Interactions Course, Second Edition
© The Regents of the University of California
Can be duplicated for classroom or workshop use.

Investigation 4: Kinetic Energy
No. 22—Notebook Master

Solid. Particles in solids have bonds holding them tightly together. The particles cannot move around. The particles are, however, moving a little. Particles in solids are always **vibrating** (moving back and forth) in place.

The vibrating motion of particles in solids is kinetic energy. Heating particles in a solid makes them vibrate faster, giving them more kinetic energy. Faster-vibrating particles bump into one another more often and hit each other harder. This pushes the particles farther apart. When particles are pushed farther apart, the solid expands.

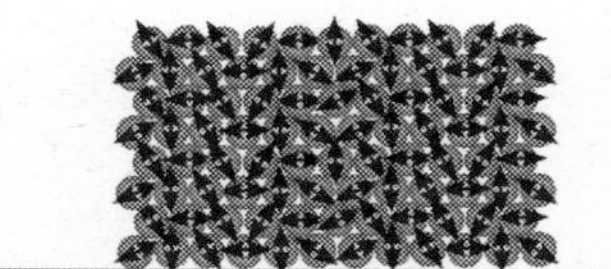

The particles in solids are bonded. Particles move by vibrating, but do not change positions.

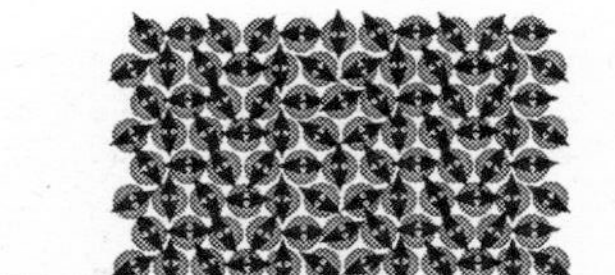

When solids get hot, the particles vibrate more. Increased vibration pushes the particles farther apart, causing the solid to expand.

Heating and Cooling

When a sample of solid, liquid, or gas matter heats up, it expands. When matter gets hot, its particles gain kinetic energy. The increased kinetic energy pushes the particles farther apart. This causes the matter to expand.

When a sample of solid, liquid, or gas matter cools down, it contracts. When matter cools down, its particles lose kinetic energy. The decreased kinetic energy lets the particles come closer together. This causes the matter to contract.

Think Questions

1. What is kinetic energy?
2. How can you increase an object's kinetic energy?
3. Explain why a balloon inflates when you set a bottle-and-balloon system in hot water.
4. What happens to a sample of matter when its particles lose kinetic energy?
5. How are particles in solids, liquids, and gases the same? How are they different?

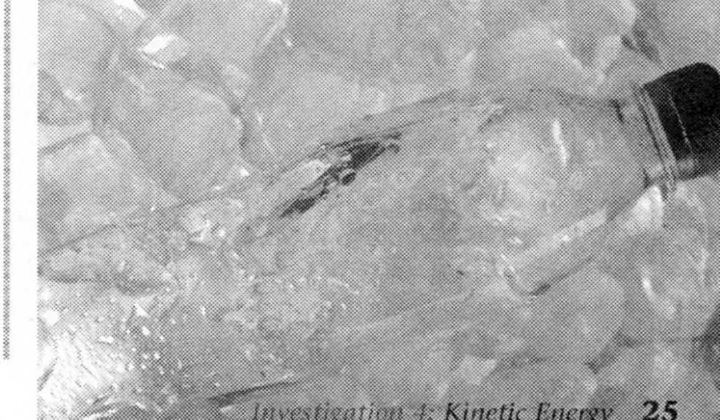

Solid. Particles in solids have bonds holding them tightly together. The particles cannot move around. The particles are, however, moving a little. Particles in solids are always **vibrating** (moving back and forth) in place.

The vibrating motion of particles in solids is kinetic energy. Heating particles in a solid makes them vibrate faster, giving them more kinetic energy. Faster-vibrating particles bump into one another more often and hit each other harder. This pushes the particles farther apart. When particles are pushed farther apart, the solid expands.

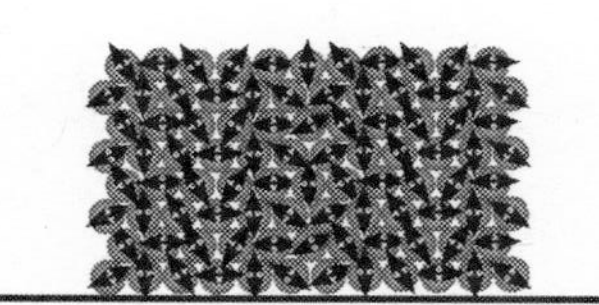

The particles in solids are bonded. Particles move by vibrating, but do not change positions.

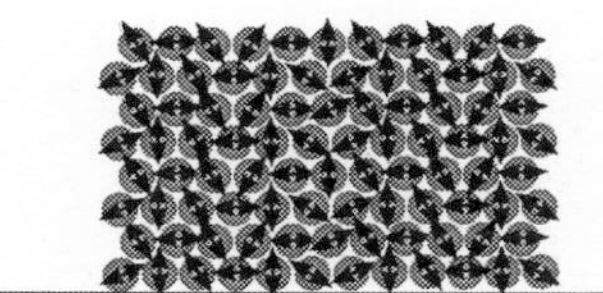

When solids get hot, the particles vibrate more. Increased vibration pushes the particles farther apart, causing the solid to expand.

Heating and Cooling

When a sample of solid, liquid, or gas matter heats up, it expands. When matter gets hot, its particles gain kinetic energy. The increased kinetic energy pushes the particles farther apart. This causes the matter to expand.

When a sample of solid, liquid, or gas matter cools down, it contracts. When matter cools down, its particles lose kinetic energy. The decreased kinetic energy lets the particles come closer together. This causes the matter to contract.

Think Questions

1. What is kinetic energy?
2. How can you increase an object's kinetic energy?
3. Explain why a balloon inflates when you set a bottle-and-balloon system in hot water.
4. What happens to a sample of matter when its particles lose kinetic energy?
5. How are particles in solids, liquids, and gases the same? How are they different?

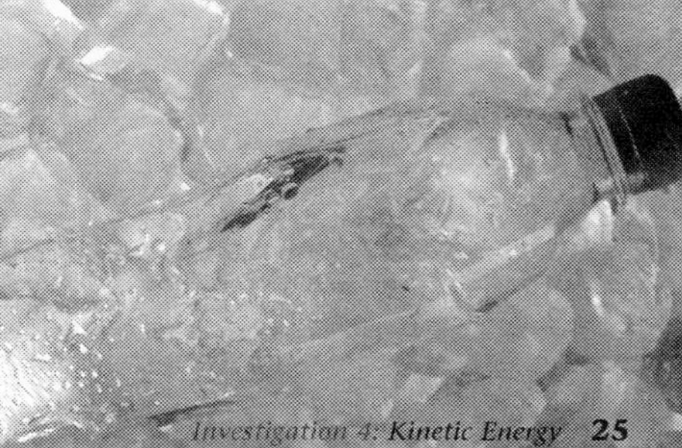

Investigation 4: Kinetic Energy **25**

FOSS Chemical Interactions Course, Second Edition
© The Regents of the University of California
Can be duplicated for classroom or workshop use.

Investigation 4: Kinetic Energy
No. 23—Notebook Master

Response Sheet—Investigation 4

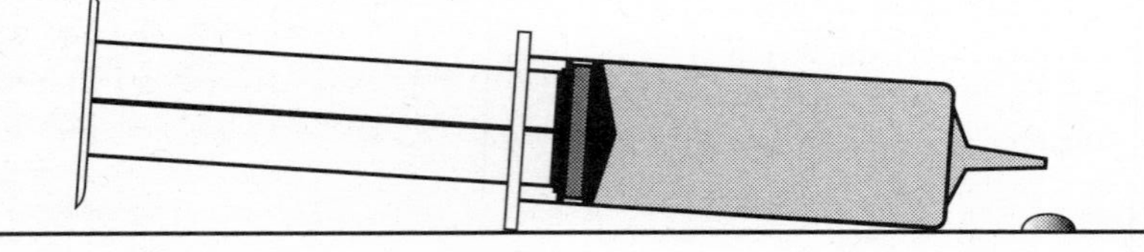

A student filled a syringe with water and left it by the sink in the sunshine. Ten minutes later she saw a little puddle of water under the syringe tip. She said,

This syringe must be broken. It's leaking.

But the syringe wasn't broken.

What do you think caused the little puddle of water to appear under the syringe tip?

NOTE: Use the words *particle* and *kinetic energy* in your explanation.

Response Sheet—Investigation 4

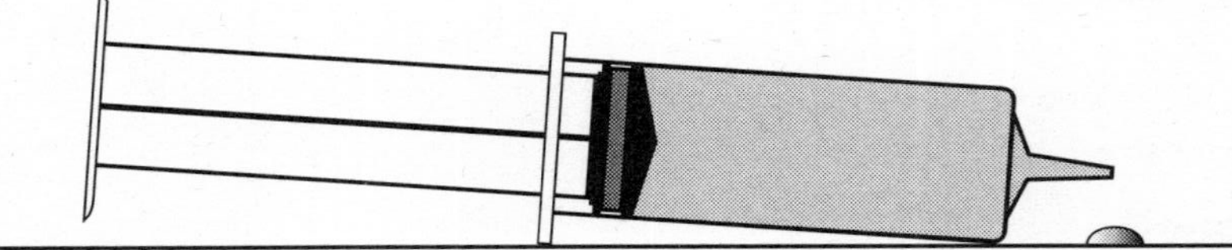

A student filled a syringe with water and left it by the sink in the sunshine. Ten minutes later she saw a little puddle of water under the syringe tip. She said,

This syringe must be broken. It's leaking.

But the syringe wasn't broken.

What do you think caused the little puddle of water to appear under the syringe tip?

NOTE: Use the words *particle* and *kinetic energy* in your explanation.

FOSS Chemical Interactions Course, Second Edition
© The Regents of the University of California
Can be duplicated for classroom or workshop use.
Investigation 4: Kinetic Energy
No. 24—Notebook Master

Mixing Water

Question

If you mixed 50 mL of 50°C hot water and 50 mL of 10°C cold water, what do you think the temperature of the mixture would be?

Prediction

Predict the temperature of the sample mixture. ________________

Reasoning

Explain the thinking behind your prediction.

Procedure

Describe an experiment you can conduct to check your prediction.

Data

We mixed ______ mL of hot water and _______ mL of cold water.

Make a prediction based on the initial temperatures immediately before mixing the two water samples.

T_{hot} (°C)	T_{cold} (°C)	Prediction (°C)	T_{final} (°C)

Write the equation for calculating final temperature when equal volumes of water are mixed.

Mixing Water

Question

If you mixed 50 mL of 50°C hot water and 50 mL of 10°C cold water, what do you think the temperature of the mixture would be?

Prediction

Predict the temperature of the sample mixture. ________________

Reasoning

Explain the thinking behind your prediction.

Procedure

Describe an experiment you can conduct to check your prediction.

Data

We mixed ______ mL of hot water and _______ mL of cold water.

Make a prediction based on the initial temperatures immediately before mixing the two water samples.

T_{hot} (°C)	T_{cold} (°C)	Prediction (°C)	T_{final} (°C)

Write the equation for calculating final temperature when equal volumes of water are mixed.

FOSS Chemical Interactions Course, Second Edition
© The Regents of the University of California
Can be duplicated for classroom or workshop use.
Investigation 5: Energy Transfer
No. 25—Notebook Master

Energy on the Move

Have you ever burned your tongue on a cup of hot cocoa? When this happens, you can cool that steaming cup to a comfortable temperature by adding a splash of cold milk. But why exactly does this work? When you mix cold milk and hot cocoa, what happens to the cold milk? And what happens to the hot cocoa?

After mixing, the cup of cocoa is warm throughout. It is cooler than the hot cocoa and hotter than the cold milk. It seems as if the hot cocoa gets colder and the cold milk gets hotter. The new temperature is between the starting temperatures of the cocoa and the milk.

How does that happen?

Kinetic Energy

Objects in motion have kinetic energy. Particles that make up substances are always moving. So the particles that make up both the hot cocoa and the cold milk have kinetic energy.

The amount of energy that a particle has depends on how fast it is moving. Faster-moving particles have more energy. Slower-moving particles have less energy.

The simple rule is that the more kinetic energy the particles have (the faster they are moving), the hotter the substance is. The particles in hot cocoa have more kinetic energy than the particles in cold milk.

This is important. *Kinetic energy of particles is directly related to temperature of a substance.*

Energy on the Move

Have you ever burned your tongue on a cup of hot cocoa? When this happens, you can cool that steaming cup to a comfortable temperature by adding a splash of cold milk. But why exactly does this work? When you mix cold milk and hot cocoa, what happens to the cold milk? And what happens to the hot cocoa?

After mixing, the cup of cocoa is warm throughout. It is cooler than the hot cocoa and hotter than the cold milk. It seems as if the hot cocoa gets colder and the cold milk gets hotter. The new temperature is between the starting temperatures of the cocoa and the milk.

How does that happen?

Kinetic Energy

Objects in motion have kinetic energy. Particles that make up substances are always moving. So the particles that make up both the hot cocoa and the cold milk have kinetic energy.

The amount of energy that a particle has depends on how fast it is moving. Faster-moving particles have more energy. Slower-moving particles have less energy.

The simple rule is that the more kinetic energy the particles have (the faster they are moving), the hotter the substance is. The particles in hot cocoa have more kinetic energy than the particles in cold milk.

This is important. *Kinetic energy of particles is directly related to temperature of a substance.*

30

FOSS Chemical Interactions Course, Second Edition
© The Regents of the University of California
Can be duplicated for classroom or workshop use.
Investigation 5: Energy Transfer
No. 26—Notebook Master

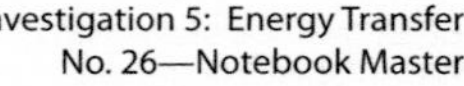

Changing Kinetic Energy

Energy is **conserved**. That means that energy is never destroyed or created during interactions. The amount of energy in a system is always the same, but it can move from place to place. When energy moves from one place to another, it is called **energy transfer**.

Energy transfer happens when particles collide. When a fast-moving particle hits a slow-moving particle, the slow-moving particle speeds up while the fast-moving particle slows down. When a particle speeds up, it has more kinetic energy. When a particle slows down, it has less kinetic energy. Energy transfers from a fast-moving particle to a slow-moving particle at the moment of impact. Visualize this situation.

1. Fast-moving particle 1 is on a collision course with slow-moving particle 2.
2. The particles collide. At the moment of impact, energy transfers from particle 1 to particle 2. As a result, particle 1 has less kinetic energy, and particle 2 has more kinetic energy.
3. The two particles are now moving at about the same speed. Energy transferred from particle 1 to particle 2 at the moment of impact.

If you add up the kinetic energy of the two particles before the collision, it is exactly the same as the kinetic energy of the two particles after the collision. No kinetic energy is created or lost as a result of the collision, only transferred. The energy of the two-particle system is conserved.

But something did change. As a result of the collision, particle 1 has less kinetic energy, and particle 2 has more kinetic energy. The collision resulted in an energy transfer. Energy transferred from particle 1 to particle 2. This kind of energy transfer, from particle to particle by contact, is called **conduction**.

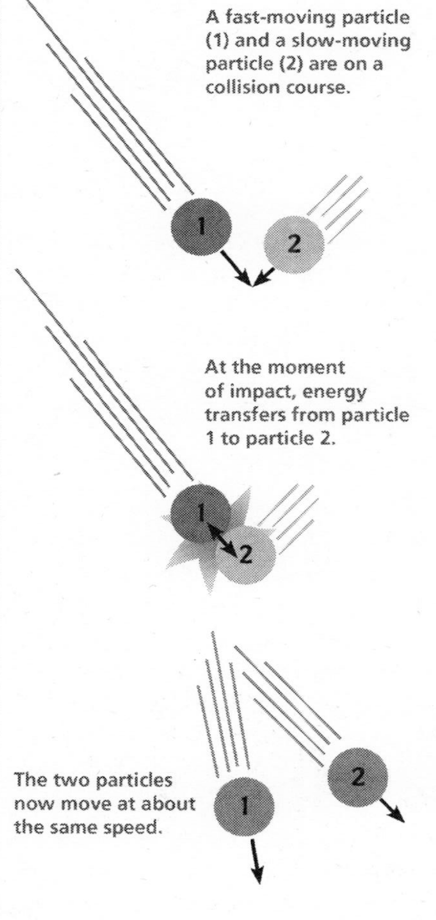

A fast-moving particle (1) and a slow-moving particle (2) are on a collision course.
1
2
At the moment of impact, energy transfers from particle 1 to particle 2.
1
2
The two particles now move at about the same speed.
1
2

Changing Kinetic Energy

Energy is **conserved**. That means that energy is never destroyed or created during interactions. The amount of energy in a system is always the same, but it can move from place to place. When energy moves from one place to another, it is called **energy transfer**.

Energy transfer happens when particles collide. When a fast-moving particle hits a slow-moving particle, the slow-moving particle speeds up while the fast-moving particle slows down. When a particle speeds up, it has more kinetic energy. When a particle slows down, it has less kinetic energy. Energy transfers from a fast-moving particle to a slow-moving particle at the moment of impact. Visualize this situation.

1. Fast-moving particle 1 is on a collision course with slow-moving particle 2.
2. The particles collide. At the moment of impact, energy transfers from particle 1 to particle 2. As a result, particle 1 has less kinetic energy, and particle 2 has more kinetic energy.
3. The two particles are now moving at about the same speed. Energy transferred from particle 1 to particle 2 at the moment of impact.

If you add up the kinetic energy of the two particles before the collision, it is exactly the same as the kinetic energy of the two particles after the collision. No kinetic energy is created or lost as a result of the collision, only transferred. The energy of the two-particle system is conserved.

But something did change. As a result of the collision, particle 1 has less kinetic energy, and particle 2 has more kinetic energy. The collision resulted in an energy transfer. Energy transferred from particle 1 to particle 2. This kind of energy transfer, from particle to particle by contact, is called **conduction**.

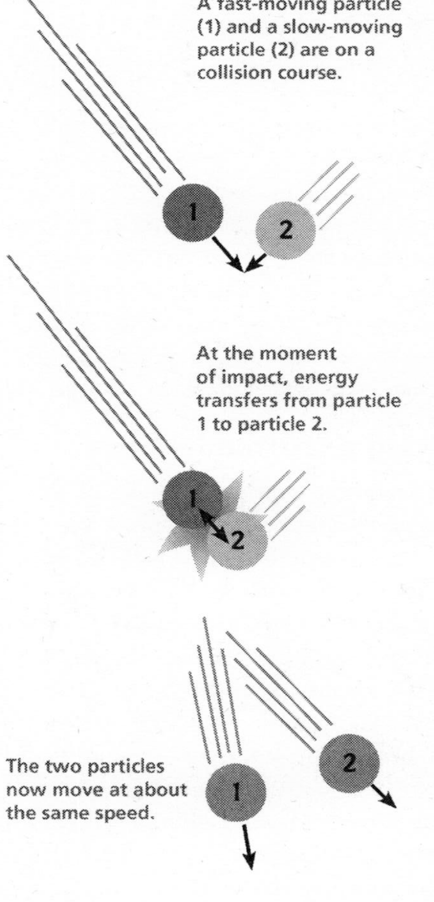

A fast-moving particle (1) and a slow-moving particle (2) are on a collision course.
1
2
At the moment of impact, energy transfers from particle 1 to particle 2.
1
2
The two particles now move at about the same speed.
1
2

Energy Transfer in Cocoa

The kinetic energy of the particles in hot cocoa is high. They are moving fast. The kinetic energy of the particles in cold milk is low. They are moving slowly.

When you pour cold milk into hot cocoa, the milk and cocoa particles start to collide. When a higher-energy cocoa particle hits a lower-energy milk particle, energy transfers by conduction. The cocoa particles slow down, and the cup of cocoa cools down.

Look back at the illustrations of the particle collision. Can you tell which particles represent a cocoa particle and which represent a milk particle? Can you see how the energy transfer reduced the speed of the cocoa particle? Remember, reduced particle speed means less kinetic energy. Lower kinetic energy means lower temperature.

Using a Thermometer

You can use a thermometer to find out if your cocoa is too hot. When you dip a thermometer in that cup of hot cocoa, it reads 90 degrees Celsius (°C). Whoa, too hot. You need to add some cold milk. Move the thermometer over to the cold milk, and the thermometer reads 10°C. That should do the job. But how does the thermometer "know" that the cocoa is 90°C and the milk is 10°C? The answer is kinetic energy. The thermometer reports the average kinetic energy of the particles in a substance. That's what temperature is: average kinetic energy of particles.

How exactly does the thermometer work? Now that we have an idea of how energy transfer takes place, let's put the thermometer into the 90°C cocoa. The cocoa particles collide with the glass particles on the outside of the thermometer stem.

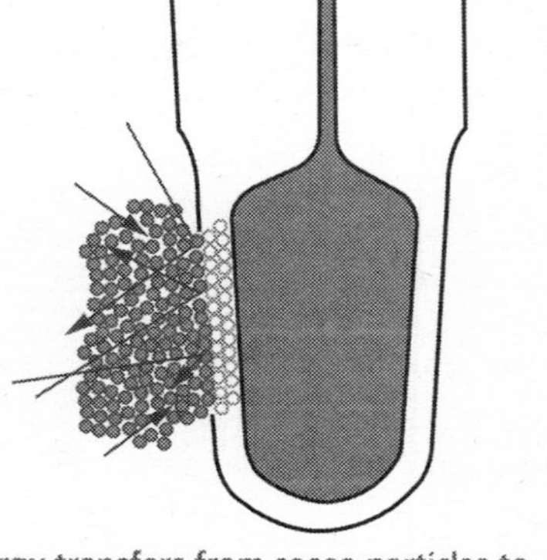

Energy transfers from cocoa particles to glass particles.

The glass particles gain kinetic energy and start vibrating more rapidly. The glass particles transfer energy to their neighbors, and those transfer energy to their neighbors by conduction. Pretty soon the whole glass stem is at 90°C.

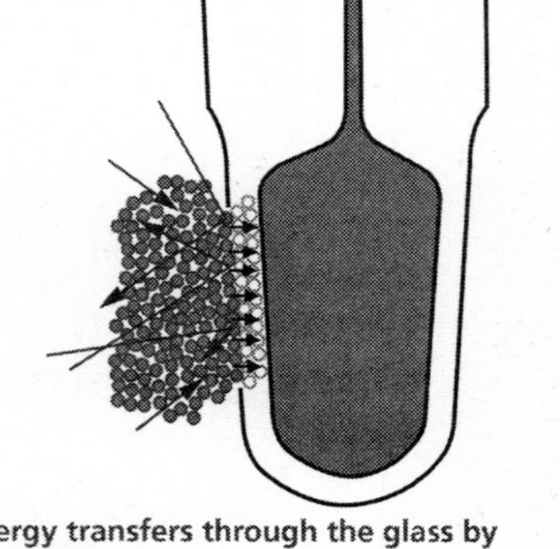

Energy transfers through the glass by conduction.

Energy Transfer in Cocoa

The kinetic energy of the particles in hot cocoa is high. They are moving fast. The kinetic energy of the particles in cold milk is low. They are moving slowly.

When you pour cold milk into hot cocoa, the milk and cocoa particles start to collide. When a higher-energy cocoa particle hits a lower-energy milk particle, energy transfers by conduction. The cocoa particles slow down, and the cup of cocoa cools down.

Look back at the illustrations of the particle collision. Can you tell which particles represent a cocoa particle and which represent a milk particle? Can you see how the energy transfer reduced the speed of the cocoa particle? Remember, reduced particle speed means less kinetic energy. Lower kinetic energy means lower temperature.

Using a Thermometer

You can use a thermometer to find out if your cocoa is too hot. When you dip a thermometer in that cup of hot cocoa, it reads 90 degrees Celsius (°C). Whoa, too hot. You need to add some cold milk. Move the thermometer over to the cold milk, and the thermometer reads 10°C. That should do the job. But how does the thermometer "know" that the cocoa is 90°C and the milk is 10°C? The answer is kinetic energy. The thermometer reports the average kinetic energy of the particles in a substance. That's what temperature is: average kinetic energy of particles.

How exactly does the thermometer work? Now that we have an idea of how energy transfer takes place, let's put the thermometer into the 90°C cocoa. The cocoa particles collide with the glass particles on the outside of the thermometer stem.

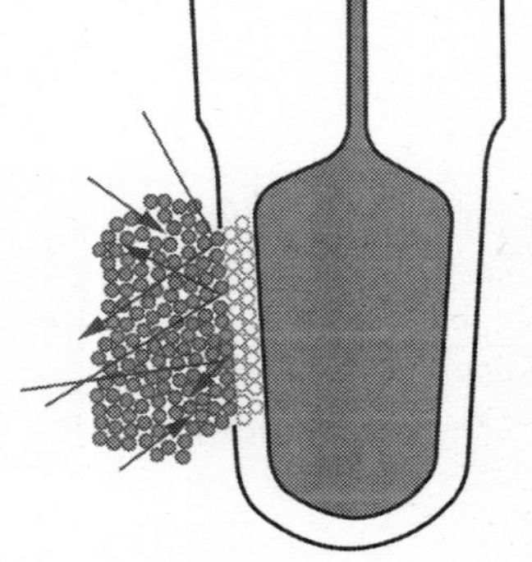

Energy transfers from cocoa particles to glass particles.

The glass particles gain kinetic energy and start vibrating more rapidly. The glass particles transfer energy to their neighbors, and those transfer energy to their neighbors by conduction. Pretty soon the whole glass stem is at 90°C.

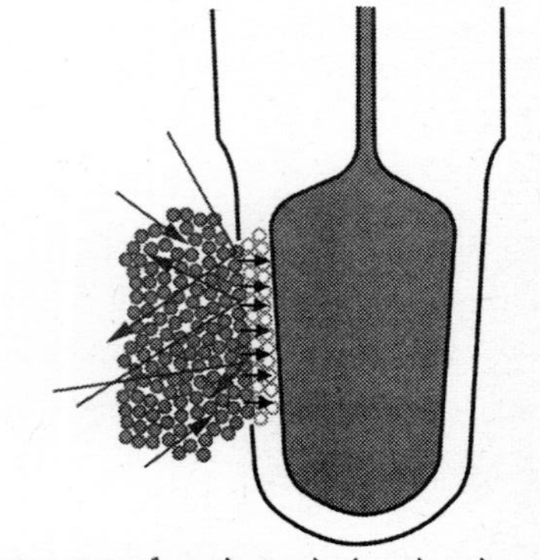

Energy transfers through the glass by conduction.

32

FOSS Chemical Interactions Course, Second Edition
© The Regents of the University of California
Can be duplicated for classroom or workshop use.

Investigation 5: Energy Transfer
No. 28—Notebook Master

The rapidly vibrating glass particles that are in contact with the alcohol inside the thermometer stem transfer kinetic energy to the alcohol particles. Kinetic energy is conducted from alcohol particle to alcohol particle.

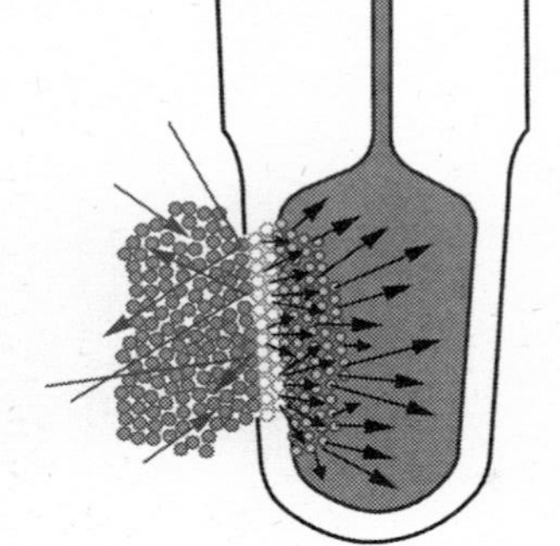

Energy transfers from the glass particles to the alcohol particles. The alcohol expands.

Soon all the alcohol particles are moving faster, pushing on each other more often and with greater force. The distance between particles increases, and the alcohol expands. As the alcohol expands, its volume increases. Alcohol pushes up the stem of the thermometer. The greater the kinetic energy of the alcohol particles, the more the alcohol expands. Energy transfers to the alcohol until the average kinetic energy of the alcohol particles is the same as the average kinetic energy of the cocoa particles. When this happens, the top of the alcohol is at the 90°C mark.

Let's make the alcohol temperature decrease. Put the thermometer into the 10°C milk. Now energy transfers from the outside of the glass thermometer stem to the milk. Energy transfers from glass particles, lowering the kinetic energy of all the glass particles. When alcohol particles collide with lower-energy glass particles, energy flows from the alcohol to the glass. The alcohol loses kinetic energy and contracts. When the average kinetic energy of the alcohol particles is the same as the average kinetic energy of the milk particles, the alcohol level is at the 10°C mark.

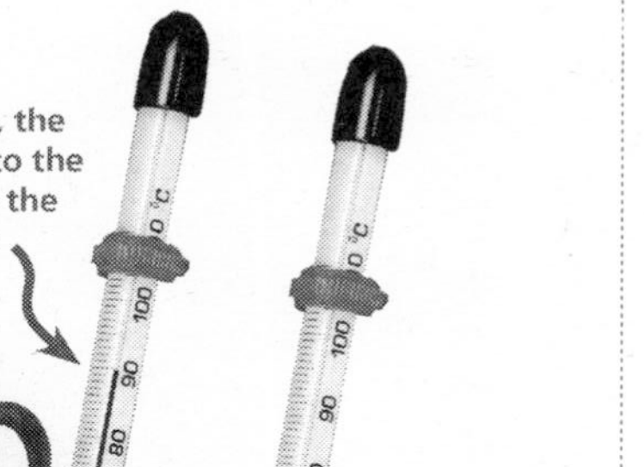

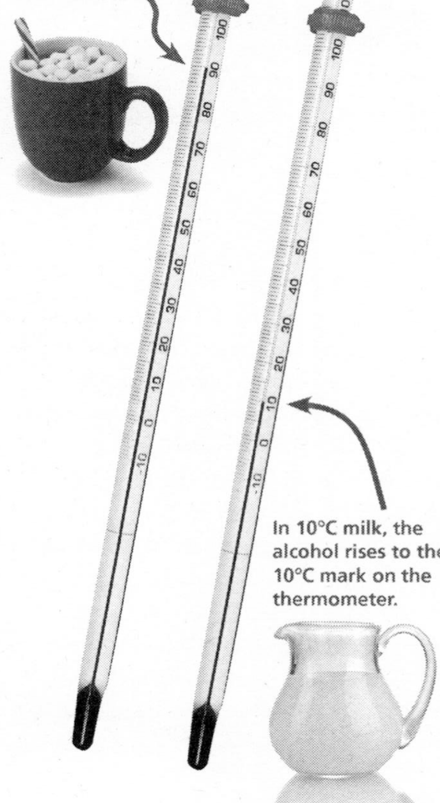

In 90°C cocoa, the alcohol rises to the 90°C mark on the thermometer.

In 10°C milk, the alcohol rises to the 10°C mark on the thermometer.

The rapidly vibrating glass particles that are in contact with the alcohol inside the thermometer stem transfer kinetic energy to the alcohol particles. Kinetic energy is conducted from alcohol particle to alcohol particle.

Energy transfers from the glass particles to the alcohol particles. The alcohol expands.

Soon all the alcohol particles are moving faster, pushing on each other more often and with greater force. The distance between particles increases, and the alcohol expands. As the alcohol expands, its volume increases. Alcohol pushes up the stem of the thermometer. The greater the kinetic energy of the alcohol particles, the more the alcohol expands. Energy transfers to the alcohol until the average kinetic energy of the alcohol particles is the same as the average kinetic energy of the cocoa particles. When this happens, the top of the alcohol is at the 90°C mark.

Let's make the alcohol temperature decrease. Put the thermometer into the 10°C milk. Now energy transfers from the outside of the glass thermometer stem to the milk. Energy transfers from glass particles, lowering the kinetic energy of all the glass particles. When alcohol particles collide with lower-energy glass particles, energy flows from the alcohol to the glass. The alcohol loses kinetic energy and contracts. When the average kinetic energy of the alcohol particles is the same as the average kinetic energy of the milk particles, the alcohol level is at the 10°C mark.

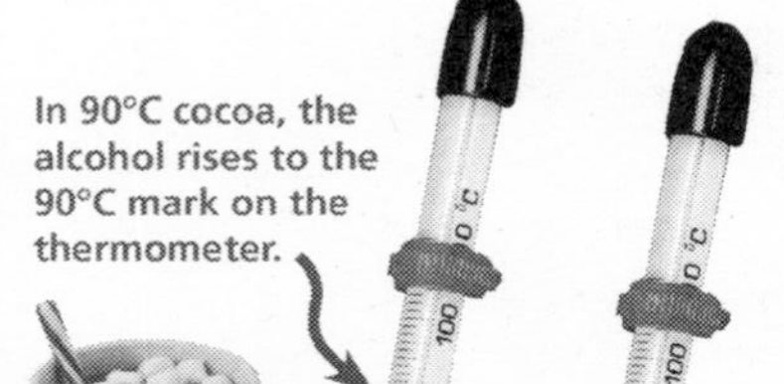

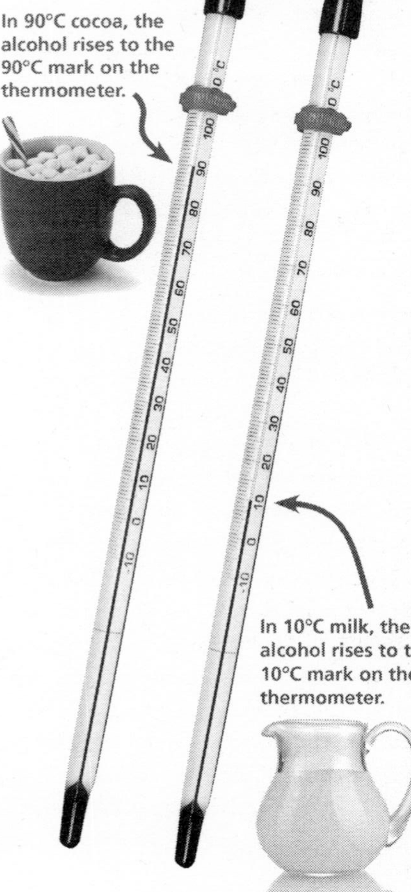

In 90°C cocoa, the alcohol rises to the 90°C mark on the thermometer.

In 10°C milk, the alcohol rises to the 10°C mark on the thermometer.

Investigation 5: Energy Transfer **33**

FOSS Chemical Interactions Course, Second Edition
© The Regents of the University of California
Can be duplicated for classroom or workshop use.

Investigation 5: Energy Transfer
No. 29—Notebook Master

Energy Flows from High to Low

When two particles collide, is it possible for the faster-moving particle to end up going even faster? Can energy transfer from a lower-energy particle to a higher-energy particle?

No. It never happens. Energy *always* transfers from a faster-moving particle to a slower-moving particle. As a result of an energy-transfer collision, the particle that was going faster before the collision will always be going slower after the collision. And the particle that was going slower before the collision will be going faster after the collision. Always.

It is sometimes useful to think of energy as flowing. Energy always flows from higher to lower, from hot to less hot (cold).

Equilibrium

When you pour cold milk into the hot cocoa, the higher-energy cocoa particles and lower-energy milk particles instantly mix with one another. They collide with each other billions of times every second. The energy flows from the higher-energy cocoa particles to the lower-energy milk particles.

Almost instantly, the average kinetic energy of the milk particles is the same as the average kinetic energy of the cocoa particles. The kinetic-energy level is uniform throughout. It is lower than the cocoa and higher than the milk.

Has energy stopped flowing? Has energy transfer between particles stopped? Not really. Even when the average kinetic energy of the mixture stays steady, some individual

Cold milk being poured into hot cocoa

particles still have high energy, and some particles have low energy. But the number of higher-energy particles is the same as the number of lower-energy particles.

When the temperature is constant, the system is in a condition called **equilibrium**. At equilibrium, temperature does not change. When a mixture of hot cocoa and cold milk has reached equilibrium, you can use a thermometer to measure the equilibrium temperature. The equilibrium temperature is a measure of the average kinetic energy of all the particles in the system. This includes the cup, the mixture of cocoa and milk, and the thermometer.

So has energy stopped flowing? Think about this. The phone rings and you talk to a friend for 20 minutes. Now the cup of cocoa is cold. Why? The room is cooler than the cocoa. Particles of air collide with the

Energy Flows from High to Low

When two particles collide, is it possible for the faster-moving particle to end up going even faster? Can energy transfer from a lower-energy particle to a higher-energy particle?

No. It never happens. Energy *always* transfers from a faster-moving particle to a slower-moving particle. As a result of an energy-transfer collision, the particle that was going faster before the collision will always be going slower after the collision. And the particle that was going slower before the collision will be going faster after the collision. Always.

It is sometimes useful to think of energy as flowing. Energy always flows from higher to lower, from hot to less hot (cold).

Equilibrium

When you pour cold milk into the hot cocoa, the higher-energy cocoa particles and lower-energy milk particles instantly mix with one another. They collide with each other billions of times every second. The energy flows from the higher-energy cocoa particles to the lower-energy milk particles.

Almost instantly, the average kinetic energy of the milk particles is the same as the average kinetic energy of the cocoa particles. The kinetic-energy level is uniform throughout. It is lower than the cocoa and higher than the milk.

Has energy stopped flowing? Has energy transfer between particles stopped? Not really. Even when the average kinetic energy of the mixture stays steady, some individual

Cold milk being poured into hot cocoa

particles still have high energy, and some particles have low energy. But the number of higher-energy particles is the same as the number of lower-energy particles.

When the temperature is constant, the system is in a condition called **equilibrium**. At equilibrium, temperature does not change. When a mixture of hot cocoa and cold milk has reached equilibrium, you can use a thermometer to measure the equilibrium temperature. The equilibrium temperature is a measure of the average kinetic energy of all the particles in the system. This includes the cup, the mixture of cocoa and milk, and the thermometer.

So has energy stopped flowing? Think about this. The phone rings and you talk to a friend for 20 minutes. Now the cup of cocoa is cold. Why? The room is cooler than the cocoa. Particles of air collide with the

34

FOSS Chemical Interactions Course, Second Edition
© The Regents of the University of California
Can be duplicated for classroom or workshop use.

Investigation 5: Energy Transfer
No. 30—Notebook Master

cup and the surface of the cocoa. Energy transfers from the cup of cocoa to the air. Energy continues to transfer to the air until the average kinetic energy of the cocoa is the same as the average kinetic energy of the air. We say the cocoa is room temperature. The cocoa is at equilibrium with everything else in the room.

Summary

All matter is made of tiny particles that are too small to see. The particles are in constant motion.

Objects in motion have kinetic energy. Particles are objects in motion, so they have kinetic energy. The faster a particle moves, the more kinetic energy it has.

Kinetic energy is related to temperature. The faster the particles in a substance move, the hotter it is.

Energy can move, or transfer, from one particle to another when particles collide. Energy always transfers from a higher-energy particle to a lower-energy particle. The transfer of kinetic energy from particle to particle as a result of contact is called conduction.

Temperature is a measure of the average kinetic energy of the particles in a mass.

Matter heats up and cools down because of energy transfer at the particle level.

What energy transfers occur when you eat hot pizza?

Think Questions

1. Explain how cold milk cools hot cocoa.
2. Why do you think an ice cube feels cold when you hold it in your hand?
3. What will happen to the balloon stretched over the mouth of this "empty" bottle when the bottle is placed in hot water? Explain all the energy transfers.

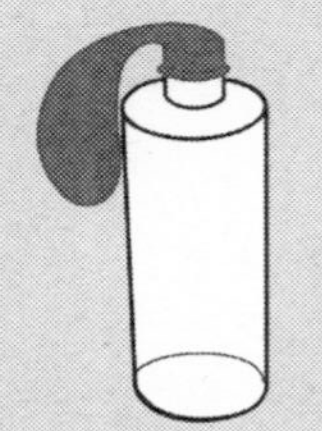

4. When does energy flow from a cold object to a hot object?
5. How does a thermometer work?

cup and the surface of the cocoa. Energy transfers from the cup of cocoa to the air. Energy continues to transfer to the air until the average kinetic energy of the cocoa is the same as the average kinetic energy of the air. We say the cocoa is room temperature. The cocoa is at equilibrium with everything else in the room.

Summary

All matter is made of tiny particles that are too small to see. The particles are in constant motion.

Objects in motion have kinetic energy. Particles are objects in motion, so they have kinetic energy. The faster a particle moves, the more kinetic energy it has.

Kinetic energy is related to temperature. The faster the particles in a substance move, the hotter it is.

Energy can move, or transfer, from one particle to another when particles collide. Energy always transfers from a higher-energy particle to a lower-energy particle. The transfer of kinetic energy from particle to particle as a result of contact is called conduction.

Temperature is a measure of the average kinetic energy of the particles in a mass.

Matter heats up and cools down because of energy transfer at the particle level.

What energy transfers occur when you eat hot pizza?

Think Questions

1. Explain how cold milk cools hot cocoa.
2. Why do you think an ice cube feels cold when you hold it in your hand?
3. What will happen to the balloon stretched over the mouth of this "empty" bottle when the bottle is placed in hot water? Explain all the energy transfers.

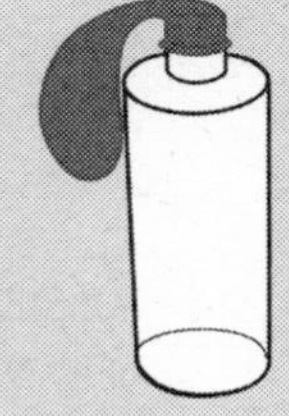

4. When does energy flow from a cold object to a hot object?
5. How does a thermometer work?

Investigation 5: Energy Transfer **35**

FOSS Chemical Interactions Course, Second Edition
© The Regents of the University of California
Can be duplicated for classroom or workshop use.

Investigation 5: Energy Transfer
No. 31—Notebook Master

Response Sheet—Investigation 5

A student said,

When you put a bottle of juice in a cooler full of ice, the juice gets cold. That's because cold transfers to the juice and slows down the kinetic energy of the juice particles.

Comment on the student's ideas and give your explanation for why the juice gets cold.

Response Sheet—Investigation 5

A student said,

When you put a bottle of juice in a cooler full of ice, the juice gets cold. That's because cold transfers to the juice and slows down the kinetic energy of the juice particles.

Comment on the student's ideas and give your explanation for why the juice gets cold.

FOSS Chemical Interactions Course, Second Edition
© The Regents of the University of California
Can be duplicated for classroom or workshop use.
Investigation 5: Energy Transfer
No. 32—Notebook Master

Calculating Energy Transfer in Calories A

Heat is measured in **calories** (cal). The calorie is the unit of heat in the metric system.

One calorie is the amount of heat needed to raise the temperature of 1 g of water 1°C. For instance, it takes 1 cal of heat to raise the temperature of 1 g of water from 25°C to 26°C.

1. Calculate the number of calories needed in each situation. Use the space below the table to write your work if necessary.

	Heat (cal)
a. Raise the temperature of 1 g of water 1°C.	
b. Raise the temperature of 2 g of water 1°C.	
c. Raise the temperature of 2 g of water 2°C.	
d. Raise the temperature of 10 g of water 1°C.	
e. Raise the temperature of 1 g of water 70°C.	
f. Raise the temperature of 100 g of water 5°C.	
g. Raise the temperature of 450 g of water 3°C.	
h. Raise the temperature of 16 g of water 62°C.	

2. What is the equation for calculating the amount of heat needed to heat up or cool down a mass of water?

Calculating Energy Transfer in Calories A

Heat is measured in **calories** (cal). The calorie is the unit of heat in the metric system.

One calorie is the amount of heat needed to raise the temperature of 1 g of water 1°C. For instance, it takes 1 cal of heat to raise the temperature of 1 g of water from 25°C to 26°C.

1. Calculate the number of calories needed in each situation. Use the space below the table to write your work if necessary.

	Heat (cal)
a. Raise the temperature of 1 g of water 1°C.	
b. Raise the temperature of 2 g of water 1°C.	
c. Raise the temperature of 2 g of water 2°C.	
d. Raise the temperature of 10 g of water 1°C.	
e. Raise the temperature of 1 g of water 70°C.	
f. Raise the temperature of 100 g of water 5°C.	
g. Raise the temperature of 450 g of water 3°C.	
h. Raise the temperature of 16 g of water 62°C.	

2. What is the equation for calculating the amount of heat needed to heat up or cool down a mass of water?

FOSS Chemical Interactions Course, Second Edition
© The Regents of the University of California
Can be duplicated for classroom or workshop use.
Investigation 5: Energy Transfer
No. 33—Notebook Master

Calculating Energy Transfer in Calories B

3. A student mixed 40 g of 60°C water with 60 g of 25°C water. The final temperature was 39°C.

   a. Calculate the change of temperature (ΔT) for the hot water.
   $\boldsymbol{\Delta T = T_f - T_i}$

   b. Calculate the amount of energy (calories) transferred *from* the hot water. Remember that heat in calories = mass of hot water × change of temperature of hot water.
   $\boldsymbol{cal = m \times \Delta T}$

   c. Calculate the change of temperature (ΔT) for the cold water.
   $\boldsymbol{\Delta T = T_f - T_i}$

   d. Calculate the amount of energy transferred *to* the cold water.
   $\boldsymbol{cal = m \times \Delta T}$

   e. Compare the amount of energy transferred from the hot water and the amount of energy transferred to the cold water.

4. A student's 600 mL cup of cocoa got cold. It was only 25°C. He put it in the microwave. How many calories must transfer to the cocoa to bring it up to 70°C?

Calculating Energy Transfer in Calories B

3. A student mixed 40 g of 60°C water with 60 g of 25°C water. The final temperature was 39°C.

   a. Calculate the change of temperature (ΔT) for the hot water.
   $\boldsymbol{\Delta T = T_f - T_i}$

   b. Calculate the amount of energy (calories) transferred *from* the hot water. Remember that heat in calories = mass of hot water × change of temperature of hot water.
   $\boldsymbol{cal = m \times \Delta T}$

   c. Calculate the change of temperature (ΔT) for the cold water.
   $\boldsymbol{\Delta T = T_f - T_i}$

   d. Calculate the amount of energy transferred *to* the cold water.
   $\boldsymbol{cal = m \times \Delta T}$

   e. Compare the amount of energy transferred from the hot water and the amount of energy transferred to the cold water.

4. A student's 600 mL cup of cocoa got cold. It was only 25°C. He put it in the microwave. How many calories must transfer to the cocoa to bring it up to 70°C?

FOSS Chemical Interactions Course, Second Edition
© The Regents of the University of California
Can be duplicated for classroom or workshop use.
Investigation 5: Energy Transfer
No. 34—Notebook Master

Calories of Energy Transfer

Results

Record the results of your group's investigation in the table below.

	Mass (g)	Initial temp (°C)	Final temp (°C)	Δ T (°C)	Calories (cal)
Hot water					
Cold water					

Calculations

1. Calculate the calories transferred from the hot water. Show your math. Record in the table.

2. Calculate the calories transferred to the cold water. Show your math. Record in the table.

Conclusions

3. Compare the energy transfer *from* the hot water and the energy transfer *to* the cold water. What do you notice?

Calories of Energy Transfer

Results

Record the results of your group's investigation in the table below.

	Mass (g)	Initial temp (°C)	Final temp (°C)	Δ T (°C)	Calories (cal)
Hot water					
Cold water					

Calculations

1. Calculate the calories transferred from the hot water. Show your math. Record in the table.

2. Calculate the calories transferred to the cold water. Show your math. Record in the table.

Conclusions

3. Compare the energy transfer *from* the hot water and the energy transfer *to* the cold water. What do you notice?

FOSS Chemical Interactions Course, Second Edition
© The Regents of the University of California
Can be duplicated for classroom or workshop use.
Investigation 5: Energy Transfer
No. 35—Notebook Master

Heat Practice A

1. What is the equation for calculating final temperature when equal masses of water are mixed?

2. What is the equation for calculating how much heat energy (calories) transferred to or from a mass of water?

3. A student mixed 30 mL of water at 15°C and 30 mL of water at 55°C. Answer the following questions. Show your work.

   a. What is the final volume of the water?

   b. What is the final temperature of the water?

   c. How many degrees did the cold water increase?

   d. How many degrees did the hot water decrease?

   e. How much heat energy transferred to the cold water?

   f. How much heat energy transferred from the hot water?

   g. What happened to the kinetic energy of the hot-water and cold-water particles?

Heat Practice A

1. What is the equation for calculating final temperature when equal masses of water are mixed?

2. What is the equation for calculating how much heat energy (calories) transferred to or from a mass of water?

3. A student mixed 30 mL of water at 15°C and 30 mL of water at 55°C. Answer the following questions. Show your work.

   a. What is the final volume of the water?

   b. What is the final temperature of the water?

   c. How many degrees did the cold water increase?

   d. How many degrees did the hot water decrease?

   e. How much heat energy transferred to the cold water?

   f. How much heat energy transferred from the hot water?

   g. What happened to the kinetic energy of the hot-water and cold-water particles?

FOSS Chemical Interactions Course, Second Edition
© The Regents of the University of California
Can be duplicated for classroom or workshop use.
Investigation 5: Energy Transfer
No. 36—Notebook Master

Heat Practice B

4. A student has a 10 L (10,000 mL) fish tank. The water needs to be 28°C for her tropical fish. When she filled the tank, the temperature of the water was 12°C. How many calories of heat must transfer to the aquarium before it is ready for the fish?

5. A student made tea. She started with 300 g of water at 20°C. She transferred 18,000 cal to the water. What was the final temperature of the water?

6. Energy "flow" is the transfer of energy from one place to another. Which direction does energy flow?

7. How does energy transfer happen?

8. What is equilibrium?

Heat Practice B

4. A student has a 10 L (10,000 mL) fish tank. The water needs to be 28°C for her tropical fish. When she filled the tank, the temperature of the water was 12°C. How many calories of heat must transfer to the aquarium before it is ready for the fish?

5. A student made tea. She started with 300 g of water at 20°C. She transferred 18,000 cal to the water. What was the final temperature of the water?

6. Energy "flow" is the transfer of energy from one place to another. Which direction does energy flow?

7. How does energy transfer happen?

8. What is equilibrium?

FOSS Chemical Interactions Course, Second Edition
© The Regents of the University of California
Can be duplicated for classroom or workshop use.
Investigation 5: Energy Transfer
No. 37—Notebook Master

Insulating Material

Material 1: ____________________ Room temperature: ________

	Initial temperature (T_i)	Final temperature (T_f)	Change in temperature (ΔT) $\Delta T = T_f - T_i$
Cold water trial 1			
Cold water trial 2			
Average cold			
Hot water trial 1			
Hot water trial 2			
Average hot			

Material 2: ____________________ Room temperature: ________

	Initial temperature (T_i)	Final temperature (T_f)	Change in temperature (ΔT) $\Delta T = T_f - T_i$
Cold water trial 1			
Cold water trial 2			
Average cold			
Hot water trial 1			
Hot water trial 2			

Insulating Material

Material 1: ____________________ Room temperature: ________

	Initial temperature (T_i)	Final temperature (T_f)	Change in temperature (ΔT) $\Delta T = T_f - T_i$
Cold water trial 1			
Cold water trial 2			
Average cold			
Hot water trial 1			
Hot water trial 2			
Average hot			

Material 2: ____________________ Room temperature: ________

	Initial temperature (T_i)	Final temperature (T_f)	Change in temperature (ΔT) $\Delta T = T_f - T_i$
Cold water trial 1			
Cold water trial 2			
Average cold			
Hot water trial 1			
Hot water trial 2			

FOSS Chemical Interactions Course, Second Edition
© The Regents of the University of California
Can be duplicated for classroom or workshop use.
Investigation 6: Thermos Engineering
No. 38—Notebook Master

Thermos Design

Design # _____

Illustration	
Plan Explanation	

Hot Water Data

		$T_{initial}$	T_{final}	ΔT
Results	Trial 1			
	Trial 2			
	Average			

Next steps	

Thermos Design

Design # _____

Illustration
Plan Explanation

Hot Water Data
Results Trial 1 Trial 2 Average
Next steps

FOSS Chemical Interactions Course, Second Edition
© The Regents of the University of California
Can be duplicated for classroom or workshop use.
Investigation 6: Thermos Engineering
No. 39—Notebook Master

Project Reflection

1. Choose a **material** and **design** that you think the thermos company should use to insulate their new container. Draw a diagram in the space below. Use evidence to support your proposal.

2. What have you learned about how engineers work?

3. If you had more time, what would you try next?

Project Reflection

1. Choose a **material** and **design** that you think the thermos company should use to insulate their new container. Draw a diagram in the space below. Use evidence to support your proposal..

2. What have you learned about how engineers work?

3. If you had more time, what would you try next?

FOSS Chemical Interactions Course, Second Edition
© The Regents of the University of California
Can be duplicated for classroom or workshop use.
Investigation 6: Thermos Engineering
No. 40—Notebook Master

Dissolve or Melt? Results

Observations. Record your observations in the table.

Material	Hot water	Cold water	Hot air	Cold air
Candy coating				
Chocolate				

Conclusions

1. What melted? ______________________

   Under what conditions? ______________________

   What happened at the particle level when it melted?

2. What dissolved? ______________________

   Under what conditions? ______________________

   What happened at the particle level when it dissolved?

Dissolve or Melt? Results

Observations. Record your observations in the table.

Material	Hot water	Cold water	Hot air	Cold air
Candy coating				
Chocolate				

Conclusions

1. What melted? ______________________

   Under what conditions? ______________________

   What happened at the particle level when it melted?

2. What dissolved? ______________________

   Under what conditions? ______________________

   What happened at the particle level when it dissolved?

FOSS Chemical Interactions Course, Second Edition
© The Regents of the University of California
Can be duplicated for classroom or workshop use.
Investigation 7: Solutions
No. 41—Notebook Master

Solubility

WARNING — This set contains chemicals that may be harmful if misused. Read cautions on individual containers carefully. Not to be used by children except under adult supervision.

Part 1. Record your observations.

Substance	Before mixing with water	After mixing with water
$CaCO_3$		
NaCl		

Part 2. Record the filtering results.

$CaCO_3$:

NaCl:

Part 3. Record the evaporation results.

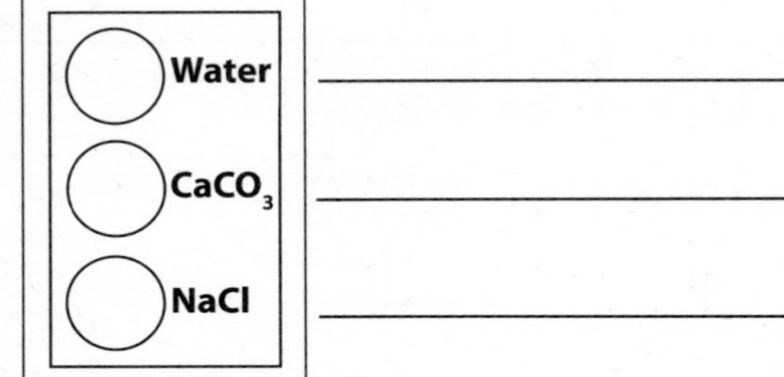

Solubility

WARNING — This set contains chemicals that may be harmful if misused. Read cautions on individual containers carefully. Not to be used by children except under adult supervision.

Part 1. Record your observations.

Substance	Before mixing with water	After mixing with water
$CaCO_3$		
NaCl		

Part 2. Record the filtering results.

$CaCO_3$:

NaCl:

Part 3. Record the evaporation results.

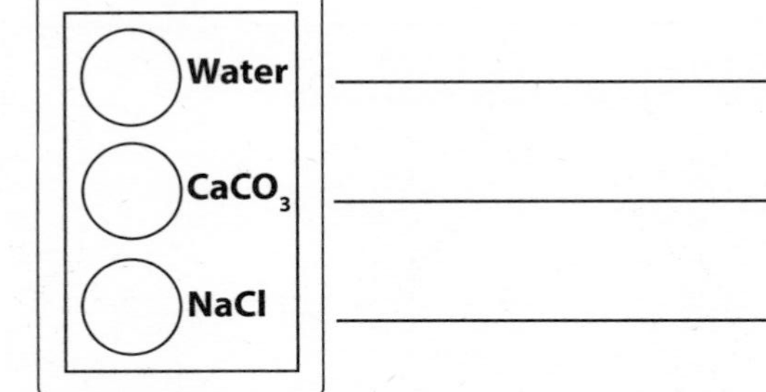

FOSS Chemical Interactions Course, Second Edition
© The Regents of the University of California
Can be duplicated for classroom or workshop use.
Investigation 7: Solutions
No. 42—Notebook Master

Melt Three Materials

Prediction

Will margarine, wax, and sucrose melt in hot water? Record your predictions in the table below.

Procedure

Write your procedure and conduct the test.

Materials	Prediction: Will it melt?	Water temperature (°C)	Observations
Margarine			
Wax			
Sucrose			

Melt Three Materials

Prediction

Will margarine, wax, and sucrose melt in hot water? Record your predictions in the table below.

Procedure

Write your procedure and conduct the test.

Materials	Prediction: Will it melt?	Water temperature (°C)	Observations
Margarine			
Wax			
Sucrose			

FOSS Chemical Interactions Course, Second Edition
© The Regents of the University of California
Can be duplicated for classroom or workshop use.
Investigation 8: Phase Change
No. 43—Notebook Master

Wax and Sucrose Questions

1. When wax melts, how do the wax particles change?

2. Why do materials melt when they get hot?

3. What happens at the particle level when a material freezes?

4. Look at the puddle of wax around the wick of your candle.
   Explain why it is solid now.

Wax and Sucrose Questions

1. When wax melts, how do the wax particles change?

2. Why do materials melt when they get hot?

3. What happens at the particle level when a material freezes?

4. Look at the puddle of wax around the wick of your candle.
   Explain why it is solid now.

FOSS Chemical Interactions Course, Second Edition
© The Regents of the University of California
Can be duplicated for classroom or workshop use.
Investigation 8: Phase Change
No. 44—Notebook Master

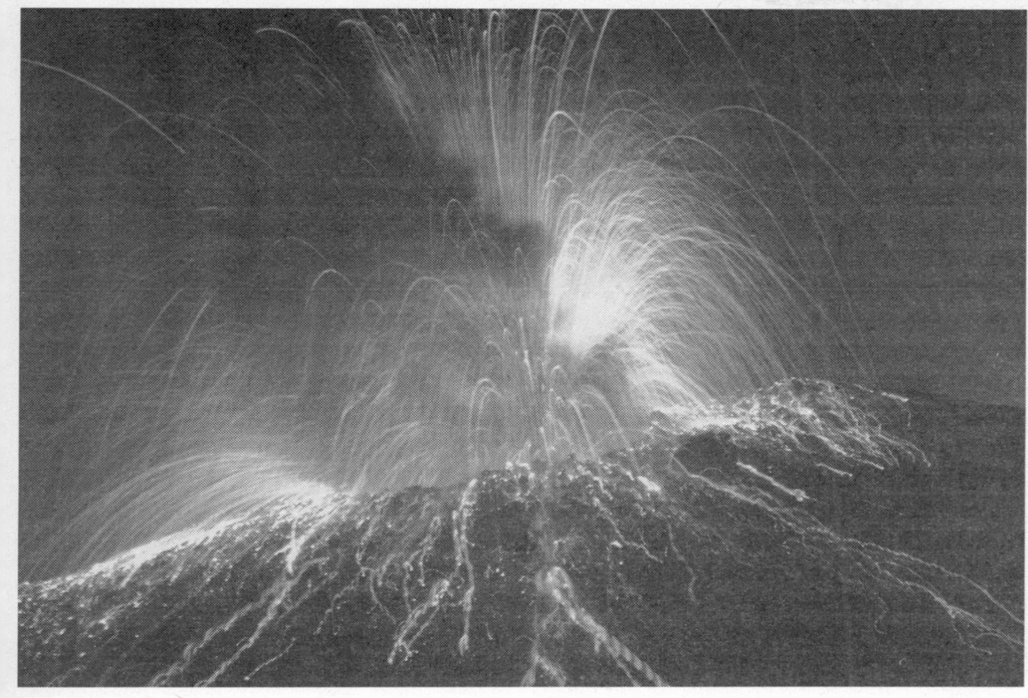

Rock Solid

What does **lava** pouring out of a volcano have in common with a snowman? They are both going to change phase in a short time. The liquid lava will **freeze** and become solid rock. The solid snowman will melt and become liquid water.

Most matter on Earth exists in one of three forms: solid, liquid, or gas. The forms are called states or phases of matter.

The clothes you wear, the forks and spoons you eat with, and your books and pencils are a few examples of matter in its solid phase.

The olive oil you put on your salad, the shampoo you use to wash your hair, and a refreshing glass of cold milk are examples of matter in its liquid phase.

The helium in a party balloon, the air you pump into a soccer ball, and the carbon dioxide in your exhaled breath are examples of matter in its gas phase.

Rock Solid

What does **lava** pouring out of a volcano have in common with a snowman? They are both going to change phase in a short time. The liquid lava will **freeze** and become solid rock. The solid snowman will melt and become liquid water.

Most matter on Earth exists in one of three forms: solid, liquid, or gas. The forms are called states or phases of matter.

The clothes you wear, the forks and spoons you eat with, and your books and pencils are a few examples of matter in its solid phase.

The olive oil you put on your salad, the shampoo you use to wash your hair, and a refreshing glass of cold milk are examples of matter in its liquid phase.

The helium in a party balloon, the air you pump into a soccer ball, and the carbon dioxide in your exhaled breath are examples of matter in its gas phase.

52

FOSS Chemical Interactions Course, Second Edition
© The Regents of the University of California
Can be duplicated for classroom or workshop use.

Investigation 8: Phase Change
No. 45—Notebook Master

Snow is solid water.

Properties of the Phases of Matter

Many substances can exist in more than one phase. The snowman, for instance, is made of solid water. We have many common names for solid water, including ice, frost, and snow.

Water can also exist as liquid. Liquid water falls from clouds as rain and flows to your home in pipes. Earth is mostly covered by an ocean filled with liquid water.

Water also exists as gas. Water in its gas phase is called water vapor. We are usually not aware of water vapor because it is invisible. Most of the water vapor on Earth is in the atmosphere as part of the air.

Ice, liquid water, and water vapor all look different. But they are all forms of water. What is the same and what is different about ice, water, and water vapor?

All three phases of water are made of exactly the same kind of particle. The chemical formula for the water particle is H_2O. Ice, water, and water vapor are all made of water particles.

The thing that is different about ice, water, and water vapor is the relationship between the water particles.

In the article "Three Phases of Matter," we considered how solids, liquids, and gases differ. In solids, the particles are attached to one another. The attachments are called bonds. The bonds in solids are so strong that the particles cannot change positions. That's why solids have definite shape and volume.

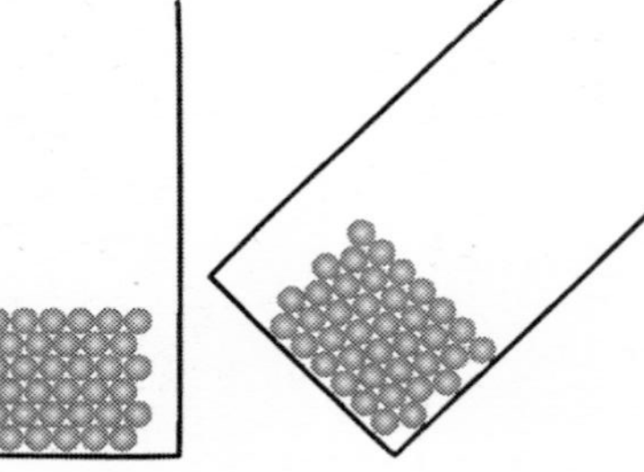

Ice in a vial will move from side to side, but will not change volume or shape.

In liquids, the bonds are weaker. The particles are still held close together, but they can move around and past one another. As a result, liquids flow. That's why liquids have definite volume, but their shape changes.

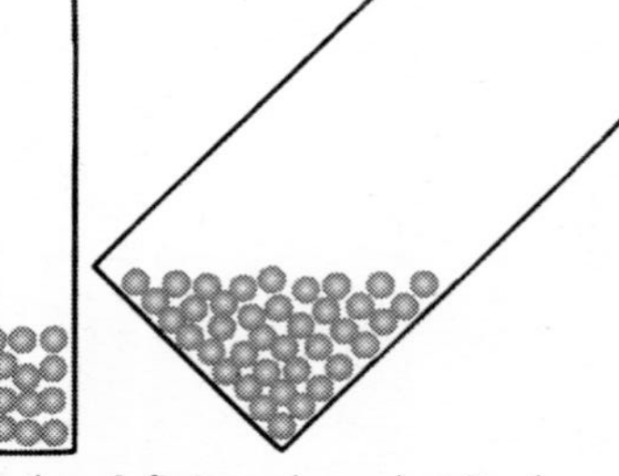

Liquid water has definite volume, but its shape changes to fit the container it is in.

Snow is solid water.

Properties of the Phases of Matter

Many substances can exist in more than one phase. The snowman, for instance, is made of solid water. We have many common names for solid water, including ice, frost, and snow.

Water can also exist as liquid. Liquid water falls from clouds as rain and flows to your home in pipes. Earth is mostly covered by an ocean filled with liquid water.

Water also exists as gas. Water in its gas phase is called water vapor. We are usually not aware of water vapor because it is invisible. Most of the water vapor on Earth is in the atmosphere as part of the air.

Ice, liquid water, and water vapor all look different. But they are all forms of water. What is the same and what is different about ice, water, and water vapor?

All three phases of water are made of exactly the same kind of particle. The chemical formula for the water particle is H_2O. Ice, water, and water vapor are all made of water particles.

The thing that is different about ice, water, and water vapor is the relationship between the water particles.

In the article "Three Phases of Matter," we considered how solids, liquids, and gases differ. In solids, the particles are attached to one another. The attachments are called bonds. The bonds in solids are so strong that the particles cannot change positions. That's why solids have definite shape and volume.

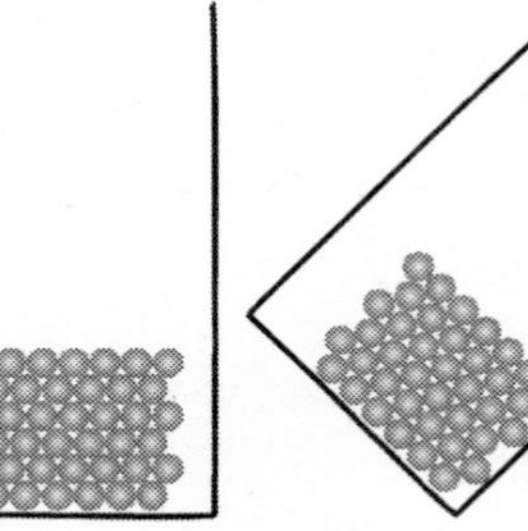

Ice in a vial will move from side to side, but will not change volume or shape.

In liquids, the bonds are weaker. The particles are still held close together, but they can move around and past one another. As a result, liquids flow. That's why liquids have definite volume, but their shape changes.

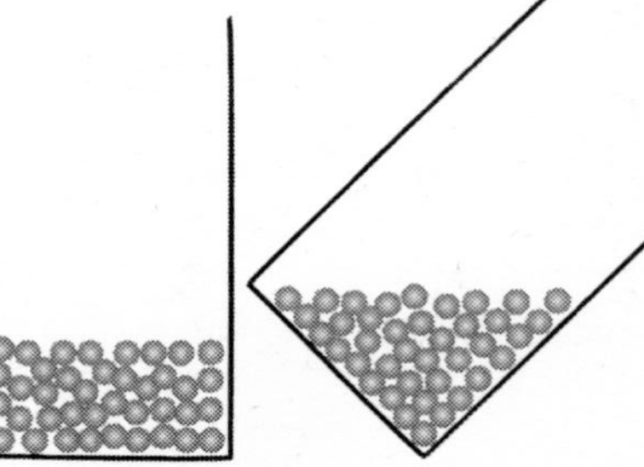

Liquid water has definite volume, but its shape changes to fit the container it is in.

Investigation 8: Phase Change **53**

FOSS Chemical Interactions Course, Second Edition
© The Regents of the University of California
Can be duplicated for classroom or workshop use.

Investigation 8: Phase Change
No. 46—Notebook Master

In gases, bonds do not hold the particles together. Individual particles of gas fly around in space. That's why gases do not have definite volume or shape.

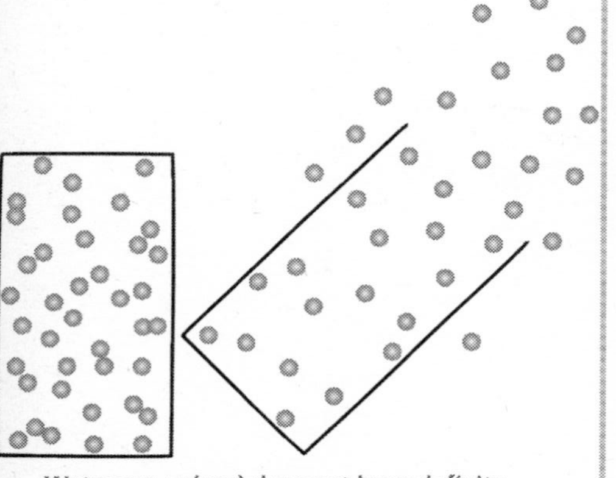

Water vapor (gas) does not have definite volume or shape. If the container is open, the gas will expand, and the particles will leave the container.

Phase Change

The snowman wasn't always solid. And it won't stay solid. The solid snowman will melt and turn into liquid water. The liquid lava wasn't always liquid. And it won't stay liquid. The liquid lava will freeze and turn to solid rock.

Change from solid to liquid and change from liquid to solid are examples of phase change. What causes substances to change phase?

Heat causes phase change. Or, more accurately, energy transfer causes phase change. Here's how it works.

When ice cubes are heated they change to liquid water.

When a piece of ice is placed in a warm room, energy transfers from the air particles to the water particles in the ice. The kinetic energy of the water particles increases until the ice reaches 0 degrees Celsius (°C).

As more and more energy transfers to the 0°C ice, the bonds holding the water particles together start to break. When most of the bonds are broken, the water particles are no longer held in place. They start to move over and around one another.

In gases, bonds do not hold the particles together. Individual particles of gas fly around in space. That's why gases do not have definite volume or shape.

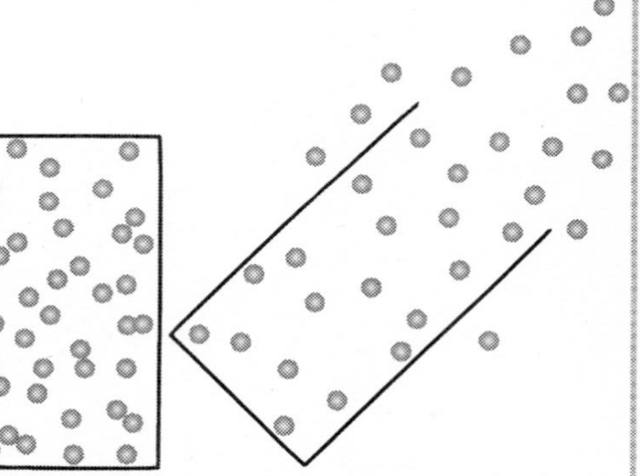

Water vapor (gas) does not have definite volume or shape. If the container is open, the gas will expand, and the particles will leave the container.

Phase Change

The snowman wasn't always solid. And it won't stay solid. The solid snowman will melt and turn into liquid water. The liquid lava wasn't always liquid. And it won't stay liquid. The liquid lava will freeze and turn to solid rock.

Change from solid to liquid and change from liquid to solid are examples of phase change. What causes substances to change phase?

Heat causes phase change. Or, more accurately, energy transfer causes phase change. Here's how it works.

When ice cubes are heated they change to liquid water.

When a piece of ice is placed in a warm room, energy transfers from the air particles to the water particles in the ice. The kinetic energy of the water particles increases until the ice reaches 0 degrees Celsius (°C).

As more and more energy transfers to the 0°C ice, the bonds holding the water particles together start to break. When most of the bonds are broken, the water particles are no longer held in place. They start to move over and around one another.

54

FOSS Chemical Interactions Course, Second Edition
© The Regents of the University of California
Can be duplicated for classroom or workshop use.

Investigation 8: Phase Change
No. 47—Notebook Master

When particles flow over and around one another, we say the substance changed from solid to liquid. The process is called melting. Substances melt when enough energy transfers to the particles of a solid and breaks the bonds holding particles in place.

That's why the snowman melts. Energy from the Sun transfers to the water particles in the snow crystals. The bonds that hold particles together as a solid are broken, and the solid water changes to liquid water. The snowman changes into a hat and scarf on top of a puddle of water.

What about the lava? How does it change phase? When lava pours out on Earth's surface, it is extremely hot (up to 1,100°C). The kinetic energy of the rock particles is so great that most of the bonds holding them together have been broken. The rock particles move over and around one another. The rock is liquid, so it flows down the side of the volcano.

Air is cooler than lava . . . a lot cooler than lava. Energy from the liquid rock particles transfers to the air particles. The rock particles lose kinetic energy, and the mass of lava cools. As the lava cools, stronger bonds form between the rock particles. When enough energy has transferred from the rock particles, the particles are locked in place by the bonds.

When particles stop flowing over and around one another, we say the substance changed from liquid to solid. The process is called freezing. Substances freeze when enough energy transfers away from the particles of a liquid.

That's why the liquid lava freezes and becomes solid rock. Energy transfers away from the rock particles, bonds hold the particles together in a fixed position, and the rock changes from liquid to solid.

Evaporation

Let's get back to the snowman. After a day or two, all that remains is the hat and scarf. Even the puddle of liquid water has disappeared. Where did the water go?

Hot, liquid lava will freeze and change to solid rock.

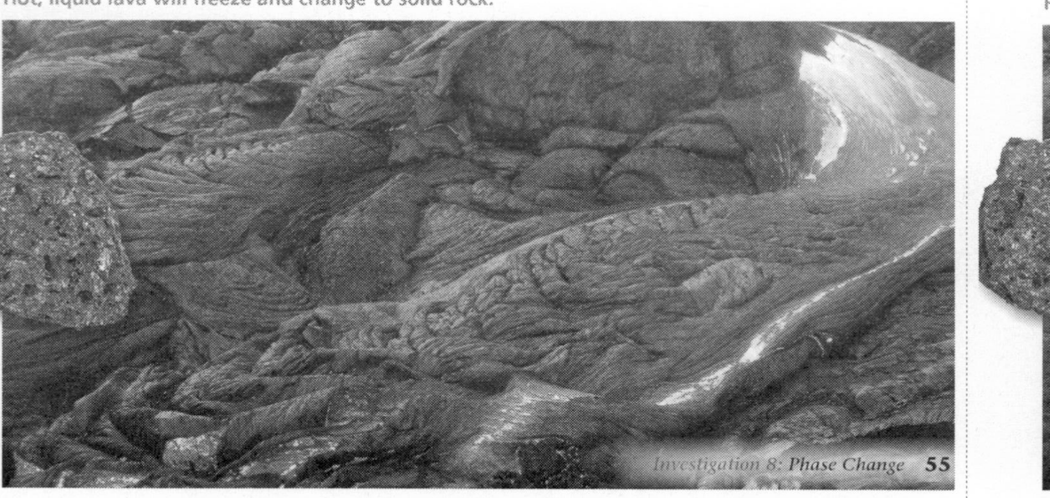

When particles flow over and around one another, we say the substance changed from solid to liquid. The process is called melting. Substances melt when enough energy transfers to the particles of a solid and breaks the bonds holding particles in place.

That's why the snowman melts. Energy from the Sun transfers to the water particles in the snow crystals. The bonds that hold particles together as a solid are broken, and the solid water changes to liquid water. The snowman changes into a hat and scarf on top of a puddle of water.

What about the lava? How does it change phase? When lava pours out on Earth's surface, it is extremely hot (up to 1,100°C). The kinetic energy of the rock particles is so great that most of the bonds holding them together have been broken. The rock particles move over and around one another. The rock is liquid, so it flows down the side of the volcano.

Air is cooler than lava . . . a lot cooler than lava. Energy from the liquid rock particles transfers to the air particles. The rock particles lose kinetic energy, and the mass of lava cools. As the lava cools, stronger bonds form between the rock particles. When enough energy has transferred from the rock particles, the particles are locked in place by the bonds.

When particles stop flowing over and around one another, we say the substance changed from liquid to solid. The process is called freezing. Substances freeze when enough energy transfers away from the particles of a liquid.

That's why the liquid lava freezes and becomes solid rock. Energy transfers away from the rock particles, bonds hold the particles together in a fixed position, and the rock changes from liquid to solid.

Evaporation

Let's get back to the snowman. After a day or two, all that remains is the hat and scarf. Even the puddle of liquid water has disappeared. Where did the water go?

Hot, liquid lava will freeze and change to solid rock.

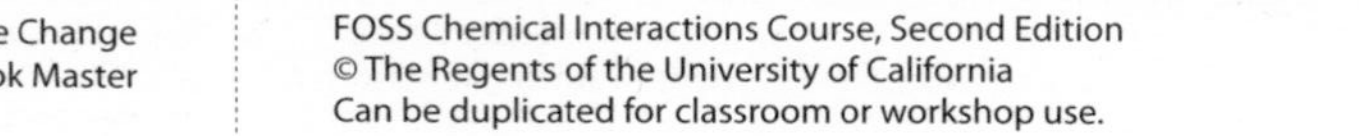

Investigation 8: Phase Change 55

FOSS Chemical Interactions Course, Second Edition
© The Regents of the University of California
Can be duplicated for classroom or workshop use.

Investigation 8: Phase Change
No. 48—Notebook Master

As sunshine falls on the puddle of liquid water, energy transfers to the water particles. The kinetic energy of the particles increases. When enough energy transfers to a particle, the particle breaks all the bonds holding it to the mass of liquid. The particle breaks free and flies into space. The water changes phase again, but this time from liquid to gas.

The phase change from liquid to gas is called **evaporation** (or vaporization). Water in the gas phase is called water vapor. The individual water particles are too small to see, so water vapor is invisible. Water vapor enters the air and becomes part of Earth's atmosphere.

Water can change from gas to liquid, too. The process involves energy transfer. Can you predict what energy transfer takes place?

When energy transfers away from the water vapor particles, they lose kinetic energy. When enough energy has transferred from the particles, bonds form between them. The water changes phase from gas to liquid. The process is called **condensation**. Substances condense when energy transfers away from the particles of a gas.

Condensation on a window

Look at the illustration of an experiment. A pan of liquid water is heated. Water evaporates. The water vapor condenses on a cup filled with ice. Study how the water particles change phase from liquid to gas, and then back to liquid. You should be able to see where evaporation and condensation are taking place.

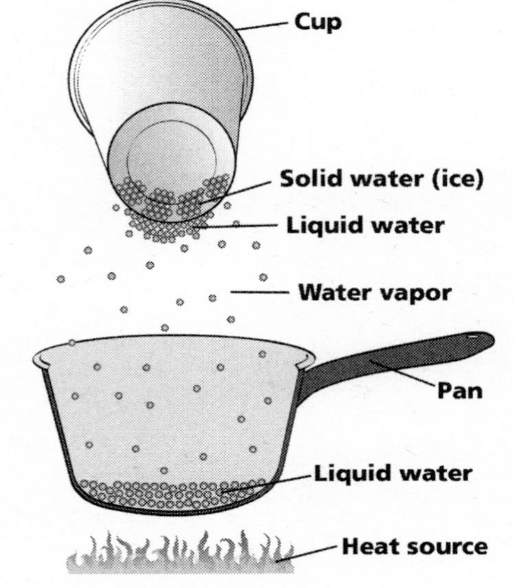

Liquid water evaporates when it is heated. Water vapor condenses on the outside of a cup containing ice.

As sunshine falls on the puddle of liquid water, energy transfers to the water particles. The kinetic energy of the particles increases. When enough energy transfers to a particle, the particle breaks all the bonds holding it to the mass of liquid. The particle breaks free and flies into space. The water changes phase again, but this time from liquid to gas.

The phase change from liquid to gas is called **evaporation** (or vaporization). Water in the gas phase is called water vapor. The individual water particles are too small to see, so water vapor is invisible. Water vapor enters the air and becomes part of Earth's atmosphere.

Water can change from gas to liquid, too. The process involves energy transfer. Can you predict what energy transfer takes place?

When energy transfers away from the water vapor particles, they lose kinetic energy. When enough energy has transferred from the particles, bonds form between them. The water changes phase from gas to liquid. The process is called **condensation**. Substances condense when energy transfers away from the particles of a gas.

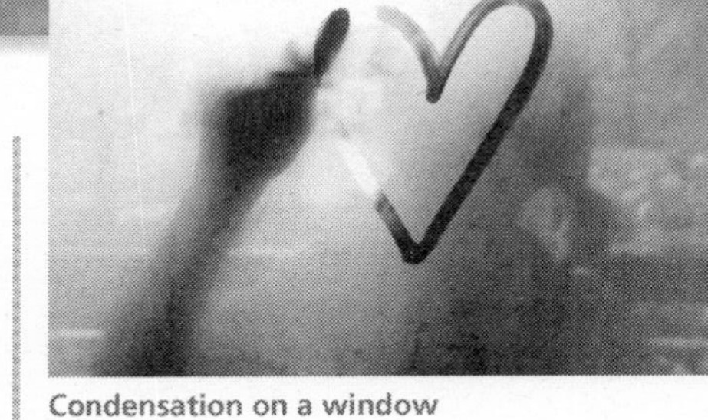

Condensation on a window

Look at the illustration of an experiment. A pan of liquid water is heated. Water evaporates. The water vapor condenses on a cup filled with ice. Study how the water particles change phase from liquid to gas, and then back to liquid. You should be able to see where evaporation and condensation are taking place.

Liquid water evaporates when it is heated. Water vapor condenses on the outside of a cup containing ice.

FOSS Chemical Interactions Course, Second Edition
© The Regents of the University of California
Can be duplicated for classroom or workshop use.

Investigation 8: Phase Change
No. 49—Notebook Master

Melt and Freeze

There are three important things to understand about melting and freezing.

Substances don't have to be cold to freeze. *Freeze* just means changing phase from liquid to solid, and this happens at different temperatures for different substances. Granite freezes at about 1,650°C. On the other hand, oxygen freezes at –218°C. Every substance has its own freezing temperature. Any solid substance is technically frozen, even a hot metal pan on the stove.

Phase is a relationship between particles. The phase of a substance is determined by what is happening between the particles in the substance. Particles in solids have strong bonds, particles in liquids have weak bonds, and particles in gases have no bonds.

Freezing temperature = melting temperature. A substance freezes and melts at the same temperature. Water, for instance, freezes and melts at 0°C. If you move a piece of ice from a freezer to a warm room, the ice will warm up until it reaches 0°C. Then it will melt. If you put a cup of warm water in a freezer, the water will cool until it gets to 0°C. Then it will freeze.

Melting gold at a foundry

The temperature at which a substance evaporates is the same as the temperature at which it condenses. Water, for instance, evaporates and condenses at 100°C, depending on if you are heating it up or cooling it down.

Substance	Freeze/melt (°C)	Condense/evaporate (°C)
Helium	–272	–269
Oxygen	–218	–183
Nitrogen	–210	–198
Carbon dioxide	—	–78
Chlorine	–101	–34
Mercury	–39	357
Water	0	100
Sodium	98	883
Lead	327	1,749
Aluminum	660	2,519
Calcium chloride	775	1,936
Sodium chloride	801	1,465
Silver	962	2,162
Gold	1,064	2,856
Copper	1,085	2,562
Iron	1,538	2,861
Tungsten	3,422	5,555

The freeze/melt temperatures and condense/evaporate temperatures for some common substances are shown here. Carbon dioxide is a special substance. Do you see that it has no freezing and melting point? Keep reading to find out why.

Melt and Freeze

There are three important things to understand about melting and freezing.

Substances don't have to be cold to freeze. *Freeze* just means changing phase from liquid to solid, and this happens at different temperatures for different substances. Granite freezes at about 1,650°C. On the other hand, oxygen freezes at –218°C. Every substance has its own freezing temperature. Any solid substance is technically frozen, even a hot metal pan on the stove.

Phase is a relationship between particles. The phase of a substance is determined by what is happening between the particles in the substance. Particles in solids have strong bonds, particles in liquids have weak bonds, and particles in gases have no bonds.

Freezing temperature = melting temperature. A substance freezes and melts at the same temperature. Water, for instance, freezes and melts at 0°C. If you move a piece of ice from a freezer to a warm room, the ice will warm up until it reaches 0°C. Then it will melt. If you put a cup of warm water in a freezer, the water will cool until it gets to 0°C. Then it will freeze.

Melting gold at a foundry

The temperature at which a substance evaporates is the same as the temperature at which it condenses. Water, for instance, evaporates and condenses at 100°C, depending on if you are heating it up or cooling it down.

Substance	Freeze/melt (°C)	Condense/evaporate (°C)
Helium	–272	–269
Oxygen	–218	–183
Nitrogen	–210	–198
Carbon dioxide	—	–78
Chlorine	–101	–34
Mercury	–39	357
Water	0	100
Sodium	98	883
Lead	327	1,749
Aluminum	660	2,519
Calcium chloride	775	1,936
Sodium chloride	801	1,465
Silver	962	2,162
Gold	1,064	2,856
Copper	1,085	2,562
Iron	1,538	2,861
Tungsten	3,422	5,555

The freeze/melt temperatures and condense/evaporate temperatures for some common substances are shown here. Carbon dioxide is a special substance. Do you see that it has no freezing and melting point? Keep reading to find out why.

Investigation 8: Phase Change **57**

FOSS Chemical Interactions Course, Second Edition
© The Regents of the University of California
Can be duplicated for classroom or workshop use.

Investigation 8: Phase Change
No. 50—Notebook Master

ENERGY TRANSFERRED **TO** THE SUBSTANCE

SUBLIME

MELT

EVAPORATE

SOLID

LIQUID

GAS

FREEZE

CONDENSE

DEPOSIT

ENERGY TRANSFERRED **FROM** THE SUBSTANCE

Phase-change vocabulary

This illustration summarizes how energy transfer affects phase change. The top half shows how substances go from solid to liquid to gas as energy transfers *to* the particles of the substance. The bottom half shows how substances go from gas to liquid to solid as energy transfers *from* the particles of the substance.

Notice that a substance can go straight from solid to gas. This process is called **sublimation**. Carbon dioxide is a substance that sublimes. And when energy transfers the other way, carbon dioxide **deposits**. It changes from a gas to a solid without going through a liquid phase. That's why solid carbon dioxide is called **dry ice**.

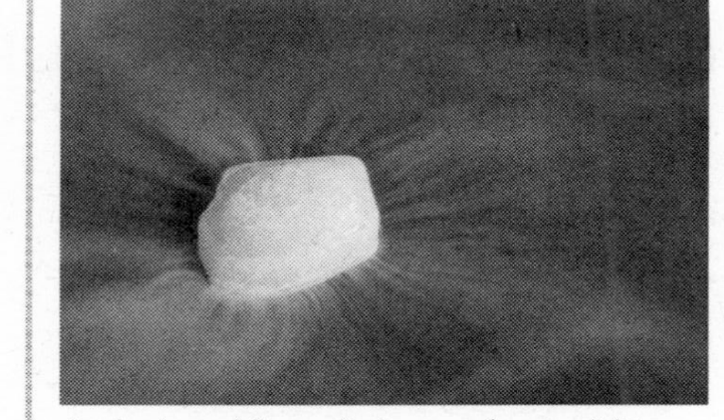

As dry ice sublimes, it changes from solid to gas without passing through a liquid phase.

Think Questions

1. What causes a substance to change from one phase to another?
2. What are the three important things to know about freezing and melting?
3. What happens to water particles as a cup of ice melts and then evaporates?

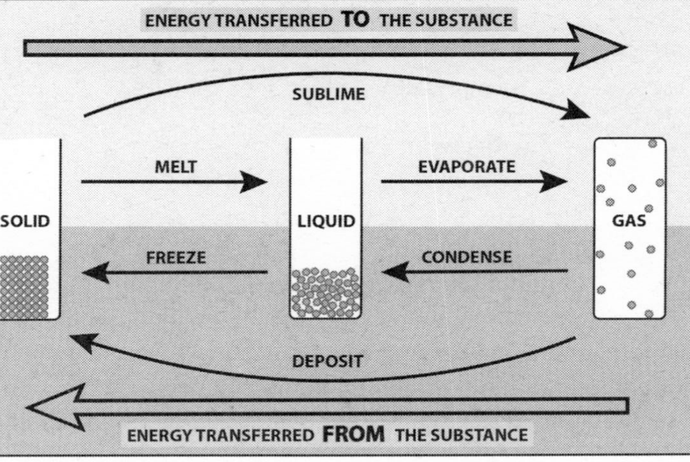

Phase-change vocabulary

This illustration summarizes how energy transfer affects phase change. The top half shows how substances go from solid to liquid to gas as energy transfers *to* the particles of the substance. The bottom half shows how substances go from gas to liquid to solid as energy transfers *from* the particles of the substance.

Notice that a substance can go straight from solid to gas. This process is called **sublimation**. Carbon dioxide is a substance that sublimes. And when energy transfers the other way, carbon dioxide **deposits**. It changes from a gas to a solid without going through a liquid phase. That's why solid carbon dioxide is called **dry ice**.

As dry ice sublimes, it changes from solid to gas without passing through a liquid phase.

Think Questions

1. What causes a substance to change from one phase to another?
2. What are the three important things to know about freezing and melting?
3. What happens to water particles as a cup of ice melts and then evaporates?

58

FOSS Chemical Interactions Course, Second Edition
© The Regents of the University of California
Can be duplicated for classroom or workshop use.

Investigation 8: Phase Change
No. 51—Notebook Master

Response Sheet—Investigation 8

A student watched his mom put a piece of wax in a pan. She put the pan on the stove. A minute later, the student looked in the pan and said,

Look, the wax is turning into water.

What would you tell the student to help him understand what happened in the pan?

Response Sheet—Investigation 8

A student watched his mom put a piece of wax in a pan. She put the pan on the stove. A minute later, the student looked in the pan and said,

Look, the wax is turning into water.

What would you tell the student to help him understand what happened in the pan?

FOSS Chemical Interactions Course, Second Edition
© The Regents of the University of California
Can be duplicated for classroom or workshop use.

Investigation 8: Phase Change
No. 52—Notebook Master

Ice and Substances

White substance tested: ______________________________

Amount tested (2 or 4 scoops): ____________

Results

Time (min)	Temperature (°C)
0 (Start)	
2	
4	
6 (Final)	

Record the initial and final temperatures on the class results table. Calculate ΔT and record it on the class table.

$\Delta T =$ __________

Which substance(s) dropped the temperature of the ice the most?

Which substance was most effective?______________________________

Questions

1. If you put a vial of room-temperature water in a cup of 0°C ice, will the water in the vial freeze? Why or why not?

2. If you put a vial of room-temperature water in a cup of ice that is colder than 0°C, will it freeze? Why or why not?

Ice and Substances

White substance tested: ______________________________

Amount tested (2 or 4 scoops): ____________

Results

Time (min)	Temperature (°C)
0 (Start)	
2	
4	
6 (Final)	

Record the initial and final temperatures on the class results table. Calculate ΔT and record it on the class table.

$\Delta T =$ __________

Which substance(s) dropped the temperature of the ice the most?

Which substance was most effective?______________________________

Questions

1. If you put a vial of room-temperature water in a cup of 0°C ice, will the water in the vial freeze? Why or why not?

2. If you put a vial of room-temperature water in a cup of ice that is colder than 0°C, will it freeze? Why or why not?

FOSS Chemical Interactions Course, Second Edition
© The Regents of the University of California
Can be duplicated for classroom or workshop use.
Investigation 8: Phase Change
No. 53—Notebook Master

Freezer Design

Design # _____

Illustration	
Plan explanation	

Did your design freeze the water in the vial? ___________________

Next steps	

Freezer Design

Design # _____

Illustration	
Plan explanation	

Did your design freeze the water in the vial? ___________________

Next steps	

FOSS Chemical Interactions Course, Second Edition
© The Regents of the University of California
Can be duplicated for classroom or workshop use.

Investigation 8: Phase Change
No. 54—Notebook Master

Phase-Change Summary

ENERGY TRANSFERRED **TO** THE SUBSTANCE

ENERGY TRANSFERRED **FROM** THE SUBSTANCE

1.
2.
3.
4.
5.
6.
7.
8.
9.

Phase-Change Summary

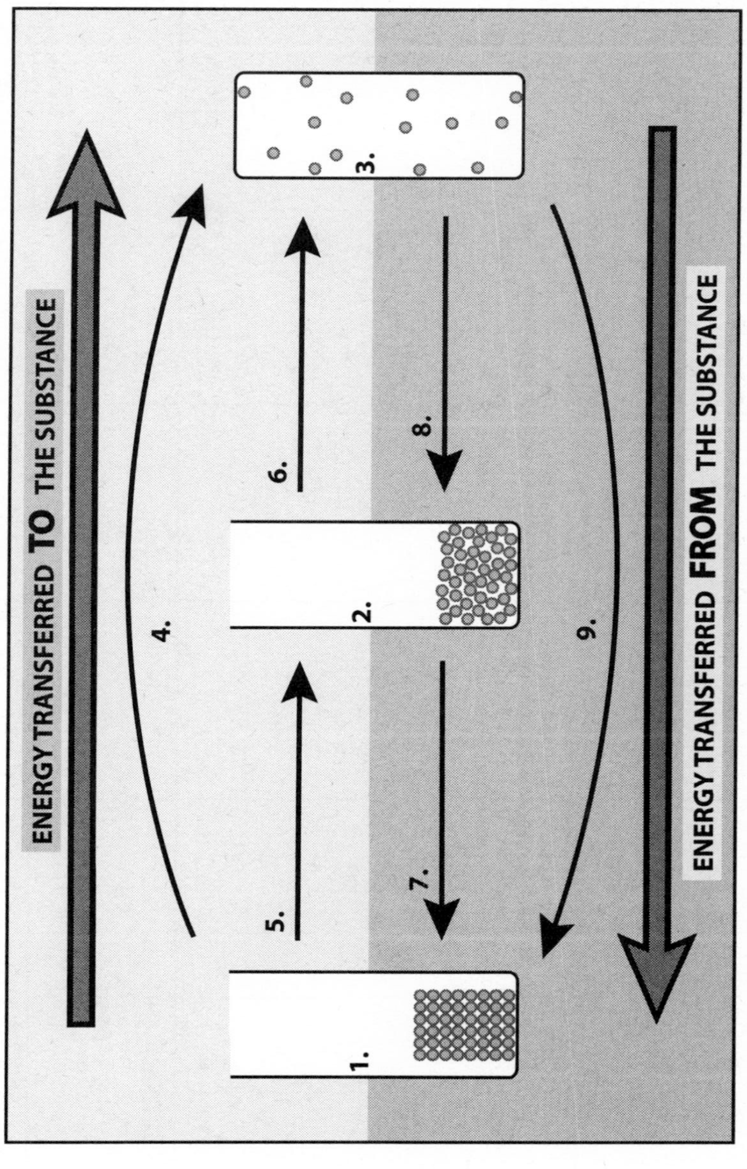

FOSS Chemical Interactions Course, Second Edition
© The Regents of the University of California
Can be duplicated for classroom or workshop use.
Investigation 8: Phase Change
No. 55—Notebook Master

Representing Substances

Substance name	Chemical formula	Representation	Number of elements	Number of atoms
Carbon	C			
Water	H_2O			
Carbon dioxide	CO_2			
Sodium chloride	NaCl			
Oxygen	O_2			
Sodium carbonate	Na_2CO_3			

Representing Substances

Substance name	Chemical formula	Representation	Number of elements	Number of atoms
Carbon	C			
Water	H_2O			
Carbon dioxide	CO_2			
Sodium chloride	NaCl			
Oxygen	O_2			
Sodium carbonate	Na_2CO_3			

FOSS Chemical Interactions Course, Second Edition
© The Regents of the University of California
Can be duplicated for classroom or workshop use.
Investigation 9: Reaction
No. 56—Notebook Master

Analyzing Substances

Substance name and Chemical formula	Representation	Number of elements	Number of atoms
	Cl Ca Cl		
	O C O		

Analyzing Substances

Substance name and Chemical formula	Representation	Number of elements	Number of atoms
	Cl Ca Cl		
	O C O		

FOSS Chemical Interactions Course, Second Edition
© The Regents of the University of California
Can be duplicated for classroom or workshop use.
Investigation 9: Reaction
No. 57—Notebook Master

Thinking about Limewater

1. Limewater is calcium hydroxide dissolved in water. The chemical formula for calcium hydroxide is $Ca(OH)_2$. Use circles labeled with atomic symbols to draw what you think a representation of one particle of calcium hydroxide might look like.

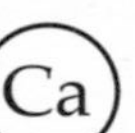

2. a. Use atom tiles to make representations of the particles that you think reacted.

   b. Rearrange the atoms to figure out what the white precipitate is.

   c. Draw representations of the reactants and the products using labeled circles. (HINT: The white precipitate does not dissolve in water. What white substance are you familiar with that doesn't dissolve?)

3. Write the limewater reaction using chemical formulas. Write the names of the reactants and products under the formulas.

$Ca(OH)_2$ +

Calcium hydroxide

4. Did new substances form? If yes, what are they?

5. Did new atoms form? If yes, what are they?

6. Did new elements form? If yes, what are they?

Thinking about Limewater

1. Limewater is calcium hydroxide dissolved in water. The chemical formula for calcium hydroxide is $Ca(OH)_2$. Use circles labeled with atomic symbols to draw what you think a representation of one particle of calcium hydroxide might look like.

2. a. Use atom tiles to make representations of the particles that you think reacted.

   b. Rearrange the atoms to figure out what the white precipitate is.

   c. Draw representations of the reactants and the products using labeled circles. (HINT: The white precipitate does not dissolve in water. What white substance are you familiar with that doesn't dissolve?)

3. Write the limewater reaction using chemical formulas. Write the names of the reactants and products under the formulas.

$Ca(OH)_2$ +

Calcium hydroxide

4. Did new substances form? If yes, what are they?

5. Did new atoms form? If yes, what are they?

6. Did new elements form? If yes, what are they?

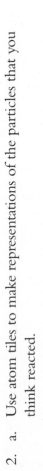

FOSS Chemical Interactions Course, Second Edition
© The Regents of the University of California
Can be duplicated for classroom or workshop use.
Investigation 9: Reaction
No. 58—Notebook Master

Acid/Baking Soda Reaction Products

WARNING — This set contains chemicals that may be harmful if misused. Read cautions on individual containers carefully. Not to be used by children except under adult supervision.

1. What happened in the *vial*? Use chemical equations to explain.

2. What happened in the *bottle*? Use chemical equations to explain.

3. Were you able to confirm all the products that formed during the reaction between baking soda and hydrochloric acid? If not, what else will you do?

Acid/Baking Soda Reaction Products

WARNING — This set contains chemicals that may be harmful if misused. Read cautions on individual containers carefully. Not to be used by children except under adult supervision.

1. What happened in the *vial*? Use chemical equations to explain.

2. What happened in the *bottle*? Use chemical equations to explain.

3. Were you able to confirm all the products that formed during the reaction between baking soda and hydrochloric acid? If not, what else will you do?

FOSS Chemical Interactions Course, Second Edition
© The Regents of the University of California
Can be duplicated for classroom or workshop use.
Investigation 9: Reaction
No. 59—Notebook Master

Response Sheet—Investigation 9

Grandmother ate too many chili peppers for supper. She moaned,

I need an antacid tablet.

Her granddaughter found the package of antacid (antacid means "against acid") tablets and read the label. The active ingredient was calcium carbonate. The granddaughter said,

This will give you some relief.

1. Explain why the granddaughter thought the antacid tablet would help Grandmother.

2. Use chemical formulas to write the equation for the reaction.

NOTE: Here are the formulas for some of the substances you have used.

CO_2	H_2O	Na_2CO_3
$CaCO_3$	HCl	$NaCl$
$CaCl_2$	$MgSO_4$	
$Ca(OH)_2$	$NaHCO_3$	

Response Sheet—Investigation 9

Grandmother ate too many chili peppers for supper. She moaned,

I need an antacid tablet.

Her granddaughter found the package of antacid (antacid means "against acid") tablets and read the label. The active ingredient was calcium carbonate. The granddaughter said,

This will give you some relief.

1. Explain why the granddaughter thought the antacid tablet would help Grandmother.

2. Use chemical formulas to write the equation for the reaction.

NOTE: Here are the formulas for some of the substances you have used.

CO_2	H_2O	Na_2CO_3
$CaCO_3$	HCl	$NaCl$
$CaCl_2$	$MgSO_4$	
$Ca(OH)_2$	$NaHCO_3$	

FOSS Chemical Interactions Course, Second Edition
© The Regents of the University of California
Can be duplicated for classroom or workshop use.
Investigation 9: Reaction
No. 60—Notebook Master

Citric Acid/Baking Soda Reaction

1. Explain why the same amount of gas was produced.

5 mL citric acid solution A + *3 midispoons* baking soda → 30 mL gas

5 mL citric acid solution A + *6 midispoons* baking soda → 30 mL gas

2. Explain why different amounts of gas were produced.

5 mL *citric acid solution A* + 3 midispoons baking soda → 30 mL gas

5 mL *citric acid solution B* + 3 midispoons baking soda → 15 mL gas

3. What might happen if you mix 5 mL of citric acid solution A with 1 midispoon of baking soda?

4. What could you do to determine which reactant was in excess at the end of a reaction between citric acid and baking soda?

Citric Acid/Baking Soda Reaction

1. Explain why the same amount of gas was produced.

5 mL citric acid solution A + *3 midispoons* baking soda → 30 mL gas

5 mL citric acid solution A + *6 midispoons* baking soda → 30 mL gas

2. Explain why different amounts of gas were produced.

5 mL *citric acid solution A* + 3 midispoons baking soda → 30 mL gas

5 mL *citric acid solution B* + 3 midispoons baking soda → 15 mL gas

3. What might happen if you mix 5 mL of citric acid solution A with 1 midispoon of baking soda?

4. What could you do to determine which reactant was in excess at the end of a reaction between citric acid and baking soda?

FOSS Chemical Interactions Course, Second Edition
© The Regents of the University of California
Can be duplicated for classroom or workshop use.
Investigation 10: Limiting Factors
No. 61—Notebook Master

Teacher Masters

FOSS SAFETY CONTRACT

Safety is an important part of participating in chemistry. Safety guidelines must be followed at all times. Read, sign, and date this contract at the bottom, indicating that you agree to use safe practices at all times.

1. Follow the safety procedures outlined by your teacher. Ask questions if you're unsure of what to do.
2. Behave in a responsible manner. No running, pushing, horseplay, or practical jokes are allowed.
3. Know where classroom safety equipment is located and know how to use it.
4. Wear safety goggles when instructed to do so by your teacher.
5. Never eat, drink, or chew gum during laboratory activities.
6. Use care and common sense when working with chemical substances.
    - Never put substances in your mouth. Do not taste any substance unless your teacher specifically tells you to do so.
    - Do not smell unknown substances. If your teacher asks you to smell a substance, wave a hand over the substance to draw the scent toward you.
    - Do not touch your face, mouth, eyes, or another person while working with chemical substances.
    - Wash your hands with soap and warm water immediately after working with chemical substances.
7. If you come in contact with a chemical substance, *immediately* rinse skin and clothing with water, and *then* inform your teacher.
8. Report all accidents and injuries to your teacher.
9. Use extra care when working with matches and around open flame.
    - Pull back and secure long hair. Remove long jewelry and scarves.
    - Do not leave an open flame unattended.
    - Do not reach over an open flame.
    - Do not use bare hands to pick up hot objects.
10. Cleanup is *your* responsibility. Handle all used and unused substances as directed by your teacher. Clean up your work area.

I, ________________________, have read and understand the FOSS Safety Contract. I agree to follow the safety guidelines and any additional instructions and precautions given by the teacher. I understand that if I do not follow the safety guidelines, I will not be allowed to participate in chemistry.

________________________________ ________________________

Student signature Date

I have reviewed the FOSS Safety Contract with my child. I understand that my child will not be allowed to participate in chemistry if he or she does not follow the safety guidelines.

________________________________ ________________________

Parent/guardian signature Date

SUBSTANCE LABELS

Calcium carbonate
(chalk)
$CaCO_3$

Chemical name
(common name)
chemical formula

TWO-SUBSTANCE REACTIONS

Ascorbic acid + calcium carbonate

$C_6H_8O_6 + CaCO_3$

Ascorbic acid + sodium bicarbonate

$C_6H_8O_6 + NaHCO_3$

Ascorbic acid + sodium carbonate

$C_6H_8O_6 + Na_2CO_3$

Calcium chloride + sodium bicarbonate

$CaCl_2 + NaHCO_3$

Citric acid + calcium carbonate

$C_6H_8O_7 + CaCO_3$

Citric acid + sodium bicarbonate

$C_6H_8O_7 + NaHCO_3$

Citric acid + sodium carbonate

$C_6H_8O_7 + Na_2CO_3$

WARNING — This set contains chemicals that may be harmful if misused. Read cautions on individual containers carefully. Not to be used by children except under adult supervision.

HOW MUCH GAS?—PROCEDURE

Materials

- 1 Jar of sodium bicarbonate
- 1 Jar of citric acid
- 2 Spoons, 2 mL
- 1 Small cup (250 mL)
- 1 Tote tray
- • Water
- 4 Safety goggles
- 1 Self-stick note
- 2 Rubber stoppers, with hole
- 2 Syringes
- 1 Container, 1/2 L
- 1 Container, 1 L
- 1 Stirring stick
- 2 Glass bottles
- 2 Paper funnels

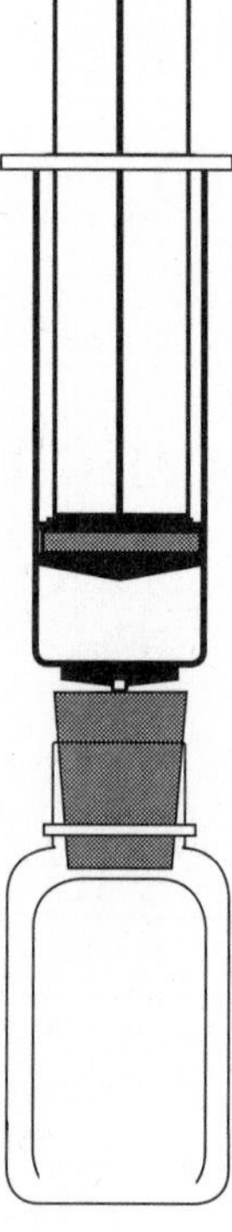

Procedure

a. Get a tray of materials for your group.

b. Construct a bottle-and-syringe system for each pair.

c. Put on safety goggles.

d. Make a citric acid solution for the group to share. Dissolve one level, 2 mL spoon of citric acid in 100 mL of water in the plastic cup. Use the self-stick note to label the cup.

e. Make a paper funnel if needed. Use the funnel to put one level, 2 mL spoon of sodium bicarbonate into the bottle. Twist the stopper into the bottle.

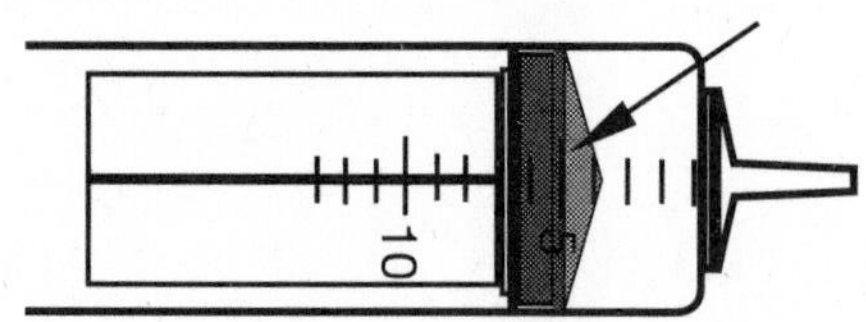

f. Take up exactly 5 mL of citric acid solution in the syringe. Insert the tip of the syringe into the hole in the stopper.

g. Push the solution into the bottle and quickly release the plunger. *Don't* remove the syringe. Observe and record the volume of gas.

h. Dump the used liquid and conduct two more trials. It is not necessary to wash out the bottle between trials.

HOW MUCH GAS?—CLASS RESULTS

Group	Average volume of gas (mL)
1	
2	
3	
4	
5	
6	
7	
8	
Average	

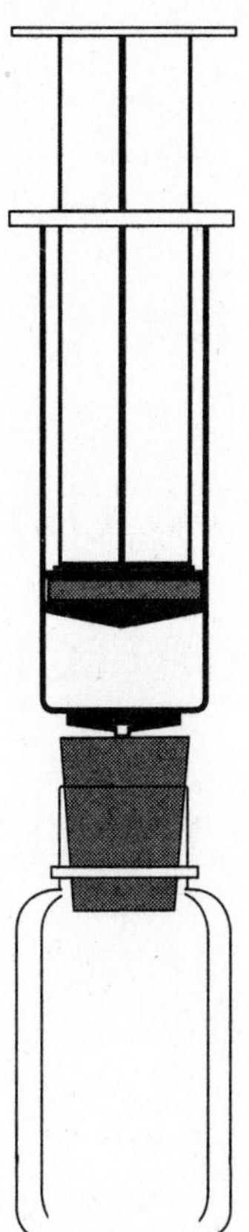

PROPERTIES OF GAS

1. How do you know when something is gas?
2. What is gas made of?
3. How do you know when something is matter?
4. Is gas matter?

PUSH AND PULL ON AIR

1. What did you learn about air using a two-syringe system?
2. What did you learn about air with a syringe system that was clamped shut?
3. Why couldn't the plunger be pushed all the way down?
4. Does air take up space?
5. What is your evidence?
6. Does air always take up the same amount of space?

HEATING AND COOLING WATER PROCEDURE

Materials

- 2 Glass bottles
- 2 Rubber stoppers
- 2 Clear pipes
- 2 Bulb pipettes
- 2 Cards, 2.5 × 8 cm
- • Tape
- • Blue water
- • Hot water
- • Cold water
- 4 Large cups
- 4 Paper towels

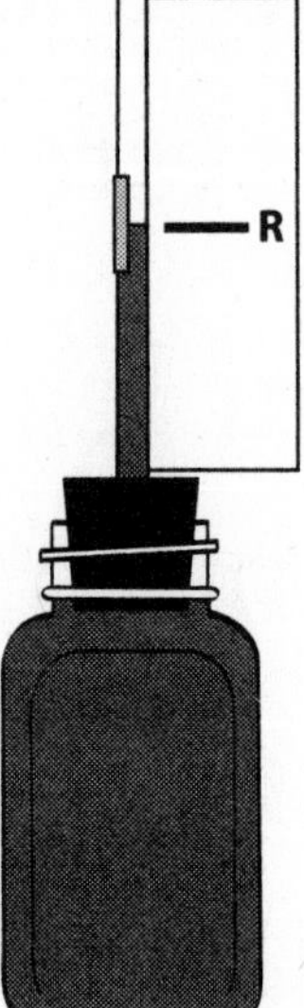

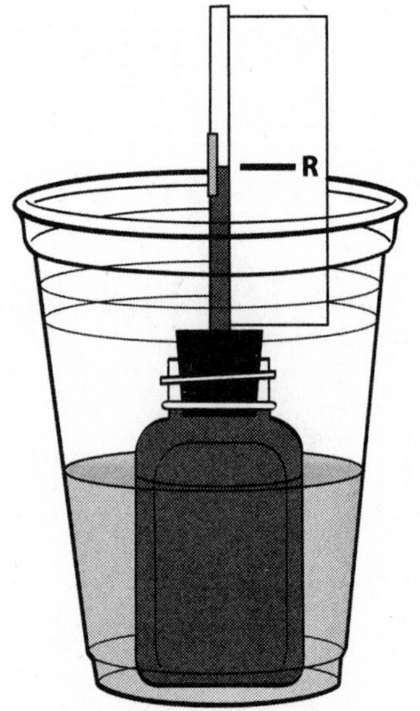

Procedure

a. Push the clear plastic pipe a short distance into the rubber stopper.

b. Use a syringe (at the materials station) to put 35 mL of blue water into the glass bottle.

c. Push the stopper into the bottle as far as it will go. Use the pipette to fine-tune the water level so it is halfway up the pipe.

d. Tape a 2.5 × 8 cm card to the clear tube. Label the water level "R."

e. Place the bottle in 150 mL of cold water. After 3 minutes, label the water level "C."

f. Move the bottle to 150 mL of hot water. In 5 minutes, label the water level "H."

KINETIC ENERGY VOCABULARY

Compression: The decrease of gas volume as a result of applied force or pressure.

Contraction: The decrease of volume due to decreased kinetic energy of particles.

Expansion: The increase of volume as a result of applied force or due to increased kinetic energy of particles.

Kinetic energy: The energy of motion.

MIXING WATER RESULTS

Group	T_{hot} (°C)	T_{cold} (°C)	Prediction (°C)	T_{final} (°C)

ENERGY VOCABULARY

Cooling: Energy transfer that decreases the kinetic energy of particles.

Heating: Energy transfer that increases the kinetic energy of particles.

Kinetic energy: The energy of motion. Hot substances have greater kinetic energy of particles than cool substances.

Temperature: A measure of the average kinetic energy of the particles in a substance.

ENERGY-TRANSFER PROCEDURE

Materials

- 2 Graduated cylinders
- 2 Bulb pipettes
- 3 Foam cups
- 1 Large cup
- 2 Thermometers (glass)
- • Hot and cold water

Procedure

a. Decide on the mass of hot water and the mass of cold water you will use.

b. Measure the hot water into one foam cup and the cold water into a second foam cup.

c. Record the mass and starting temperatures in the table on your notebook sheet.

d. Pour the cold water and the hot water into the third foam cup.

e. Put the third foam cup into the large cup.

f. Measure and record the final temperature.

ENERGY-TRANSFER DEMONSTRATION

Start time: ___________ **End time:** ___________

Hot water temperature

Start ___________

End ___________

Air temperature

Start ___________

End ___________

Cold water temperature

Start ___________

End ___________

THERMOS ENGINEERING PROBLEM

Problem: Create an insulating device that most effectively reduces the transfer of energy between the surrounding atmosphere and the liquid within the container. (Liquid may be hot or cold.)

MATERIALS TEST CONSIDERATIONS

Materials

- 2 Small cups
- 2 Large cups
- 2 Foam cups
- 2 Thermometers (glass)
- • Hot and cold water
- 1 Timer (clock or stopwatch)

Pointers

1. Each team will test one insulating material with both hot and cold water. Set up two identical cup systems (small cup within the large cup) with your material between the cups.
2. You cannot change the cups or the arrangement of insulating material.
3. Use 100 mL of water for each test.
4. Starting temperature must be approximately 50°C for hot water and 0°C for cold water.
5. Measure and record the temperatures at the start and at the end of 5 minutes.
6. Do two hot-water trials and two cold-water trials for your material. Start with new water for the second trial.
7. After you do two hot-water and two cold-water trials for a material, test another material if there is time.

CLASS MATERIALS DATA

Material		Average ΔT (°C)	Rank (1 = least transfer per 5 minutes)
1.	Hot:		
	Cold:		
2.	Hot:		
	Cold:		
3.	Hot:		
	Cold:		
4.	Hot:		
	Cold:		
5.	Hot:		
	Cold:		
6.	Hot:		
	Cold:		
7.	Hot:		
	Cold:		
8.	Hot:		
	Cold:		

ENGINEERING CRITERIA AND CONSTRAINTS

Criteria, or design requirements, for the thermos design challenge:

- Minimize energy transfer between the contents of the cup and the surrounding environment.
- Use the standard outer container (large cup).
- Inner cup of test container must hold at least 100 mL of liquid.

Constraints for the thermos design challenge:

- All teams will follow the same procedure for measuring energy transfer (temperature change after 5 minutes).
- Use only one period for testing.
- All insulating materials must be recycled materials (already used for something else).

BRAINSTORMING GUIDELINES

The purpose of a brainstorm is to generate as **many** ideas as possible as **quickly** as possible.

- Choose someone on your design team to write down the ideas that your team members come up with.
- Write down ***all*** ideas. Do not comment on any ideas. Any type of comment such as "That is a great idea!" or "I don't think that will work," may keep other members of the team from wanting to share their ideas.
- Even an idea that has no chance of working can trigger someone else to think of a new idea that just might work.
- Make sure everyone has a chance to share their ideas.

CLASS DESIGN DATA

Team	Average ΔT (°C)	Rank (1 = least transfer per 5 minutes)
1		
2		
3		
4		
5		
6		
7		
8		

ENGINEERING DESIGN PROCESS

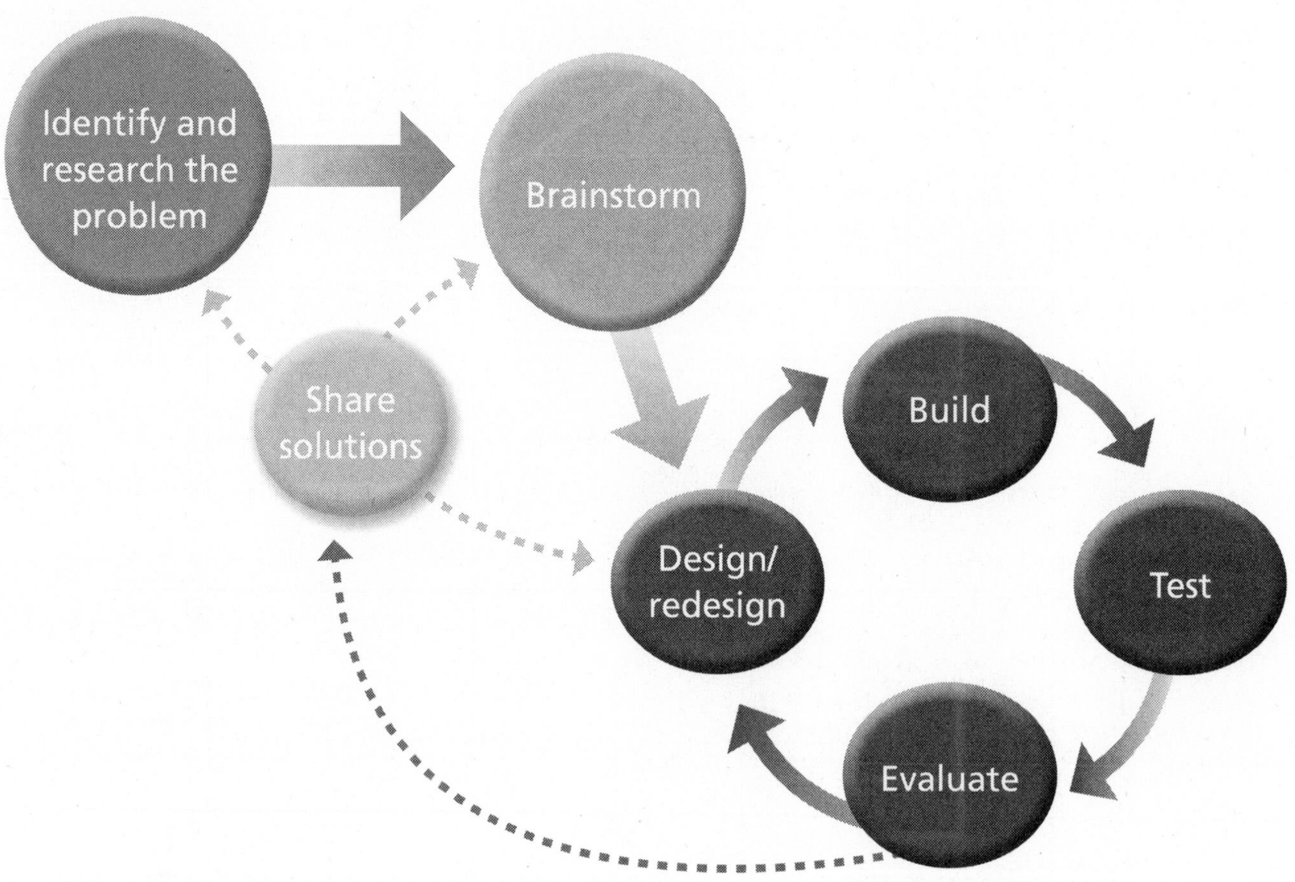

DISSOLVE OR MELT? PROCEDURE

Materials

2 Plastic cups, small, 60 mL

2 Plastic cups, 250 mL

4 Candies, all one color

- Hot water
- Cold water
- Paper towels

Procedure

a. Put about 150 mL of hot water in one 250 mL plastic cup; put about 150 mL of cold water in the other 250 mL plastic cup.

b. Put a small 60 mL plastic cup in each cup of water. Make sure the small cups don't have water in them before you go to the next step.

c. Get four candies, all one color. Put one candy in each 60 mL cup and one in the bottom of each of the cups of water.

d. Don't stir, poke, or shake the candies or the cups. Record your observations.

e. When your teacher says to squash each candy, use paper towels. Record your observations.

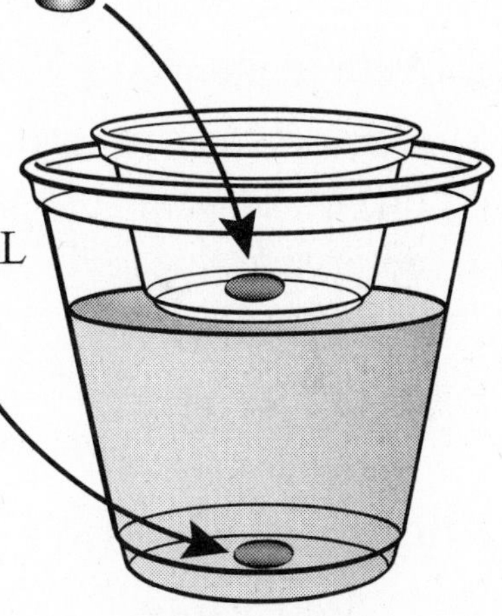

Hot water

Cold water

WARNING — This set contains chemicals that may be harmful if misused. Read cautions on individual containers carefully. Not to be used by children except under adult supervision.

SOLUBILITY PROCEDURE

Part 1

Materials

- 2 Plastic cups, 250 mL
- 2 Self-stick notes
- 2 Craft sticks
- 2 Hand lenses
- 4 Safety goggles
- 1 Syringe
- 1 Container, 1/2 L
- • Calcium carbonate ($CaCO_3$)
- • Sodium chloride (NaCl)
- • Water

Procedure

a. Label two cups "$CaCO_3$" and "NaCl," using self-stick notes.

b. Put on safety goggles.

c. Measure one level, 2 mL spoon of calcium carbonate into one plastic cup.

d. Measure one level, 2 mL spoon of sodium chloride into a second plastic cup.

e. Observe the two solid materials with a hand lens. Record your observations.

f. Use a syringe to add 30 mL of water to each cup. Stir, let cups sit for a minute or so, observe, and record.

Parts 2 and 3

Additional Materials

- 2 Small cups
- 2 Self-stick notes
- 1 Funnel stand
- 2 Filter papers
- 1 Well tray
- 3 Bulb pipettes

Procedure

a. Label two cups "$CaCO_3$" and "NaCl," using self-stick notes.

b. Set up the funnel stand and place a filter paper in the funnel.

c. Place the empty cup labeled "NaCl" under the filter funnel. Stir the sodium chloride mixture and pour it into the filter.

d. Repeat the process with the calcium carbonate mixture.

e. Prepare evaporation samples according to your teacher's instructions.

WARNING — This set contains chemicals that may be harmful if misused. Read cautions on individual containers carefully. Not to be used by children except under adult supervision.

WELL-TRAY ORGANIZATION FOR EVAPORATION

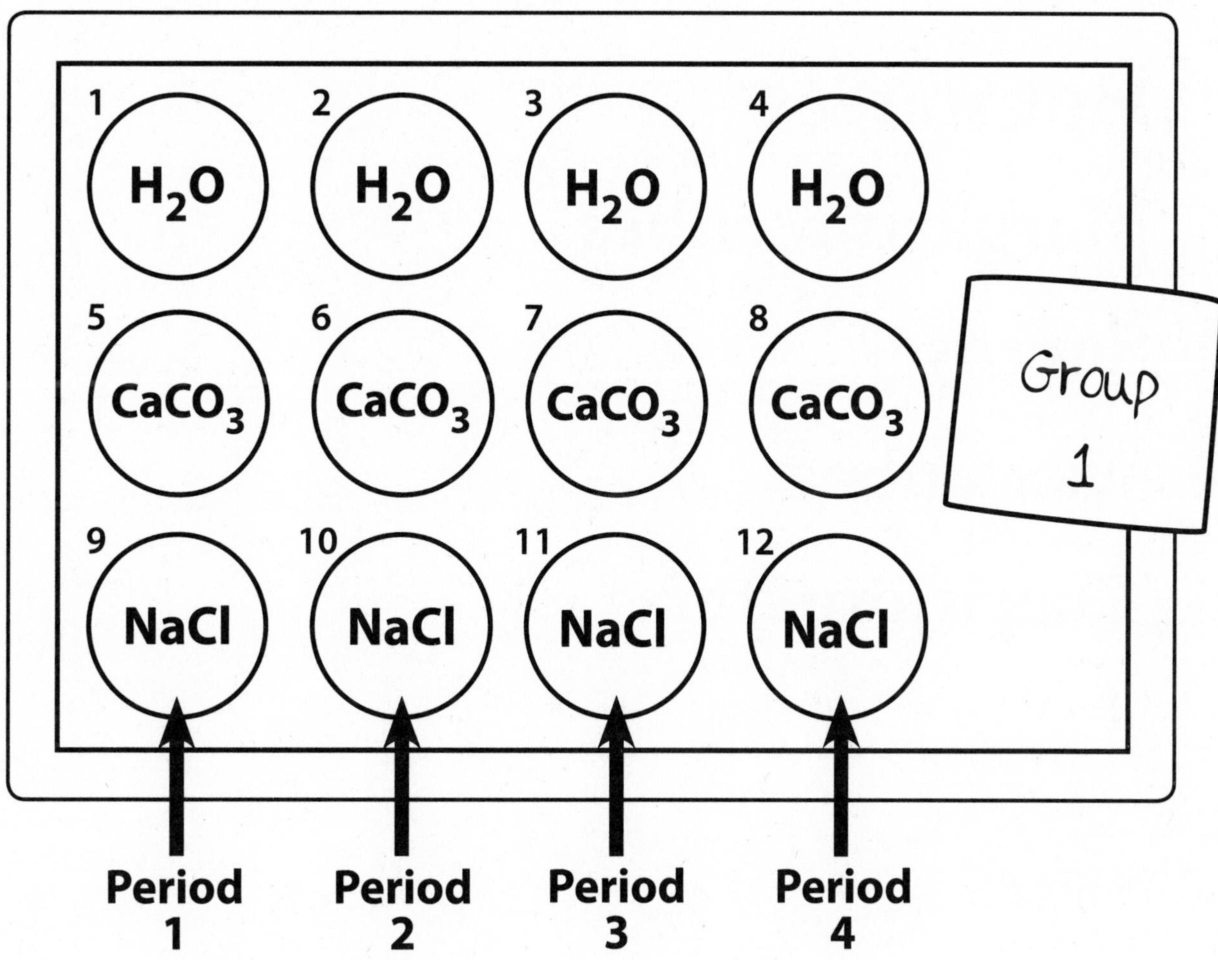

MELTING EXPERIMENT MATERIALS

- Containers, 1/2-liter
- Paper cups
- Hot water
- Margarine cubes
- Sucrose
- Wax cubes
- Thermometers

ALUMINUM-FOIL SPOON

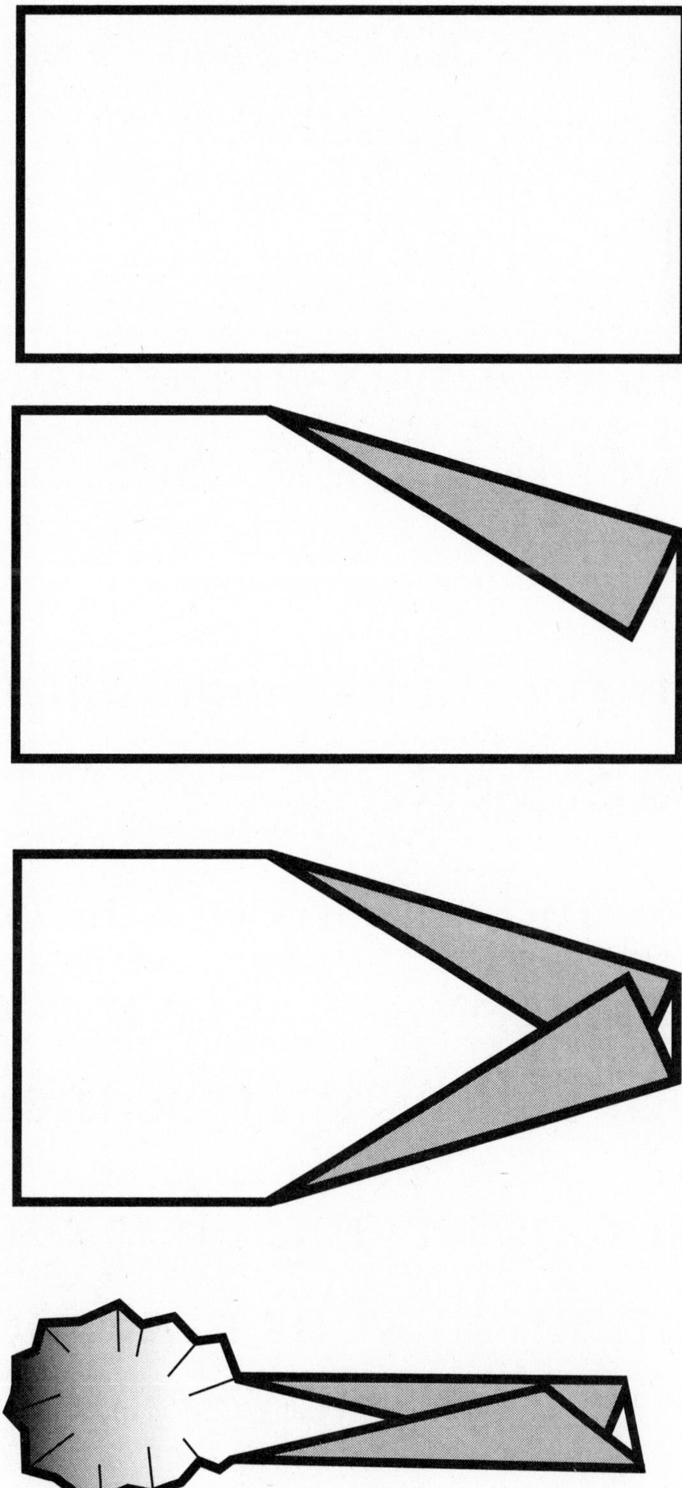

WAX AND SUCROSE MELTING PROCEDURE

a. Make two foil spoons.

b. Put on safety goggles.

c. Light the candle.

d. Put a cube of wax in one foil spoon. Place over the flame. See if the wax melts.

e. If a material melts, *immediately* remove it from the heat.

f. Put two midispoons of sucrose in another foil spoon. Place over the flame. See if the sucrose melts.

g. Continue observing. Record your observations in your notebook.

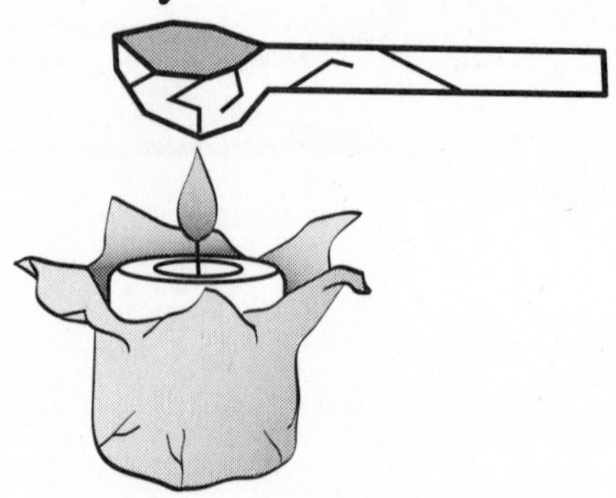

WAX AND SUCROSE DISCUSSION

1. What does the word **melt** mean?
2. Did the wax melt? List your evidence.
3. Did the sucrose melt? List your evidence.
4. Do all solids melt? How could you find out?
5. Do all solids melt at the same temperature?
6. Did the melted wax and sucrose *stay* liquid?
7. When liquids change state from liquid to solid, we call that **freezing**. Did the melted wax and sucrose freeze? List your evidence.
8. Do all liquids freeze? How could you find out?
9. Do all liquids freeze at the same temperature?

EQUILIBRIUM

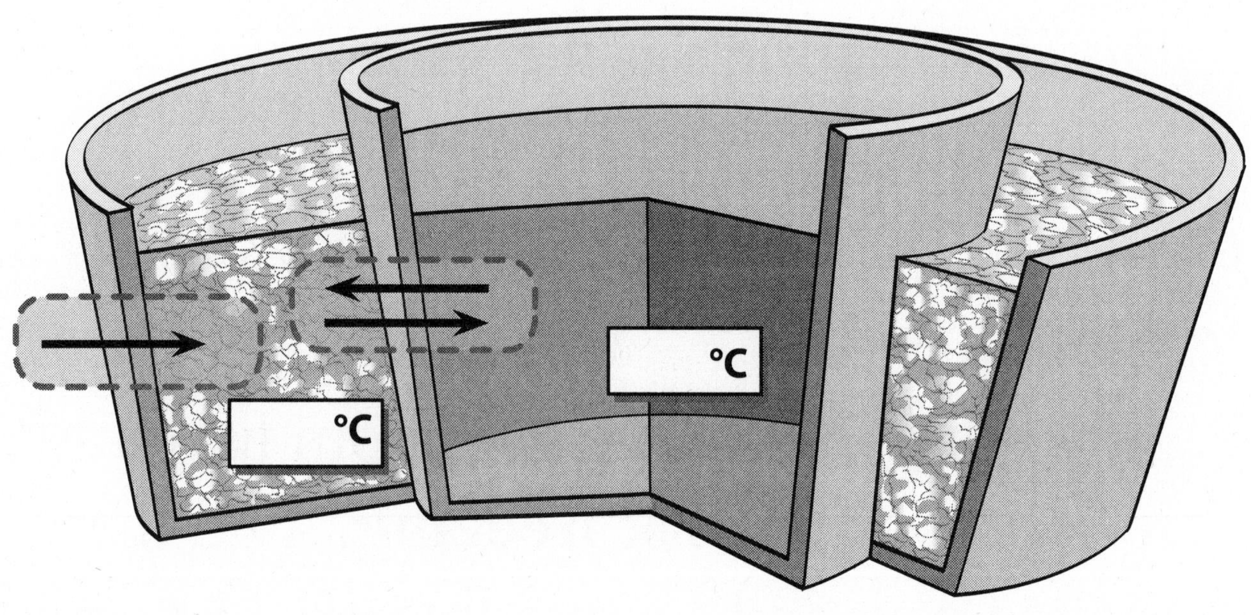

WHITE SUBSTANCES TO TEST

Calcium carbonate (chalk)

Calcium chloride (road salt)

Citric acid (citric acid)

Magnesium sulfate (Epsom salts)

Sodium bicarbonate (baking soda)

Sodium carbonate (washing soda)

Sodium chloride (table salt)

Sucrose (sugar)

WARNING — This set contains chemicals that may be harmful if misused. Read cautions on individual containers carefully. Not to be used by children except under adult supervision.

ICE AND SUBSTANCES PROCEDURE

Materials

2 Thermometers (metal-backed)
2 Small cups, plastic, with line
2 Stirring sticks
2 Spoons, 2 mL

- White substance
- Ice, crushed

4 Safety goggles

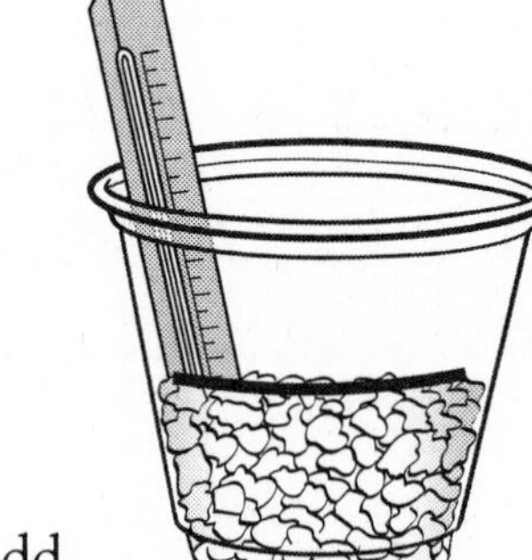

Procedure (work in pairs)

a. Fill a cup with ice to the marked line.

b. Measure and record the start temperature (time 0).

c. Collect your group's white substance and spoons. Do NOT add the substance to your cup yet.

d. When start time is called, add the assigned amount of substance to the cup. Stir thoroughly with the stirring stick. (Do not use the thermometer or spoon to stir.)

- One pair adds two 2 mL scoops.
- One pair adds four 2 mL scoops.

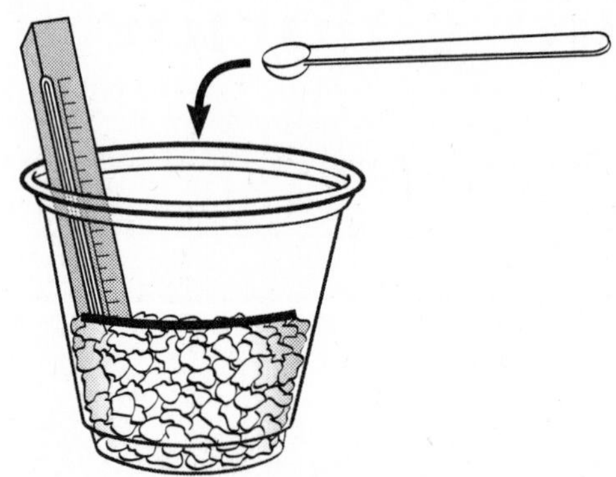

e. Measure and record the temperature of the ice at each time interval.

f. Record initial and final temperatures and ΔT on the class results table.

ICE AND SUBSTANCES CLASS RESULTS

Substance	Amount (# of scoops)	$T_{initial}$	T_{final}	ΔT
Calcium carbonate	2			
Calcium carbonate	4			
Calcium chloride	2			
Calcium chloride	4			
Citric acid	2			
Citric acid	4			
Magnesium sulfate	2			
Magnesium sulfate	4			
Sodium bicarbonate	2			
Sodium bicarbonate	4			
Sodium carbonate	2			
Sodium carbonate	4			
Sodium chloride	2			
Sodium chloride	4			
Sucrose	2			
Sucrose	4			

FREEZER DESIGN CHALLENGE

Criterion

- The device must freeze 10 mL of water in a plastic vial in 20 minutes.

Constraints

- Choose a white substance from those tested.
- Use no more than four 2 mL spoonfuls of the white substance.
- Use no more than one half-full small cup of ice.
- Testing stops after 20 minutes.

FREEZER DESIGN QUESTIONS

1. What substance (and how much) does your freezer use? How might this affect the cost of your device?

2. How does your freezer decrease energy transfer between the water and the atmosphere?

3. What elements of your design came from your experience designing a thermos?

ATOMS AND COMPOUNDS

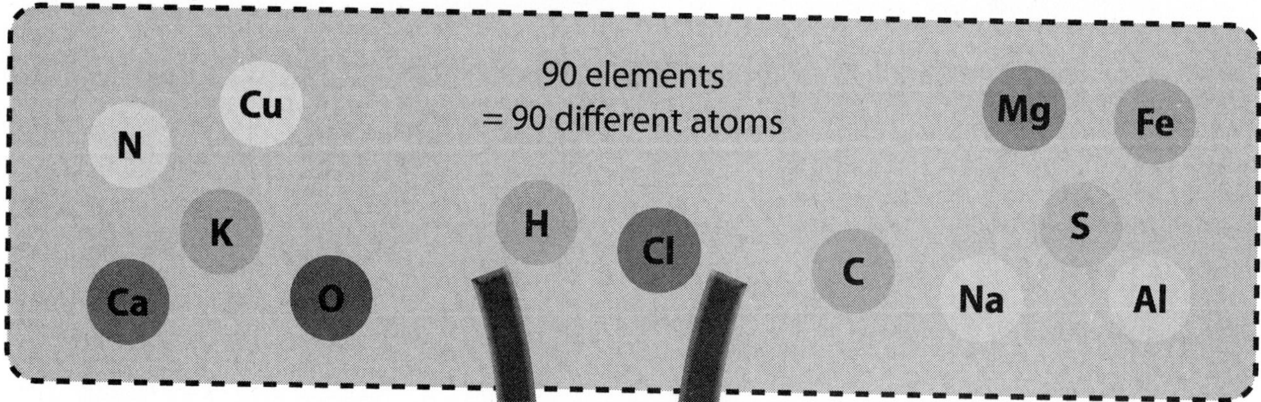

Atoms combine
to make
new substances

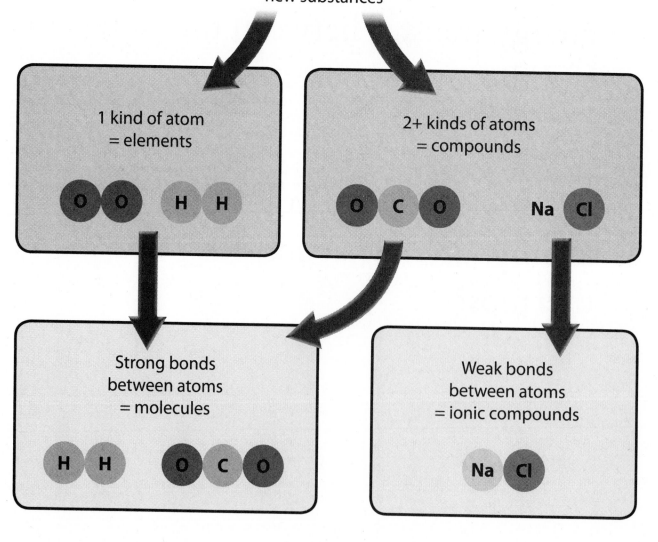

1 kind of atom
= elements

O O H H

2+ kinds of atoms
= compounds

O C O Na Cl

Strong bonds
between atoms
= molecules

H H O C O

Weak bonds
between atoms
= ionic compounds

Na Cl

NAMING PARTICLES

1. What are the basic particles from which all matter is made?

2. What is a compound?

3. What kinds of particles are made of two or more kinds of atoms?

4. What kinds of particles are made of just one kind of atom?

5. How are molecules and ionic compounds the same?

6. How are molecules and ionic compounds different?

COMPOUND STRUCTURE

Some compounds form molecules.

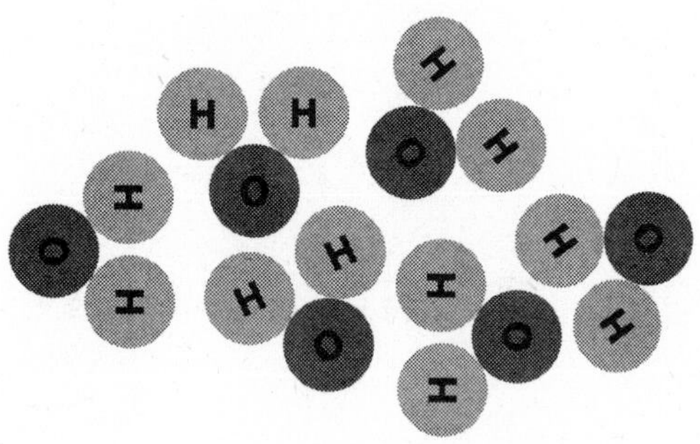

water (liquid)

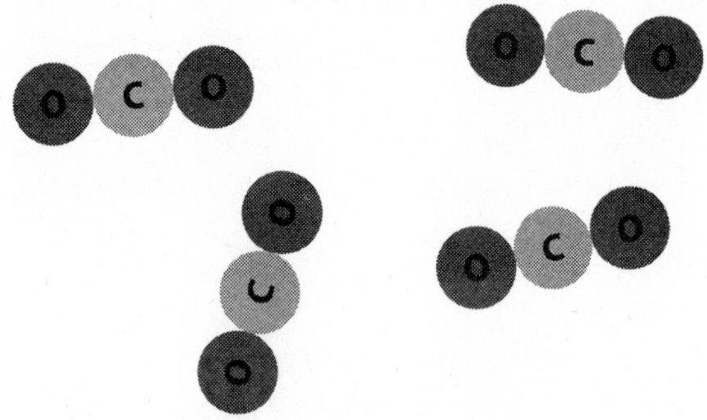

carbon dioxide (gas)

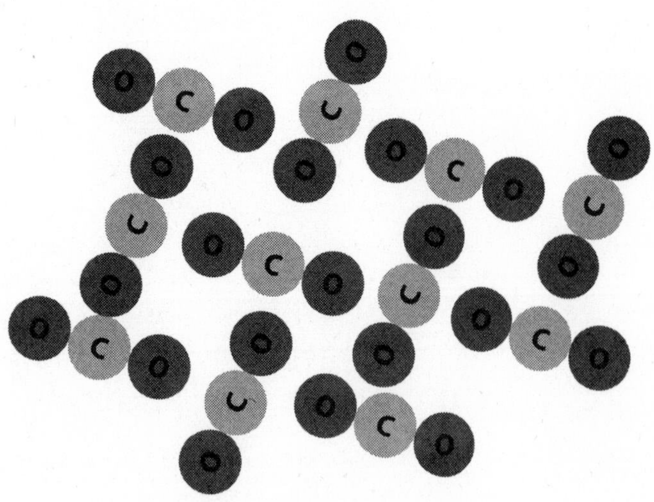

carbon dioxide (solid)

Some compounds form unique extended structures such as crystals.

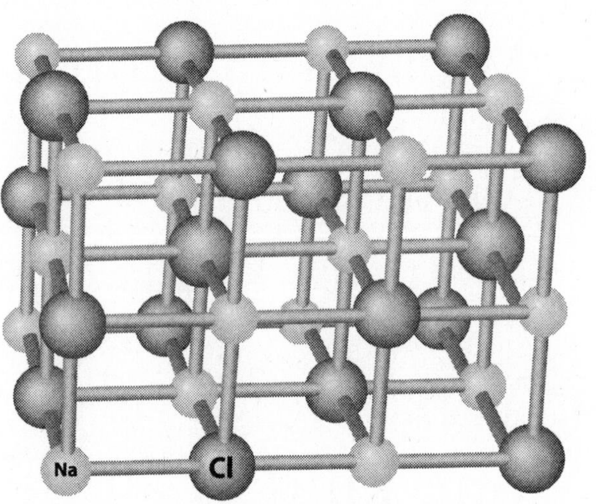

sodium chloride (solid)

What shape crystals does sodium chloride form?

ATOM-TILE INVENTORY

Atom-Tile Inventory

4 Hydrogen—H (blue)
1 Carbon—C (orange)
5 Oxygen—O (red)
2 Chlorine—Cl (green)
2 Sodium—Na (yellow)
1 Calcium—Ca (dark purple)

Atom-Tile Inventory

4 Hydrogen—H (blue)
1 Carbon—C (orange)
5 Oxygen—O (red)
2 Chlorine—Cl (green)
2 Sodium—Na (yellow)
1 Calcium—Ca (dark purple)

Atom-Tile Inventory

4 Hydrogen—H (blue)
1 Carbon—C (orange)
5 Oxygen—O (red)
2 Chlorine—Cl (green)
2 Sodium—Na (yellow)
1 Calcium—Ca (dark purple)

Atom-Tile Inventory

4 Hydrogen—H (blue)
1 Carbon—C (orange)
5 Oxygen—O (red)
2 Chlorine—Cl (green)
2 Sodium—Na (yellow)
1 Calcium—Ca (dark purple)

Atom-Tile Inventory

4 Hydrogen—H (blue)
1 Carbon—C (orange)
5 Oxygen—O (red)
2 Chlorine—Cl (green)
2 Sodium—Na (yellow)
1 Calcium—Ca (dark purple)

Atom-Tile Inventory

4 Hydrogen—H (blue)
1 Carbon—C (orange)
5 Oxygen—O (red)
2 Chlorine—Cl (green)
2 Sodium—Na (yellow)
1 Calcium—Ca (dark purple)

Atom-Tile Inventory

4 Hydrogen—H (blue)
1 Carbon—C (orange)
5 Oxygen—O (red)
2 Chlorine—Cl (green)
2 Sodium—Na (yellow)
1 Calcium—Ca (dark purple)

Atom-Tile Inventory

4 Hydrogen—H (blue)
1 Carbon—C (orange)
5 Oxygen—O (red)
2 Chlorine—Cl (green)
2 Sodium—Na (yellow)
1 Calcium—Ca (dark purple)

Atom-Tile Inventory

4 Hydrogen—H (blue)
1 Carbon—C (orange)
5 Oxygen—O (red)
2 Chlorine—Cl (green)
2 Sodium—Na (yellow)
1 Calcium—Ca (dark purple)

WARNING — This set contains chemicals that may be harmful if misused. Read cautions on individual containers carefully. Not to be used by children except under adult supervision.

LIMEWATER INVESTIGATION PROCEDURE

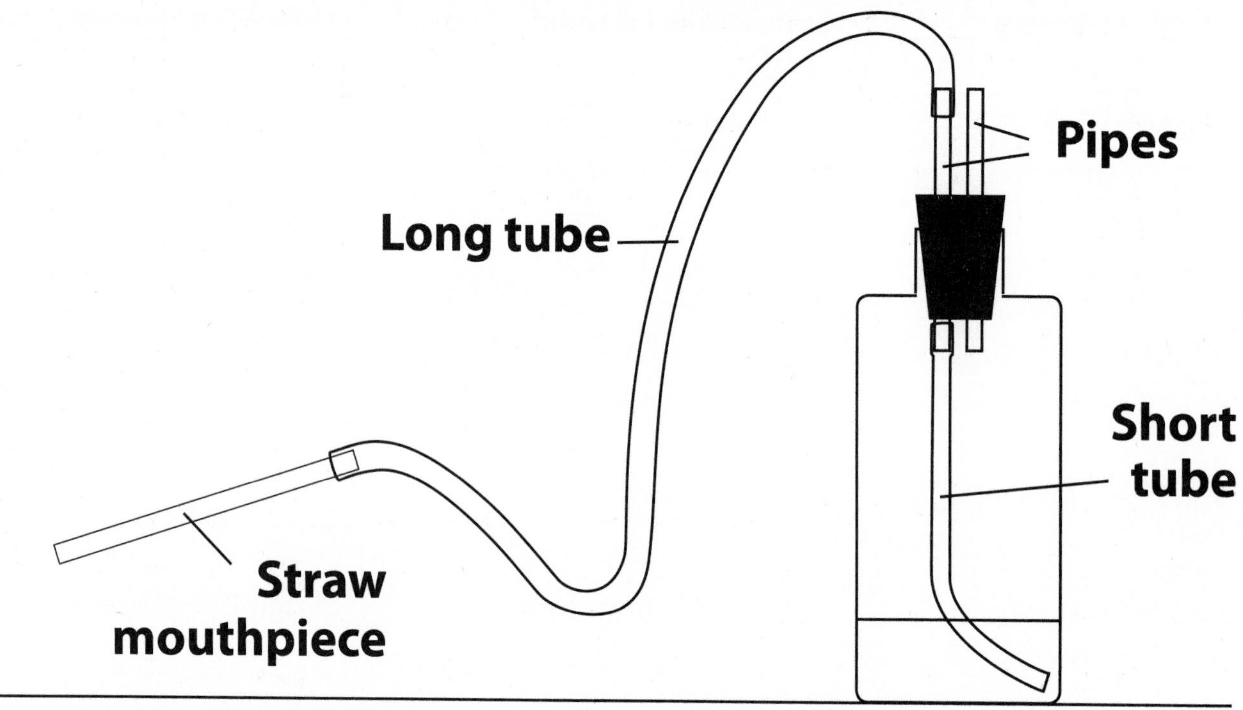

a. Push the two clear plastic pipes through the holes in the rubber stopper.

b. Attach a long tube and a short tube to one pipe, as illustrated.

c. Put on safety goggles. Measure 30 mL of limewater into the bottle. Insert the rubber stopper in the bottle.

d. Take turns using your straw mouthpieces to gently bubble one breath of air into the bottle through the long tube. Everyone should have at least two turns.

BAKING SODA AND HYDROCHLORIC ACID

Here are some possible reactions. Which one is correct?

a. $NaHCO_3 + HCl \rightarrow CO_2\uparrow + H_2O + NaCl$

b. $NaHCO_3 + 2HCl \rightarrow NaHCO_3 + Cl_2\uparrow + H_2\uparrow$

c. $NaHCO_3 + HCl \rightarrow NaCl + O_2\uparrow + H_2O + C$

d. $NaHCO_3 + HCl \rightarrow CO\uparrow + H_2O_2 + NaCl$

e. $2NaHCO_3 + 2HCl \rightarrow$
$C_2H_2\uparrow + 2O_2\uparrow + H_2O_2 + 2NaCl$

WARNING — This set contains chemicals that may be harmful if misused. Read cautions on individual containers carefully. Not to be used by children except under adult supervision.

CARBON DIOXIDE TEST PROCEDURE

Materials

1 Bottle
1 Syringe
1 Small cup
1 Midispoon
1 Stopper with tubes
1 Vial
1 Vial holder
• Hydrochloric acid (HCl)
• Baking soda ($NaHCO_3$)
• Limewater ($Ca(OH)_2$)
4 Safety goggles

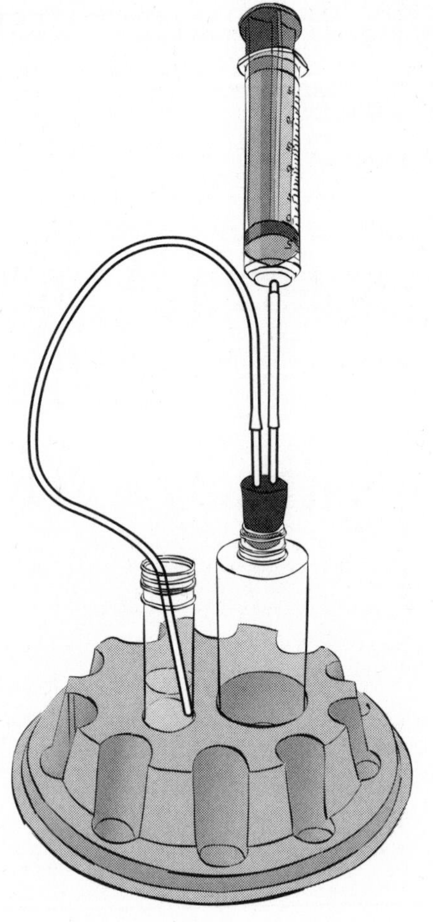

Procedure

a. Place three *level* midispoons of baking soda in the bottle.

b. Place 10 mL of limewater in the vial.

c. Insert the bottle and the vial into the cavities in the vial holder.

d. Take up 5 mL of HCl in a syringe. Place the syringe in a cup to carry to your table.

e. Draw 30 mL of air into the syringe.

f. Slowly put the acid and air into the bottle. Observe. Record your observations in your notebook.

CITRIC ACID/BAKING SODA POINTERS

Materials

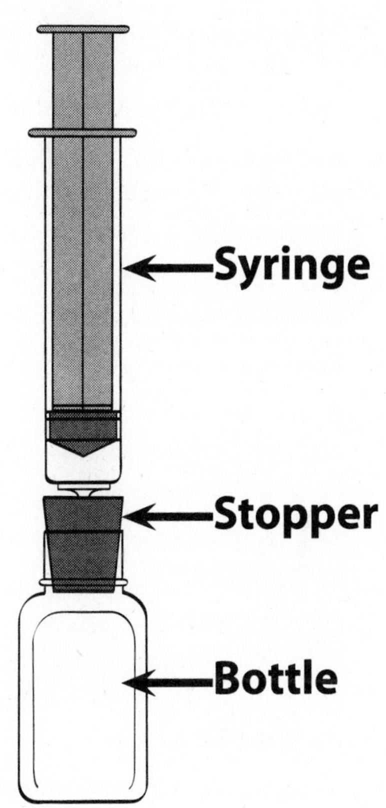

2 Bottle-and-syringe systems
2 Small cups
2 Self-stick notes
- Citric acid solution A
- Citric acid solution B
- Sodium bicarbonate

1 Midispoon
1 Water container, 1/2 L
1 Waste container, 1 L
4 Safety goggles

Pointers

1. Each pair works with one bottle-and-syringe system.
2. Each group shares a cup of solution A and a cup of solution B.
3. Use exactly three level midispoons of sodium bicarbonate.
4. Use exactly 5 mL of citric acid solution.
5. Do two or three trials with each solution.
6. Rinse the bottle between each trial.
7. Record results.

CHEMICAL INTERACTIONS KEY IDEAS

- **Matter** is anything that has mass and occupies space. The specific forms of matter are called **substances**. There are millions of different substances on Earth, and every one is identified by a unique **chemical formula**.
- **Elements** are the basic building blocks of all matter. Ninety different elements occur naturally on Earth. Elements combine to form substances. Every different combination of elements forms a different substance.
- The smallest piece of a substance is a **particle** of that substance. The simplest substances are elements. The basic particle of an element is an **atom**.
- Particles of new substances form when atoms rearrange during **chemical reactions**.
- Atoms are not *within* substances; substances are made of atoms and atoms only. There is nothing between atoms except space.
- Particles are in constant motion. The motion gives particles **kinetic energy.** The greater the motion, the greater the kinetic energy.
- The kinetic energy of the particles in a sample of matter affects the phase of that matter. Particles with relatively low kinetic energy are bonded tightly together in the **solid** phase. Particles with greater kinetic energy are touching, but can move around and past one another in the **liquid** phase. Particles with high kinetic energy move independently through space in the **gas** phase.
- **Temperature** is a measure of the average kinetic energy of the particles in a substance.
- When particles collide, kinetic energy **transfers** from the particle with more energy to the particle with less energy. Energy transfer by contact is **conduction**.
- **Insulating** materials can reduce energy transfer by conduction.
- When kinetic energy increases in a sample of matter, particles collide more often and hit harder, which pushes the particles farther apart. This causes the matter to **expand**. When energy transfers from matter, it **contracts**.
- **Phase change** is affected by energy transfer. As energy transfers to a substance, it typically changes from solid to liquid to gas. As energy transfers from a substance, it typically changes from gas to liquid to solid. Phase changes include **melting**, **evaporation**, **condensation**, **freezing**, **sublimation**, and **deposition**.
- Substances can be put together to make **mixtures**. In some mixtures, one substance (**solute**) **dissolves** in another substance (**solvent**) to form a **solution**. In a solution, the solute is broken down to particles, which are distributed uniformly throughout the solvent.
- Atoms are neither created nor destroyed during chemical reactions, only rearranged, matter is conserved.
- Starting substances change into new substances during chemical reactions. The starting substances are **reactants**; new substances are **products**.
- Engineers test and modify designs that meet a set of **criteria** and work within the **constraints** of the problem.

Assessment Masters

Embedded Assessment Notes

Chemical Interactions, Second Edition

Investigation ___, Part ___	Date ____________
Concept:	
Tally: Got it	Doesn't get it
Misconceptions/incomplete ideas:	
Reflections/next steps:	

Investigation ___, Part ___	Date ____________
Concept:	
Tally: Got it	Doesn't get it
Misconceptions/incomplete ideas:	
Reflections/next steps:	

Investigation ___, Part ___	Date ____________
Concept:	
Tally: Got it	Doesn't get it
Misconceptions/incomplete ideas:	
Reflections/next steps:	

Science and Engineering Practices Checklist

Chemical Interactions, Second Edition

Start Date ______________

End Date ______________

Class	Asking questions and defining problems	Developing and using models	Planning and carrying out investigations	Analyzing and interpreting data	Using mathematics and computational thinking	Constructing explanations and designing solutions	Engaging in argument from evidence	Obtaining, evaluating, and communicating information

NOTE: See the Assessment chapter for a discussion about how to use this checklist.

Name ______________________________

SURVEY/POSTTEST
CHEMICAL INTERACTIONS

Date ____________ Class __________

1. a. A chemical reaction is _____.
   (Mark the one best answer.)

   ❍ **A** a process in which starting substances change into different substances

   ❍ **B** a form of matter with a unique composition

   ❍ **C** an interaction between two substances in which one breaks apart and intermingles with the other

   ❍ **D** the result of a change of energy in the particles in a substance

   b. Mark an **X** next to each word or phrase that describes evidence that a chemical reaction occurred.

   _____ bubbles　　　_____ a precipitate forms

   _____ color change　　　_____ temperature change

   _____ one substance melts　　　_____ a new substance

   c. What happens to the atoms in substances when a chemical reaction occurs?

   ____

   ____

   ____

   ____

   ____

2. When air is heated in a basketball _____.
   *(Mark an **X** next to all correct answers.)*

   _____ the air particles move faster

   _____ the air particles hit each other more frequently

   _____ the air particles get larger

   _____ the air particles get farther apart

   _____ the number of air particles increases

Name ____________________

SURVEY/POSTTEST
CHEMICAL INTERACTIONS

3. Which of the following is made up of atoms?
*(Mark an **X** next to all correct answers.)*

_____ Solids

_____ Matter

_____ Gas

_____ Heat

_____ Liquid

4. Two students each conducted an experiment. They measured the amount of gas produced when they mixed different amounts of liquids A and B. Their results are shown below.

Student 1

Liquid A	Liquid B	Gas produced
5 mL	5 mL	8 mL
5 mL	10 mL	12 mL
5 mL	15 mL	16 mL

Student 2

Liquid A	Liquid B	Gas produced
5 mL	5 mL	8 mL
10 mL	5 mL	8 mL
15 mL	5 mL	8 mL

Which liquid limited the amount of gas produced?
(Mark the one best answer.)

❍ **A** Liquid A

❍ **B** Liquid B

❍ **C** Neither liquid

5. Explain what happens to the particles in a solid block of gold as it melts.

____

____

____

____

Name ______________________________

SURVEY/POSTTEST

CHEMICAL INTERACTIONS

6. A student heated 25 mL of water from 10°C to 20°C. How much energy did she use to heat the water? Remember: $cal = m \times \Delta T$

   (Use the space below to show your math and your final answer.)

7. When water boils, bubbles rise up through the water. What is inside those bubbles? *(Mark the one best answer.)*

   ❍ **A** Air particles

   ❍ **B** Carbon dioxide particles

   ❍ **C** Water particles

   ❍ **D** Oxygen particles and hydrogen particles

8. Look at the list below and mark an **X** to indicate the following.

   a. Which are substances?

   b. Which are particles?

   c. Which are single elements?

   d. Which are compounds?

Chemical formula	a. Substance	b. Particle	c. Element	d. Compound
H_2O				
He				
$C_6H_8O_7$				
NaCl				
O_2				
CO_2				

Name ______________________

SURVEY/POSTTEST
CHEMICAL INTERACTIONS

9. Imagine that you remove all the particles that make up a wooden table. What remains?
(Mark the one best answer.)

   ❍ **A** A table that looks the same, but has less volume

   ❍ **B** A table that weighs less

   ❍ **C** Sawdust

   ❍ **D** Nothing

10. The diagram below shows a chemical reaction. The different-shaded circles represent different kinds of atoms. When circles are touching, that indicates that those atoms form a molecule.

   ◎◎ + ● + ● → ●◎ ●◎

   If this reaction occurs in a sealed chamber, what happens to the mass of the matter inside and why?
   (Mark the one best answer.)

   ❍ **A** The mass will stay the same because the number of each kind of atom stays the same.

   ❍ **B** The mass will decrease because two substances combine to form one substance.

   ❍ **C** The mass will increase because a new kind of molecule is formed.

   ❍ **D** More information is needed to tell if the mass will change.

11. Engineers use scientific discoveries to develop solutions to real-life problems. After they discover a good solution, should they consider their work done? Why or why not?

____

____

____

____

____

Name ______________________________

SURVEY/POSTTEST
CHEMICAL INTERACTIONS

12. The water and the air in this system are at equilibrium.

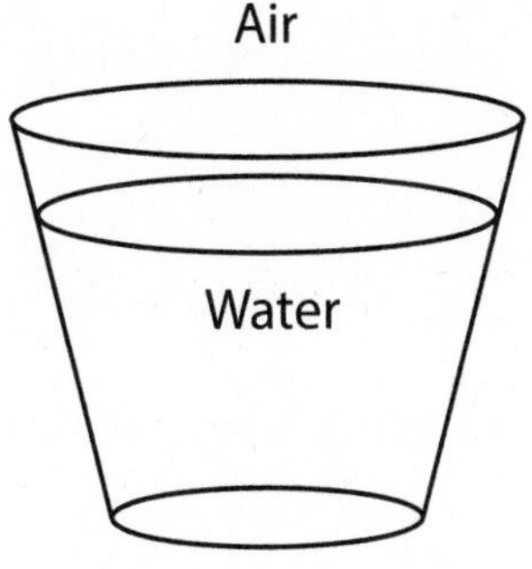

   a. Which particles have more average kinetic energy?
      (Mark the one best answer.)

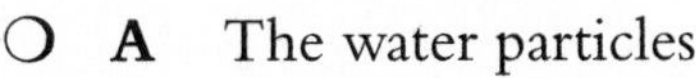

      ❍ **A** The water particles

      ❍ **B** The air particles

      ❍ **C** They have the same

      Why did you choose that answer?

      ____

      ____

   b. Describe the energy transfer between the water and the air.

      ____

      ____

13. How do particles of cold air differ from particles of hot air?
    *(Mark an **X** next to each correct answer.)*

    _____ The particles of cold air are closer together than the particles of hot air.

    _____ The particles of cold air have less mass than the particles of hot air.

    _____ The particles of cold air have less kinetic energy than the particles of hot air.

    _____ The particles of cold air are smaller than the particles of hot air.

    _____ The particles of cold air move slower than the particles of hot air.

    _____ The particles of cold air move at the same speed as the particles of hot air.

Name ____________________________

SURVEY/POSTTEST

CHEMICAL INTERACTIONS

14. Sugar can melt, and sugar can dissolve. Mark an **X** next to each statement that explains what happens at the particle level when melting or dissolving occurs.

_____ Sugar melts when its particles get soft enough to turn into liquid.

_____ Sugar melts when a liquid breaks particles away from the solid substance.

_____ Sugar melts when kinetic energy increases enough for the particles to move past one another.

_____ Sugar dissolves when a liquid breaks particles away from the solid substance.

_____ Sugar dissolves when its particles get soft enough to turn into liquid.

_____ Sugar dissolves when its particles are heated until the bonds holding them together as a solid break.

15. Solid water (ice) does not flow. Liquid water does flow because the particles of liquid water _____.

(Mark the one best answer.)

❍ **A** are not as hard as the particles of solid ice

❍ **B** weigh less than the particles of solid ice

❍ **C** are moving, but the particles of solid ice are not

❍ **D** can easily move past one another, but the particles of solid ice cannot

16. When a syringe is filled with air, you can compress the air by pushing the plunger down. If you fill the syringe with water, you cannot compress the water. The difference is because the water particles _____.

(Mark the one best answer.)

❍ **A** are packed less closely together than air particles

❍ **B** can't be pushed closer using only your hands like air particles can

❍ **C** can no longer move, but air particles can

❍ **D** don't shrink like air particles do when you squeeze the syringe

Name ______________________

INVESTIGATIONS 1–2 I-CHECK

CHEMICAL INTERACTIONS

Date ____________ Class __________

Instructions: Use the periodic table of the elements on page 3 to help you answer these questions.

1. What is the difference between the substances represented by the symbols Co and CO?

____

____

____

2. What elements are found in the following substances?

Substance	Chemical formula	Names of the elements
Water	H_2O	
Sodium chloride	NaCl	
Carbon dioxide	CO_2	

3. Which Venn diagram best represents the relationship between an element and a substance?

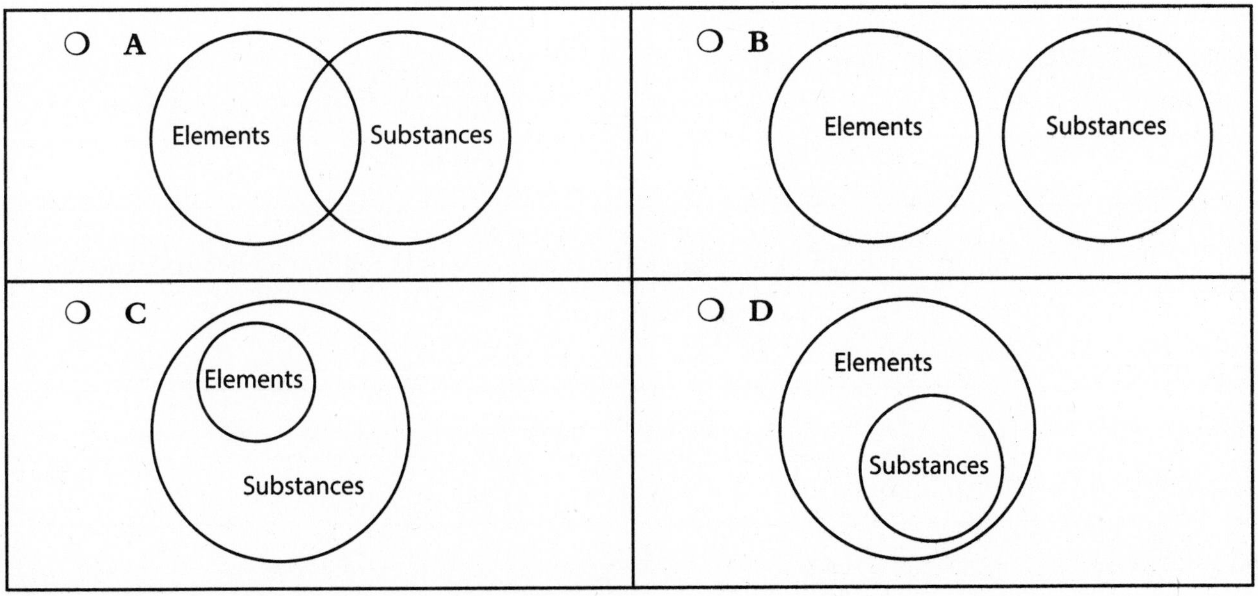

Name ______________________

INVESTIGATIONS 1–2 I-CHECK

CHEMICAL INTERACTIONS

4. What are three ways that substances can be identified or labeled?

____

____

5. a. What was Mendeleyev's purpose for reorganizing the periodic table? *(Mark the one best answer.)*

   ❍ **A** He wanted to fit all of the elements on one page instead of in a long line.

   ❍ **B** He wanted to put elements with similar characteristics in the same column.

   ❍ **C** He wanted to order the elements from the lightest to the heaviest.

   ❍ **D** He wanted to put all the metals on one side of the table and gases on the other.

   b. When Mendeleyev changed the layout, there were gaps (no known element fit in those places). How did the gaps help scientists look for undiscovered elements?

____

____

____

6. a. What is a chemical reaction?

____

____

   b. If you mix two substances together, what evidence would tell you a chemical reaction occurred? *(List as many examples as you can.)*

____

____

____

____

INVESTIGATIONS 1–2 I-CHECK
CHEMICAL INTERACTIONS

The Periodic Table of the Elements

1	2	3	4	5	6	7	8	9	10	11	12	13	14	15	16	17	18
1 **H** Hydrogen																	2 **He** Helium
3 **Li** Lithium	4 **Be** Beryllium											5 **B** Boron	6 **C** Carbon	7 **N** Nitrogen	8 **O** Oxygen	9 **F** Fluorine	10 **Ne** Neon
11 **Na** Sodium	12 **Mg** Magnesium											13 **Al** Aluminum	14 **Si** Silicon	15 **P** Phosphorus	16 **S** Sulfur	17 **Cl** Chlorine	18 **Ar** Argon
19 **K** Potassium	20 **Ca** Calcium	21 **Sc** Scandium	22 **Ti** Titanium	23 **V** Vanadium	24 **Cr** Chromium	25 **Mn** Manganese	26 **Fe** Iron	27 **Co** Cobalt	28 **Ni** Nickel	29 **Cu** Copper	30 **Zn** Zinc	31 **Ga** Gallium	32 **Ge** Germanium	33 **As** Arsenic	34 **Se** Selenium	35 **Br** Bromine	36 **Kr** Krypton
37 **Rb** Rubidium	38 **Sr** Strontium	39 **Y** Yttrium	40 **Zr** Zirconium	41 **Nb** Niobium	42 **Mo** Molybdenum	43 **Tc** Technetium	44 **Ru** Ruthenium	45 **Rh** Rhodium	46 **Pd** Palladium	47 **Ag** Silver	48 **Cd** Cadmium	49 **In** Indium	50 **Sn** Tin	51 **Sb** Antimony	52 **Te** Tellurium	53 **I** Iodine	54 **Xe** Xenon
55 **Cs** Cesium	56 **Ba** Barium	71 **Lu** Lutetium	72 **Hf** Hafnium	73 **Ta** Tantalum	74 **W** Tungsten	75 **Re** Rhenium	76 **Os** Osmium	77 **Ir** Iridium	78 **Pt** Platinum	79 **Au** Gold	80 **Hg** Mercury	81 **Tl** Thallium	82 **Pb** Lead	83 **Bi** Bismuth	84 **Po** Polonium	85 **At** Astatine	86 **Rn** Radon
87 **Fr** Francium	88 **Ra** Radium	103 **Lr** Lawrencium	104 **Rf** Rutherfordium	105 **Db** Dubnium	106 **Sg** Seaborgium	107 **Bh** Bohrium	108 **Hs** Hassium	109 **Mt** Meitnerium	110 **Ds** Darmstadtium	111 **Rg** Roentgenium	112 **Cn** Copernicium	113 **Nh** Nihonium	114 **Fl** Flerovium	115 **Mc** Moscovium	116 **Lv** Livermorium	117 **Ts** Tennessine	118 **Og** Oganesson

57 **La** Lanthanum	58 **Ce** Cerium	59 **Pr** Praseodymium	60 **Nd** Neodymium	61 **Pm** Promethium	62 **Sm** Samarium	63 **Eu** Europium	64 **Gd** Gadolinium	65 **Tb** Terbium	66 **Dy** Dysprosium	67 **Ho** Holmium	68 **Er** Erbium	69 **Tm** Thulium	70 **Yb** Ytterbium
89 **Ac** Actinium	90 **Th** Thorium	91 **Pa** Protactinium	92 **U** Uranium	93 **Np** Neptunium	94 **Pu** Plutonium	95 **Am** Americium	96 **Cm** Curium	97 **Bk** Berkelium	98 **Cf** Californium	99 **Es** Einsteinium	100 **Fm** Fermium	101 **Md** Mendelevium	102 **No** Nobelium

Name ____________________

INVESTIGATION 3 I-CHECK
CHEMICAL INTERACTIONS

Date ____________ Class __________

1. A student trapped air inside a syringe (illustration A). She pushed the plunger down (illustration B) and then pulled the plunger up (illustration C).

   a. Draw the air particles inside the syringes in illustrations B and C.

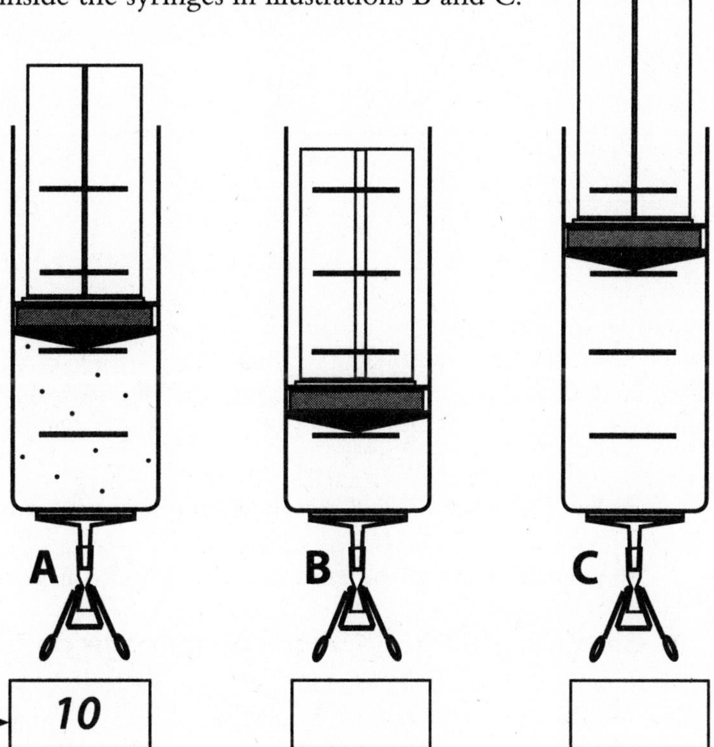

Record the number of particles in each syringe → | 10 | | |

   b. What happens to the particles when you push the plunger down (B)?

   ____

   ____

   c. What happens to the particles when you pull the plunger back up (C)?

   ____

   ____

   d. Between the air particles in each syringe is _____.
   (Mark the one best answer.)

   ❍ **A** Matter ❍ **B** More air

   ❍ **C** Space ❍ **D** Atoms

Name ______________________

INVESTIGATION 3 I-CHECK
CHEMICAL INTERACTIONS

2. a. What is between the helium particles in a helium-filled balloon?

____

b. Can helium be compressed? ________

Why or why not?

____

____

____

3. Mark an **X** next to each statement that describes the particles if a gas is placed in a sealed container.

_____ The particles are packed closely throughout the container.

_____ The particles are spread far apart throughout the container.

_____ Almost all of the particles are at the top of the container.

_____ Almost all of the particles are at the bottom of the container.

_____ All of the particles are spread evenly throughout the container.

4. Which of the following always results from a chemical reaction? *(Mark the one best answer.)*

❍ **A** Bubbles

❍ **B** Fire or smoke

❍ **C** Temperature change

❍ **D** A new substance

Name ____________________

INVESTIGATION 3 I-CHECK
CHEMICAL INTERACTIONS

5. a. What do we mean when we talk about a particle?

____

____

   b. Describe the motion of air particles inside a soccer ball.

____

____

____

6. A student was investigating air in a closed syringe. He compressed the air by pushing the plunger in as far as he could and then let go. The plunger returned to its original position.

   a. Why did the plunger return to its original position?
   (Mark the one best answer.)

   ❍ **A** The air particles outside the syringe pulled the plunger up.

   ❍ **B** The air particles inside the syringe pushed the plunger up.

   ❍ **C** More air particles rushed into the syringe and pushed the plunger up.

   ❍ **D** The air pushed the plunger up when it tried to get out.

   b. Explain why you chose that answer.

____

____

____

____

____

Name ______________________

Date ____________ Class __________

INVESTIGATION 4 I-CHECK
CHEMICAL INTERACTIONS

1. A student put room-temperature water into a bottle. She pushed a stopper and tube into the bottle until the water came halfway up the tube.

   The student turned the bottle system sideways and put a cold wrap around the bottle for 2 minutes. She then put a hot wrap around the bottle.

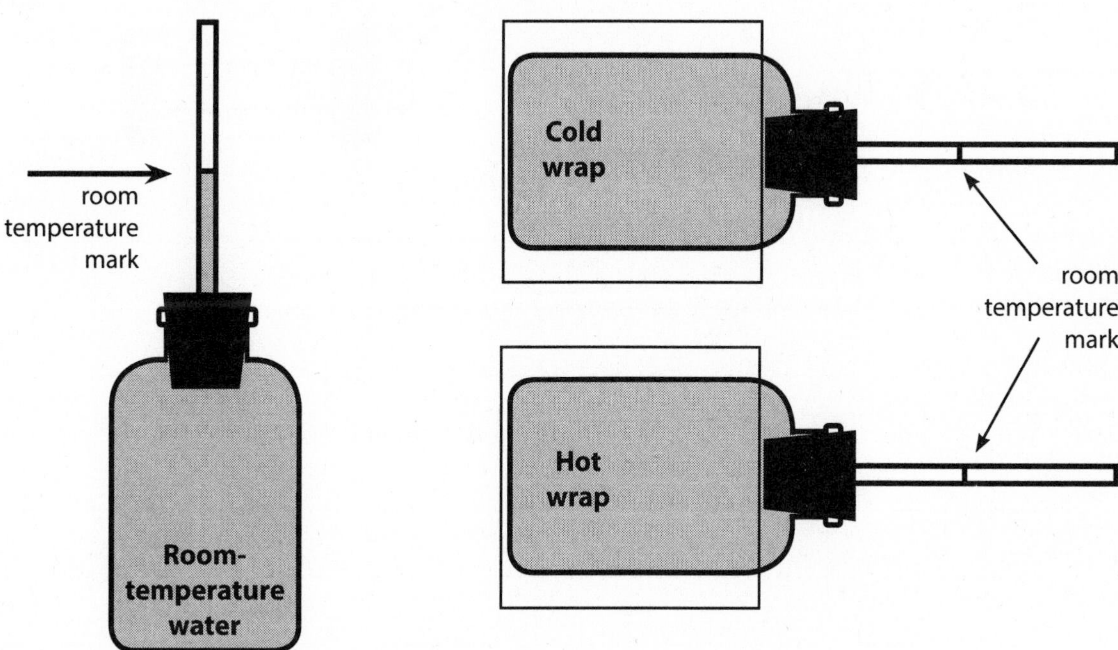

   a. Draw the water level in the tube with the cold wrap and with the hot wrap.

   b. What happened to the kinetic energy of the water particles when the student put the hot wrap on the cold bottle?
   (Mark the one best answer.)

   ❍ **A** The kinetic energy of the water particles increased.

   ❍ **B** The kinetic energy of the water particles decreased.

   ❍ **C** There was no change in the kinetic energy of the water particles.

   c. What caused the water level in the tube to change when the student put the hot wrap on the bottle?

   ____

   ____

   ____

Name ____________________

INVESTIGATION 4 I-CHECK
CHEMICAL INTERACTIONS

2. An aluminum nut and bolt are stuck together.

   a. To get them apart, would you put ice on the nut or on the bolt?
   (Mark the one best answer.)

   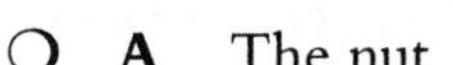
   ❍ **A** The nut

   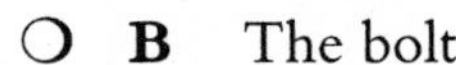
   ❍ **B** The bolt

   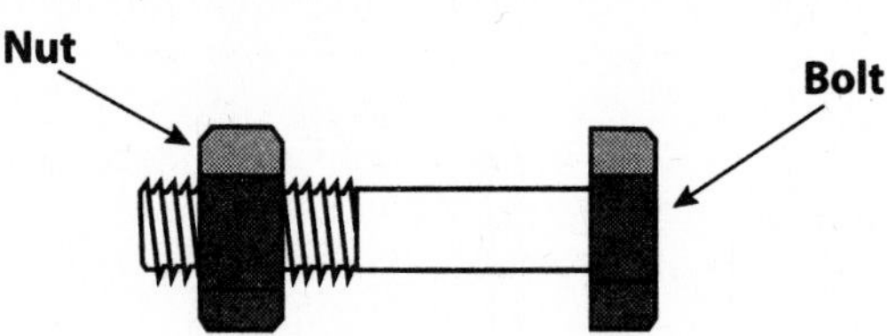

   Why did you choose that answer?

   ____

   ____

   ____

   b. What role does kinetic energy play in getting the nut and bolt apart?

   ____

   ____

   ____

   ____

3. What happens to the particles in a cup of cold juice as it warms up to room temperature?
   (Mark the one best answer.)

   ❍ **A** The number of juice particles decreases.

   ❍ **B** The size of the juice particles increases.

   ❍ **C** The motion of the juice particles decreases.

   ❍ **D** The space between the juice particles increases.

Name ___________________________

INVESTIGATION 4 I-CHECK
CHEMICAL INTERACTIONS

4. A student put a cap on a bottle, trapping room-temperature air inside. He put the bottle in the freezer for 15 minutes, then took it out and saw that the bottle looked different. What caused the bottle to change shape?
(Mark the one best answer.)

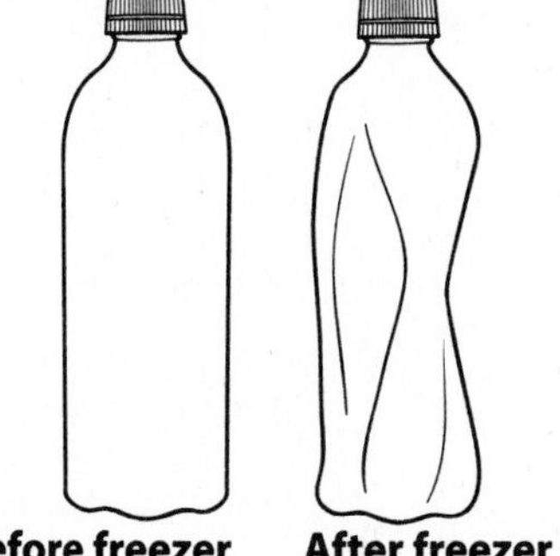

❍ **A** Some of the air particles got out of the bottle.

❍ **B** The air particles in the bottle got closer together.

❍ **C** The air particles settled to the bottom of the bottle.

❍ **D** The air particles cooled and became smaller.

5. Compare the particles in a sample of liquid water and the particles in a sample of solid water (ice).
(Mark the one best answer.)

❍ **A** Particles in the liquid are smaller than the particles in the solid.

❍ **B** Particles in the liquid move past each other, and particles in the solid cannot.

❍ **C** Particles in the liquid are less firm than particles in the solid.

❍ **D** Particles in the liquid are moving, and the particles in the solid are not moving.

6. When a piece of solid lead is heated (but not melted), the lead particles _____.
(Mark all that apply.)

_____ move slower

_____ get farther apart

_____ have fewer collisions

_____ get closer together

_____ bump into each other more

Name ____________________

INVESTIGATION 4 I-CHECK
CHEMICAL INTERACTIONS

7. a. What is the difference between compression and contraction?

____

____

____

____

b. Give an example of compression.

____

Give an example of contraction.

____

8. In what phase of matter are the particles spaced farthest apart?
(Mark the one best answer.)

❍ **A** A gas

❍ **B** A liquid

❍ **C** A solid

❍ **D** All are equal

9. A jeweler heats a silver strip and bends it into a bracelet. The bracelet cools down when the jeweler is finished. What happens to the kinetic energy of the silver particles as the solid silver cools? The kinetic energy of the particles _____.
(Mark the one best answer.)

❍ **A** increases

❍ **B** decreases until the particles stop moving

❍ **C** decreases, but the particles still move

❍ **D** does not change

Name ______________________

Date ____________ Class __________

INVESTIGATION 5 I-CHECK
CHEMICAL INTERACTIONS

1. A student put a vial of plain water into a container of ice. She put the container into a freezer. The starting temperatures are listed below.

   - Water in the vial 22°C
   - Ice 0°C
   - Freezer environment −17°C

   In the diagram, draw arrows in the blank boxes to show the direction of energy transfer between

   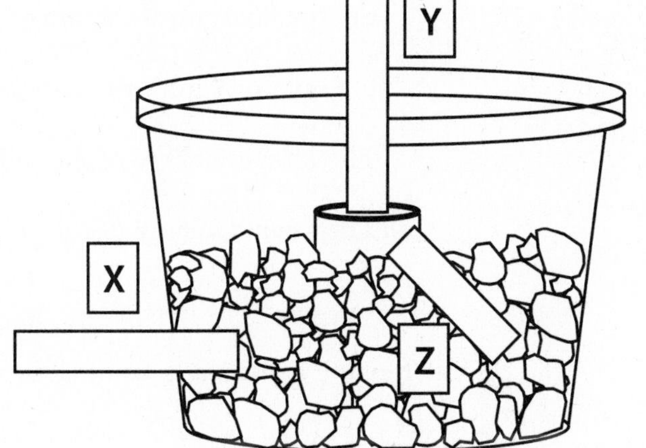

   - the freezer and the ice (X)

   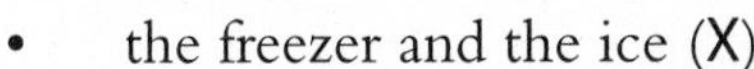

   - the freezer and the water in the vial (Y)
   - the ice and the water in the vial (Z)

2. A closed container of water is kept at a constant temperature. Which of the following statements about the water particles is true?
   (Mark the one best answer.)

   ❍ **A** The average kinetic energy of the water particles stays the same.

   ❍ **B** The average kinetic energy of the water particles increases a little bit.

   ❍ **C** The average kinetic energy of the water particles decreases a little bit.

   ❍ **D** The water particles stop moving.

3. A plastic bottle filled with warm air is placed into cold water.

   The temperature of the air gets ______________________________.

   The temperature of the water gets ______________________________.

   Describe the energy transfer between the air particles and the water particles.

   ____

   ____

   ____

Name ______________________

INVESTIGATION 5 I-CHECK
CHEMICAL INTERACTIONS

4. What happens when cold milk is poured into hot chocolate?
(Mark an **X** *next to each correct answer.)*

_____ Energy flows from the milk to the chocolate.

_____ Energy flows from the chocolate to the milk.

_____ The kinetic energy of the milk increases.

_____ The kinetic energy of the chocolate increases.

5. A fast-moving particle (A) and a slow-moving particle (B) collide.

a. Which particle has more kinetic energy before the collision?
(Mark the one best answer.)

❍ **A** Particle A

❍ **B** Particle B

❍ **C** A and B have the same kinetic energy.

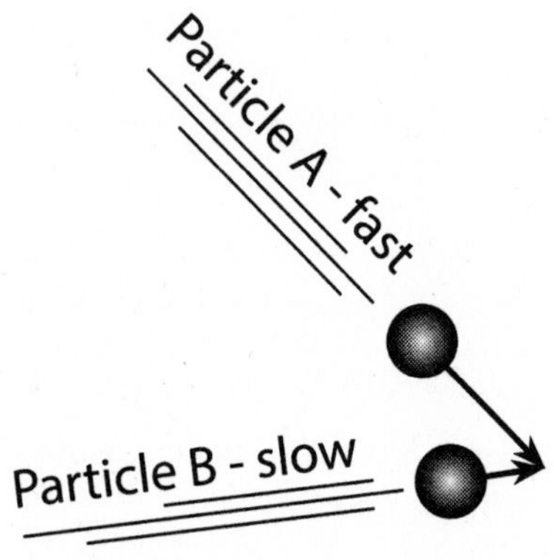

b. What happens to the kinetic energy when the particles collide?

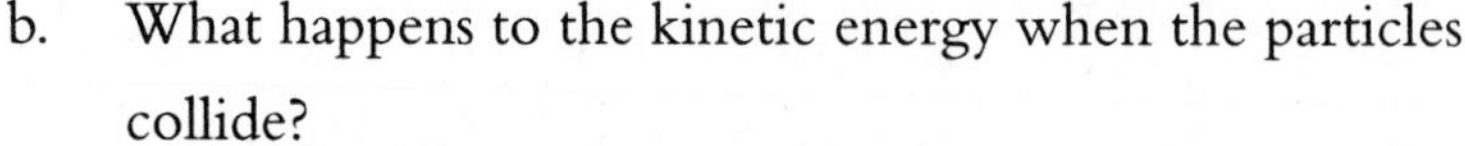

❍ **A** Energy transfers to particle A.

❍ **B** Energy transfers to particle B.

❍ **C** Energy transfers to both particles.

c. Describe the change in speed of each particle after the collision.

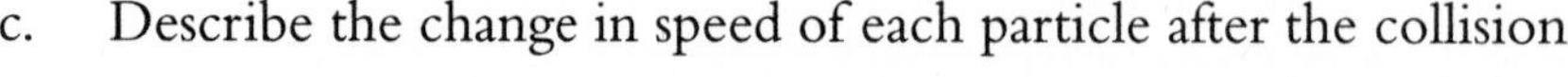

____

____

____

____

Name ______________________________

INVESTIGATION 5 I-CHECK
CHEMICAL INTERACTIONS

6. A baker has two identical cakes except that one cake is hot, and the other cake is room temperature. He places both cakes on a cold plate. What happens?
(Mark the one best answer.)

❍ **A** Only the hot cake transfers energy to the plate.

❍ **B** The plate transfers energy to the room-temperature cake.

❍ **C** Both cakes transfer energy to the plate.

❍ **D** Neither cake transfers energy to the plate.

Why did you choose that answer?

____

____

____

____

7. A student heated 50 mL of water from 0°C to 60°C. How much energy did she use to heat the water? Remember: $cal = m \times \Delta T$
(Use the space below to show your math and your final answer.)

Name ______________________

INVESTIGATION 5 I-CHECK
CHEMICAL INTERACTIONS

8. Things heat up and cool down as a result of energy transfer. Energy flows _____.
   (Mark the one best answer.)

   ❍ **A** from hot materials to cold materials

   ❍ **B** from cold materials to hot materials

   ❍ **C** in both directions

   ❍ **D** only until equilibrium is reached

9. The iron and water in this system are at the same temperature.

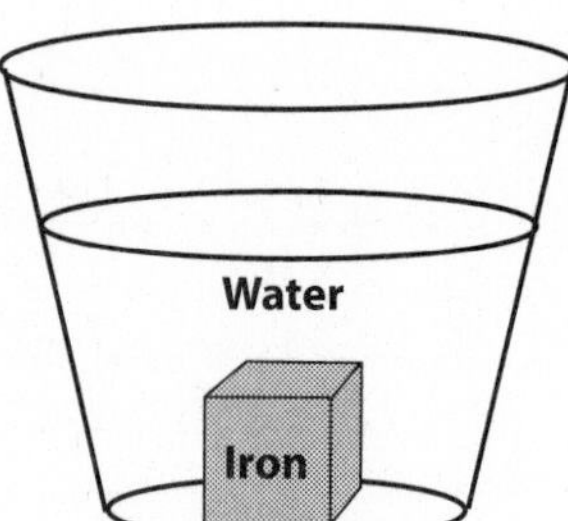

   a. Which particles have more average kinetic energy?
   (Mark the one best answer.)

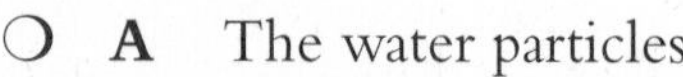

   ❍ **A** The water particles

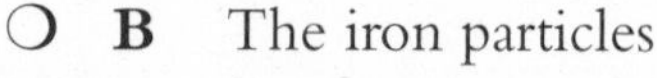

   ❍ **B** The iron particles

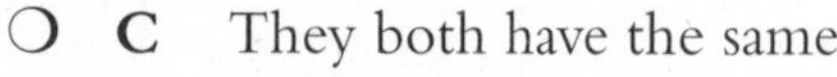

   ❍ **C** They both have the same

   Why did you choose that answer?

   ____

   ____

   ____

   b. Describe the energy transfer between the water and the iron.

   ____

   ____

   ____

Name ______________________

INVESTIGATIONS 7–8 I-CHECK

CHEMICAL INTERACTIONS

Date ____________ Class __________

1. The melting/freezing point of mercury is –39°C. A scientist put liquid mercury into a freezer that is kept at a constant temperature of –35°C.

   Will the liquid mercury freeze? __________

   Why or why not?

   ____

   ____

   ____

   ____

2. What is between the water particles in a glass of pure water?

   ____

   ____

   ____

3. When a substance changes from a liquid to a solid, which of the following is true? *(Mark an **X** next to each true statement.)*

   _____ The particles change shape.

   _____ The particles change from soft to hard.

   _____ The particles are held more strongly to one another.

   _____ The particles have more kinetic energy.

   _____ The particles have less kinetic energy.

   _____ The substance is freezing.

   _____ The substance is melting.

Name ______________________

INVESTIGATIONS 7–8 I-CHECK
CHEMICAL INTERACTIONS

4. Some people confuse what happens during melting and dissolving.

   a. How would you explain what happens to the particles during each process to someone who is confused?

   ____

   ____

   ____

   ____

   ____

   b. How would you explain the role of kinetic energy in each process?

   ____

   ____

   ____

   ____

   ____

   ____

5. You wash a T-shirt. You hang the wet T-shirt on a clothesline. A few hours later, the T-shirt is dry. Mark an **X** next to each statement that explains what happens to the water particles after you hang the shirt up.

   _____ The water particles are absorbed by the T-shirt.

   _____ The water particles evaporate into the air.

   _____ The water particles disappear and no longer exist.

   _____ The water particles melt into the T-shirt.

   _____ The water particles moved faster and become part of the air.

   _____ The water particles break down to hydrogen and oxygen particles and move into the air.

Name ______________________

INVESTIGATIONS 7–8 I-CHECK
CHEMICAL INTERACTIONS

6. Explain what happens to the particles in liquid water when it changes to ice.

____

____

____

7. A student dissolved 20 g of salt in a cup of water. She left the cup uncovered in an area where nobody could touch it. When she returned to the cup 10 days later, she found that all the water was gone, and there were crystals in the bottom of the cup. What is the best conclusion, based on her observations?
(Mark the one best answer.)

   ❍ **A** The water evaporated, and there is 20 g of salt in the cup.

   ❍ **B** The water and some salt evaporated, but some salt is left in the cup.

   ❍ **C** There was a chemical reaction, and a precipitate was left behind.

   ❍ **D** The water and salt separated and then the water evaporated, but there is no way to know what is left in the cup.

8. There are three vials of the same substance in the diagram: one solid, one liquid, and one gas.

   In the four boxes above and below the arrows, write the name of the process that results in the phase change.

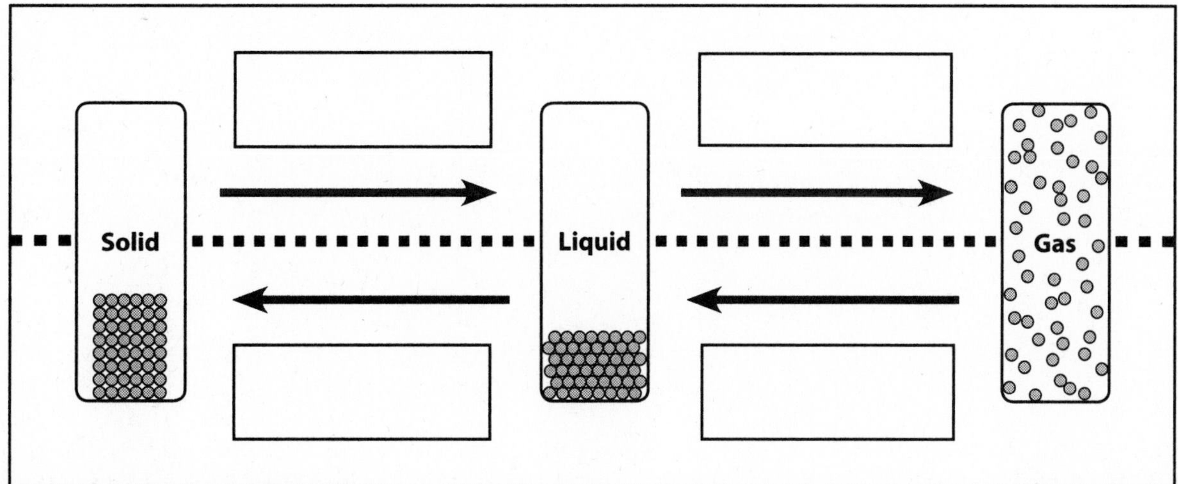

Name ____________________

INVESTIGATION 9 I-CHECK
CHEMICAL INTERACTIONS

Date ____________ Class ____________

1. What holds the atoms together in molecules and compounds?
   (Mark the one best answer.)

   ❍ **A** Glue

   ❍ **B** Freezing

   ❍ **C** Bonds

   ❍ **D** Magnetism

2. Below are the models for four common substances. In the columns, write

   a. the chemical formula.

   b. the total number of atoms present.

   c. the total number of elements present.

   d. the name of each element present.

Model	a. Chemical formula	b. Number of atoms	c. Number of elements	d. Element names
Cl Ca Cl				
O / H Na C O / O				
O C O				
O / Ca C O / O				

Name ______________________

INVESTIGATION 9 I-CHECK
CHEMICAL INTERACTIONS

3. Which of the following statements about atoms are true?
   (Mark an **X** *next to each correct answer.)*

   _____ Atoms are not matter.

   _____ Atoms are inside matter.

   _____ Atoms make up only living things.

   _____ Atoms make up only nonliving things.

   _____ Atoms make up all matter.

4. The chemical formula for tin chloride is $SnCl_4$.

   a. Mark the model you think represents tin chloride. *(Mark the one best answer.)*

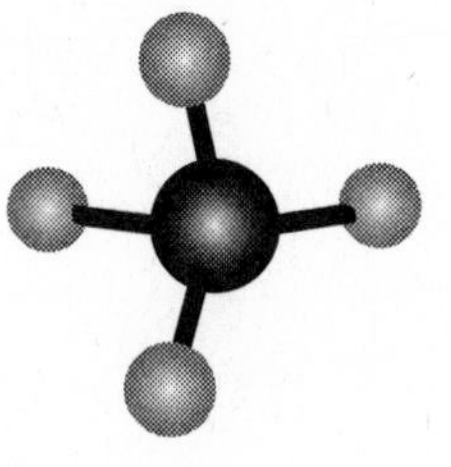

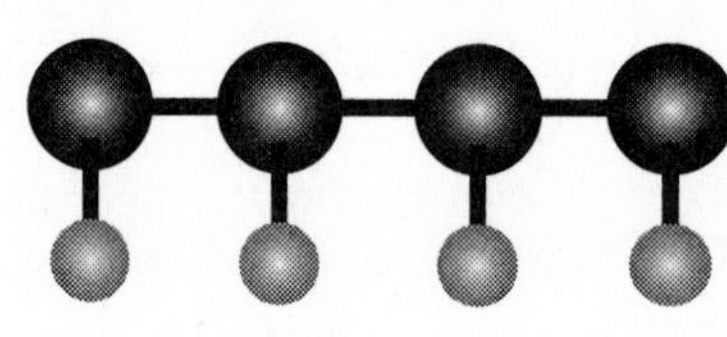

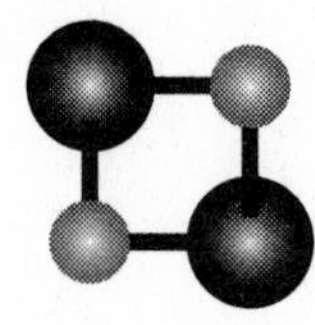

❍ A ❍ B ❍ C

   b. Why did you select that model?

   ____

   ____

   ____

5. What happens to the atoms in substances when a chemical reaction occurs?

   ____

   ____

   ____

Name ____________________________

INVESTIGATION 9 I-CHECK
CHEMICAL INTERACTIONS

6. Which of the following are examples of a chemical reaction?
   (Mark an **X** *next to each correct answer.)*

   _____ Sugar turning black when heated over a fire

   _____ Water evaporating from a pot on a hot stove

   _____ A snowman melting into a puddle of water

   _____ The surface of a penny changing color after many years

   _____ Melted butter becoming a solid when placed in the refrigerator

   _____ A white substance left behind after water evaporates from a solution

   _____ A spoonful of sugar dissolving in a glass of water

   _____ Bubbles forming when substances are mixed together

7. a. The reaction below is shown with atomic models. Write the chemical equation on the line below the model.

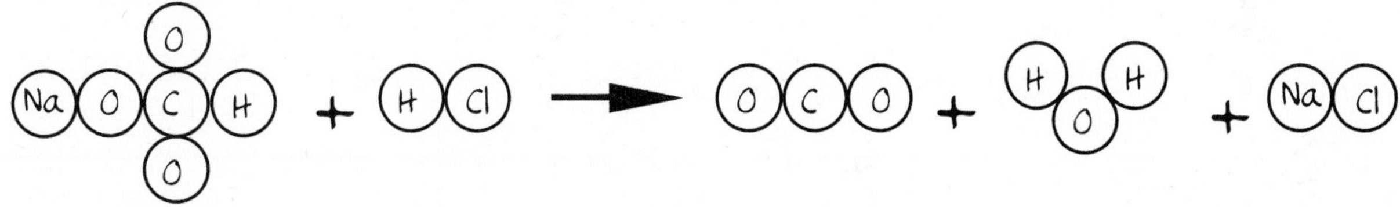

____

   b. The reaction below is shown using a chemical equation. Draw the atomic model that describes the equation.

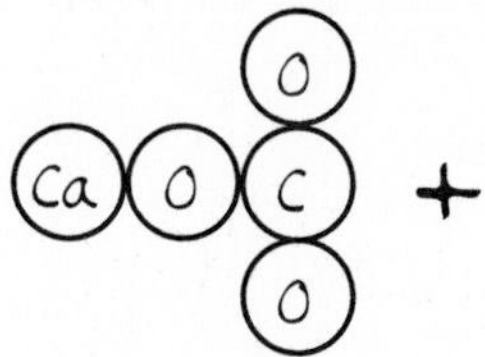

$$CaCO_3 + 2\,HCl \rightarrow CO_2 + H_2O + CaCl_2$$

Name ______________________

INVESTIGATION 9 I-CHECK
CHEMICAL INTERACTIONS

8. A student dropped an eggshell into hydrochloric acid (HCl). An eggshell is made of calcium carbonate ($CaCO_3$). Bubbles formed on the shell.

   a. What gas was in the bubbles?
   (Mark the one best answer.)

   ❍ **A** $CaCl_2$

   ❍ **B** O_2

   ❍ **C** CO_2

   ❍ **D** H_2

   b. Write the chemical equation that supports your choice.

   c. What test could you perform to confirm your prediction?

   ____

   ____

   ____

   ____

9. The different-shaded circles represent different kinds of atoms. When circles are touching, they indicate that those atoms form a molecule. Which of the following could accurately represent a chemical reaction?
(Mark the one best answer.)

   ❍ **A** ●● + ○○ → ◍◍ + ◍◍

   ❍ **B** ●● + ○○ → ◍◍◍◍

   ❍ **C** ●● + ○○ → ○○ + ●●

   ❍ **D** ●● + ○○ → ○●
○●

Name ______________________________

INVESTIGATION 9 I-CHECK

CHEMICAL INTERACTIONS

10. A scientist prepares a chamber where a chemical reaction can take place and no matter can escape. During the reaction, bubbles form. What will happen to the mass of the materials in the container?

    (Mark the one best answer.)

    ❍ **A** The mass will increase.

    ❍ **B** The mass will decrease.

    ❍ **C** The mass will stay the same.

    ❍ **D** It will depend on what the chemical reaction was.

11. When a thermometer is heated, the volume of the liquid inside of the thermometer increases, and the level of the liquid rises. As the volume increases, what happens to the mass of the liquid in the thermometer?

    (Mark the one best answer.)

    ❍ **A** The mass increases.

    ❍ **B** The mass decreases.

    ❍ **C** The mass stays the same.

    ❍ **D** The change in mass depends on the type of liquid.

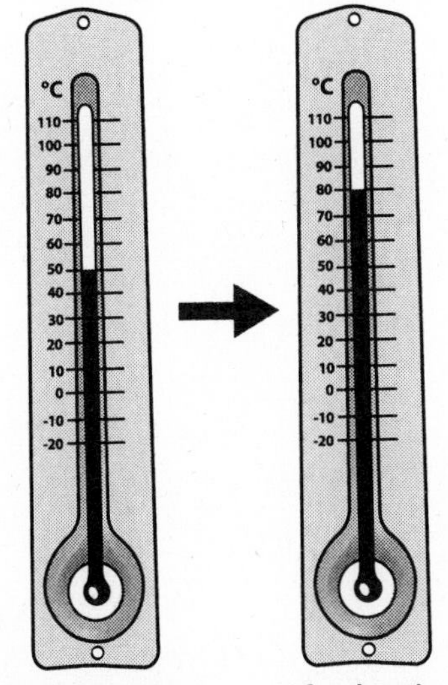

Notebook Answers

Mystery Mixture

WARNING — This set contains chemicals that may be harmful if misused. Read cautions on individual containers carefully. Not to be used by children except under adult supervision.

Part 1. Observe the unknown mixture.

1. Put on your safety goggles.
2. Put one 5 mL spoon of the mystery mixture into a cup.
3. Observe the mixture. (Do not touch or taste the mixture.)
4. Record your observations.

Answers will vary but should include white substance, powdery, two different sizes of particles, some crystals.

Part 2. Add water.

1. Add one pipette of water to the mystery mixture in the cup. Do not use the pipette to stir the mixture.
2. Observe. Take turns putting additional pipettes of water into the cup. Observe after each pipette of water.
3. Record your observations.

Answers will vary, but may include bubbling, fizzing, cup gets cold on bottom, stop fizzing after a few pipettes of water, clear liquid.

This page is intentionally left blank.

FOSS Chemical Interactions Course, Second Edition
© The Regents of the University of California
Can be duplicated for classroom or workshop use.

Mystery-Mixture Summary B

WARNING — This set contains chemicals that may be harmful if misused. Read cautions on individual containers carefully. Not to be used by children except under adult supervision.

Well	Substances	Description of fizzing	Other observations	Large-scale observations
6	Citric acid + sodium bicarbonate $C_6H_8O_7 + NaHCO_3$			
7	Citric acid + sodium carbonate $C_6H_8O_7 + Na_2CO_3$			
8	Mystery mixture			

Answers will vary.

Identify the two substances in the mystery mixture and explain how you identified them.

Mystery-Mixture Summary A

WARNING — This set contains chemicals that may be harmful if misused. Read cautions on individual containers carefully. Not to be used by children except under adult supervision.

Well	Substances	Description of fizzing	Other observations	Large-scale observations
1	Ascorbic acid + calcium carbonate $C_6H_8O_6 + CaCO_3$			
2	Ascorbic acid + sodium bicarbonate $C_6H_8O_6 + NaHCO_3$			
3	Ascorbic acid + sodium carbonate $C_6H_8O_6 + Na_2CO_3$			
4	Calcium chloride + sodium bicarbonate $CaCl_2 + NaHCO_3$			
5	Citric acid + calcium carbonate $C_6H_8O_7 + CaCO_3$			

Answers will vary.

Mystery-Mixture Elements

Chemical name	Chemical formula	Elements
Calcium carbonate	$CaCO_3$	Calcium, carbon, oxygen
Sodium carbonate	Na_2CO_3	Sodium, carbon, oxygen
Sodium bicarbonate	$NaHCO_3$	Sodium, hydrogen, carbon, oxygen
Magnesium sulfate	$MgSO_4$	Magnesium, sulfur, oxygen
Calcium chloride	$CaCl_2$	Calcium, chlorine
Sodium chloride	NaCl	Sodium, chlorine
Ascorbic acid	$C_6H_8O_6$	Carbon, hydrogen, oxygen
Citric acid	$C_6H_8O_7$	Carbon, hydrogen, oxygen
Sucrose	$C_{12}H_{22}O_{11}$	Carbon, hydrogen, oxygen

Mystery-Mixture Element Questions

1. Which substance has the greatest number of elements?

   $NaHCO_3$ –Four elements.

2. Altogether, how many different elements are in the nine substances?

   8

3. Which element is found in the greatest number of substances?

   Oxygen

4. How many elements are in the substance carbon dioxide (CO_2)?

   2 (carbon and oxygen)

5. How many elements are in the substance water (H_2O)?

   2 (hydrogen and oxygen)

6. Which of the nine substances are made of two elements?

   NaCl (sodium chloride)

   CaCl (calcium chloride)

7. Which of the nine substances are made of three elements?

   $CaCO_3$ (calcium carbonate), Na_2CO_3 (sodium carbonate), $MgSO_4$ (magnesium sulfate), $C_6H_8O_6$ (citric acid), $C_{12}H_{22}O_{11}$ (sucrose)

8. Which of the nine substances are made of four elements?

   $NaHCO_3$ (sodium bicarbonate)

FOSS Chemical Interactions Course, Second Edition

Elements in Products

Part 1. List the elements found in several products.

Product	Elements
Answers will vary.	

Part 2. Analyze the elements in the products.

1. How many different elements did you find in all the products you investigated?

   Answers will vary.

2. What is the most common element in the products you investigated?

   Answers will vary.

3. How many metals did you find in the product you investigated? List them. Answers will vary.

Response Sheet—Investigation 2

A student studied the ingredients on a box of cereal. She made a list of the elements she found. She told her friend,

This cereal contains eight different elements. I wonder what the rest of the cereal is made of.

If you were the student's friend, what would you tell her?

All matter is made only of elements. Elements are not sprinkled into substances like raisins in cookies. Products list some of the elements that make up the products. The rest of the matter in the product is made of elements, too. No common matter is made of anything besides elements.

WARNING — This set contains chemicals that may be harmful if misused. Read cautions on individual containers carefully. Not to be used by children except under adult supervision.

How Much Gas?

Challenge. Determine how much gas is produced in a citric acid and sodium bicarbonate reaction. Answers will vary.

Record results.

Volume of gas produced (mL)			
Trial 1	**Trial 2**	**Trial 3**	**Average**

My group's average volume of gas Answers will vary.

Class average volume of gas Answers will vary.

Answer the questions on the next page in your notebook.

1. What happened to the syringe plunger during the reaction between citric acid and sodium bicarbonate?
2. What caused that to happen?
3. Why is a syringe more useful than a balloon to conduct this experiment?
4. What errors might have occurred while gathering data?
5. What do you think might happen if you doubled the amount of either the citric acid solution or the sodium bicarbonate powder? Why do you think so?

How Much Gas?

1. The reaction produced a gas. The gas takes up space, so it pushed up the plunger to create the space it needed.
2. The syringe is marked off in milliliters (cubic centimeters). Using the syringe tells you how much gas forms. That way you can compare different reactions.
3. Answers will vary. In fact, the amount of gas will double.
4. Answers will vary. There was still sodium bicarbonate in the bottom of the bottle. The acid was used up before the soda.
5. Answers will vary. No change—same amount of gas.

   Answers will vary. There was still sodium bicarbonate in the bottom of the bottle. More soda on top of unused soda will not produce more reaction.

FOSS Chemical Interactions Course, Second Edition
© The Regents of the University of California
Can be duplicated for classroom or workshop use.
Investigation 3: Particles
No. 12—Notebook Master

What's in the Bubbles?

1. Make a list of the gases you know about or have heard about.
   Answers will vary.

2. How would you define *gas*?
   Matter composed of particles that fly through space independently. Gas has no definite shape or volume.

3. Everything is made of elements. What elements could be in the gas that forms when sodium bicarbonate ($NaHCO_3$) and citric acid ($C_6H_8O_7$) react?
   Possibly sodium, hydrogen, carbon, and oxygen.

4. What gas do you think is in the bubbles that form when $NaHCO_3$ and $C_6H_8O_7$ react?
   carbon dioxide (CO_2)

Discuss Air as Particles

1. What is the air in the syringe and the air in the bubble made of?
   air particles, mostly nitrogen and oxygen

2. What happens to the air particles in the syringe when you push on the plunger?
   Air particles get forced closer together; they are compressed into a smaller volume.

3. What happens to the air particles in the bubble when you pull up on the plunger?
   Pulling creates a larger volume. Air particles expand to fill the larger volume.

4. Are there more air particles in the bubble when it is compressed or when it is expanded?
   The syringe is a closed system, so the number of particles does not change.

5. When you push on the plunger, are the air particles closer together in the syringe or in the bubble?
   closer together in both subsystems, but equally close together in both

6. What is between air particles?
   space; distance; vacuum; void; nothing (except possibly other air particles)

7. What happens to air particles when a volume of air is compressed?
   Nothing happens to the particles themselves; they just get closer together.

   When a volume of air expands?
   Nothing happens to the particles themselves; they just get farther apart.

Air in a Syringe A

A student had a syringe barrel. She drew a picture (A) of her idea of how air filled the room and the syringe.

She put the plunger into the barrel (B) and then clamped the syringe shut (C).

She pushed the plunger down (D) and pulled the plunger up (E).

Draw air particles in syringes B–E.

Particles are represented in rows for easy counting. Students need not put them in rows. The number (20) and the distribution (uniform density) are important.

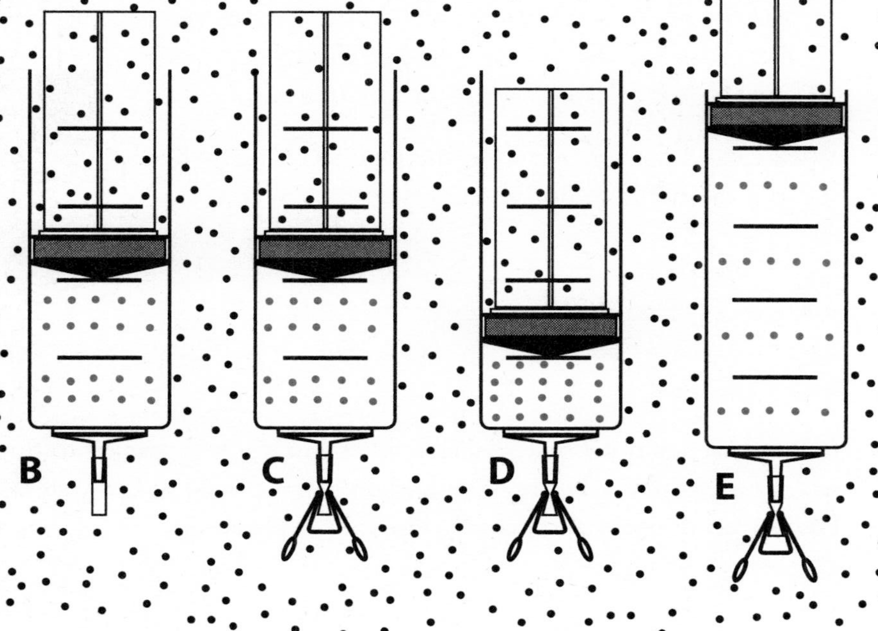

Air in a Syringe B

1. Why did you draw the particles in syringe B the way you did?

Nothing changed to change the number of particles in a given volume (space). The number of particles in half a syringe was 20 at the start, and still is. They fill the space evenly.

2. Why did you draw the particles in syringe C the way you did?

The syringe was clamped shut, but nothing changed to change the number of particles in a given volume (space). The number of particles in half a syringe was 20 at the start, and still is. They fill the space evenly.

3. Why did you draw the particles in syringe D the way you did?

The volume was reduced in half. The 20 particles had no place to go, so they were compressed into the smaller space (pushed closer together). They fill the space evenly.

4. Why did you draw the particles in syringe E the way you did?

The volume was doubled. The 20 particles expanded to fill the space. The particles are farther apart, but still fill the space evenly.

5. What happens to the air particles when air expands?

Nothing happens to the particles; they just fly farther apart.

6. What happens to the air particles when air is compressed?

Nothing happens to the particles; they just get pushed closer together.

Heating and Cooling Air

Investigation Question

What happens to a volume of air when it is heated? When it is cooled?

When air is heated, the mass of air increases in volume, or expands. When air is cooled, the mass of air decreases in volume, or contracts.

Part 1

Work with the materials to explore what happens to the air when it is heated and when it is cooled.

Part 2

Choose one demonstration to show fourth graders. Draw and label your setup.

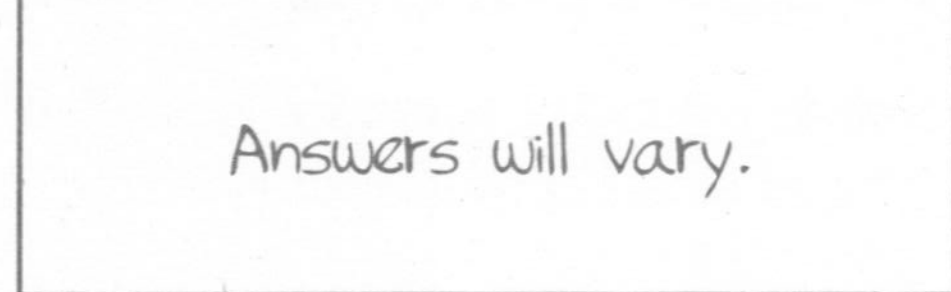

Part 3

In your science notebook, describe what happens to air when it gets hot and when it gets cold. Use drawings and labels to help you explain. Make sure it can be understood by fourth graders. Use the words *expand*, *expansion*, *contract*, and *contraction* in your explanation.

Heating and Cooling Water

Think about the bottle system

1. What happened when you placed your bottle system in cold water?
   Draw and explain. Water in the bottle cooled and contracted. It took up less volume, so the water moved down in the pipe.

2. What happened when you placed your bottle system in hot water?
   Draw and explain. Water in the bottle warmed and expanded. It took up more volume, so the water moved up higher in the pipe.

3. What caused the water level in the pipe to change when you put the bottle in cold water? Water cooled down and contracted. When water contracts, its volume decreases. When the volume of the water in the bottle system decreases, the water is pulled farther down the clear pipe.

4. What caused the water level in the pipe to change when you put the bottle in hot water? When water heated up, the kinetic energy of the water particles increased. More kinetic energy resulted in more and harder collisions between particles. Harder hitting pushed the water particles farther apart, causing the volume of the water to increase, or expand, and push up the pipe.

5. In your science notebook, describe what you think happened to the water *particles* in the bottle system when it was placed in hot water. Discuss *kinetic energy* and *expansion* in your explanation.

Response Sheet—Investigation 4

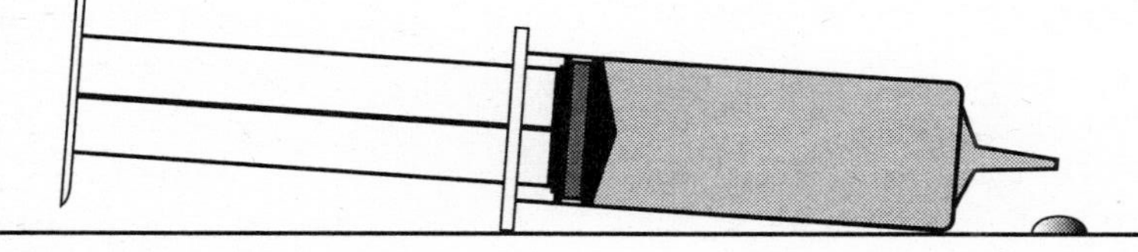

A student filled a syringe with water and left it by the sink in the sunshine. Ten minutes later she saw a little puddle of water under the syringe tip. She said,

This syringe must be broken. It's leaking.

But the syringe wasn't broken.

What do you think caused the little puddle of water to appear under the syringe tip?

NOTE: Use the words *particle* and *kinetic energy* in your explanation.

The water was warmed by the sunshine. The heat increased the kinetic energy of the water particles in the syringe. The particles pushed on one another harder, pushing them farther apart. The volume of water increased (expanded), causing the drop of water to be pushed out of the syringe.

Mixing Water

Question

If you mixed 50 mL of 50°C hot water and 50 mL of 10°C cold water, what do you think the temperature of the mixture would be?

Prediction

Predict the temperature of the sample mixture. Answers will vary.

Reasoning

Explain the thinking behind your prediction. Answers will vary.

Procedure

Describe an experiment you can conduct to check your prediction.

Answers will vary.

Data

We mixed ______ mL of hot water and _______ mL of cold water.

Make a prediction based on the initial temperatures immediately before mixing the two water samples.

T_{hot} (°C)	T_{cold} (°C)	Prediction (°C)	T_{final} (°C)

Write the equation for calculating final temperature when equal volumes of water are mixed.

$$T_f = \frac{T_1 + T_2}{2}$$

Response Sheet—Investigation 5

A student said,

When you put a bottle of juice in a cooler full of ice, the juice gets cold. That's because cold transfers to the juice and slows down the kinetic energy of the juice particles.

Comment on the student's ideas and give your explanation for why the juice gets cold.

No, there is no such thing as cold. Heat from the juice transfers to the ice in the cooler. First the particles of the bottle in contact with the ice transfer energy to the ice particles. Then the particles of juice collide with the bottle particles, and energy transfers from the warm juice to the bottle particles. The kinetic energy of the juice particles decreases, and the juice gets cold.

Calculating Energy Transfer in Calories A

Heat is measured in **calories** (cal). The calorie is the unit of heat in the metric system.

One calorie is the amount of heat needed to raise the temperature of 1 g of water 1°C. For instance, it takes 1 cal of heat to raise the temperature of 1 g of water from 25°C to 26°C.

1. Calculate the number of calories needed in each situation. Use the space below the table to write your work if necessary.

	Heat (cal)
a. Raise the temperature of 1 g of water 1°C.	1
b. Raise the temperature of 2 g of water 1°C.	2
c. Raise the temperature of 2 g of water 2°C.	4
d. Raise the temperature of 10 g of water 1°C.	10
e. Raise the temperature of 1 g of water 70°C.	70
f. Raise the temperature of 100 g of water 5°C.	500
g. Raise the temperature of 450 g of water 3°C.	1350
h. Raise the temperature of 16 g of water 62°C.	992

2. What is the equation for calculating the amount of heat needed to heat up or cool down a mass of water?

$$cal = m \times \Delta T$$

Calculating Energy Transfer in Calories B

3. A student mixed 40 g of 60°C water with 60 g of 25°C water. The final temperature was 39°C.

   a. Calculate the change of temperature (ΔT) for the hot water.
   $\boldsymbol{\Delta T = T_f - T_i}$

   $\Delta T = T_f - T_i = 39°C - 60°C = -21°C$

   b. Calculate the amount of energy (calories) transferred *from* the hot water. Remember that heat in calories = mass of hot water × change of temperature of hot water.
   ***cal* = *m* × ΔT** = 40 g × −21°C = −840 cal

   c. Calculate the change of temperature (ΔT) for the cold water.
   $\boldsymbol{\Delta T = T_f - T_i}$ ΔT = 39°C − 25°C = 14°C

   d. Calculate the amount of energy transferred *to* the cold water.
   ***cal* = *m* × ΔT**

   cal = m × ΔT = 60 g × 14°C = 840 cal

   e. Compare the amount of energy transferred from the hot water and the amount of energy transferred to the cold water.

   same

4. A student's 600 mL cup of cocoa got cold. It was only 25°C. He put it in the microwave. How many calories must transfer to the cocoa to bring it up to 70°C?

   $\Delta T = T_f - T_i = 70°C - 25°C = 45°C$

   cal = m × ΔT = 600 g × 45°C = 27,000 cal

Calories of Energy Transfer

Results

Record the results of your group's investigation in the table below.

	Mass (g)	Initial temp (°C)	Final temp (°C)	Δ T (°C)	Calories (cal)
Hot water					
Cold water					

Answers will vary.

Calculations

1. Calculate the calories transferred from the hot water. Show your math. Record in the table.

   Answers will vary.

2. Calculate the calories transferred to the cold water. Show your math. Record in the table.

   Answers will vary.

Conclusions

3. Compare the energy transfer *from* the hot water and the energy transfer *to* the cold water. What do you notice?

   The amount of energy transferred is the same.

Heat Practice A

1. What is the equation for calculating final temperature when equal masses of water are mixed?

$$T_f = \frac{T_1 + T_2}{2}$$

2. What is the equation for calculating how much heat energy (calories) transferred to or from a mass of water?

$cal = m \times \Delta T$

3. A student mixed 30 mL of water at 15°C and 30 mL of water at 55°C. Answer the following questions. Show your work.

   a. What is the final volume of the water?

   30 mL + 30 mL = 60 mL

   b. What is the final temperature of the water?

   $$T_f = \frac{T_1 + T_2}{2} = \frac{15 + 55}{2} = \frac{70}{2} = 35°C$$

   c. How many degrees did the cold water increase?

   $\Delta T = T_f - T_i = 35°C - 15°C = 20°C$

   d. How many degrees did the hot water decrease?

   $\Delta T = T_f - T_i = 35°C - 55°C = -20°C$

   e. How much heat energy transferred to the cold water?

   $cal = m \times \Delta T = 30\ g \times 20°C = 600\ cal$

   f. How much heat energy transferred from the hot water?

   $cal = m \times \Delta T = 30\ g \times -20°C = -600\ cal$

   g. What happened to the kinetic energy of the hot-water and cold-water particles?

   increased in cold-water particles; decreased in hot-water particles

Heat Practice B

4. A student has a 10 L (10,000 mL) fish tank. The water needs to be 28°C for her tropical fish. When she filled the tank, the temperature of the water was 12°C. How many calories of heat must transfer to the aquarium before it is ready for the fish?

$\Delta T = T_f - T_i = 28°C - 12°C = 16°C$

$cal = m \times \Delta T = 10{,}000g \times 16°C = 160000\ cal$

5. A student made tea. She started with 300 g of water at 20°C. She transferred 18,000 cal to the water. What was the final temperature of the water?

$cal = m \times \Delta T = 300g \times \Delta T = 18{,}000\ cal$

$\Delta T = 18{,}000\ cal/300g$

$T_f = T_i + \Delta T = 20°C + 60°C = 80°C$

6. Energy "flow" is the transfer of energy from one place to another. Which direction does energy flow?

from hot to cold; from particles with higher kinetic energy to particles with lower kinetic energy

7. How does energy transfer happen?

Between particles during collisions (contact). Energy transfer as a result of contact between particles is conduction.

8. What is equilibrium?

Equilibrium is the condition of a system in which nothing is changing. When a system is in (thermal) equilibrium, the temperature is not changing.

Dissolve or Melt? Results

Observations. Record your observations in the table.

Material	Hot water	Cold water	Hot air	Cold air
Candy coating				
Chocolate				

Answers will vary.

Conclusions

1. What melted? chocolate

   Under what conditions? when it got hot

   What happened at the particle level when it melted?

   Heat transferred from hot-water particles to chocolate particles. Chocolate particles moved faster (broke some bonds) and started to move over and around one another as a liquid.

2. What dissolved? colored candy shell

   Under what conditions? when it got wet

   What happened at the particle level when it dissolved?

   Water particles banged into candy particles and broke them away one at a time. Water particles carried candy particles into the mass of water.

Solubility

WARNING — This set contains chemicals that may be harmful if misused. Read cautions on individual containers carefully. Not to be used by children except under adult supervision.

Part 1. Record your observations.

Substance	Before mixing with water	After mixing with water
$CaCO_3$	white powder	cloudy liquid
NaCl	white crystals	clear liquid

Part 2. Record the filtering results.

$CaCO_3$: clear liquid

NaCl: clear liquid

Part 3. Record the evaporation results.

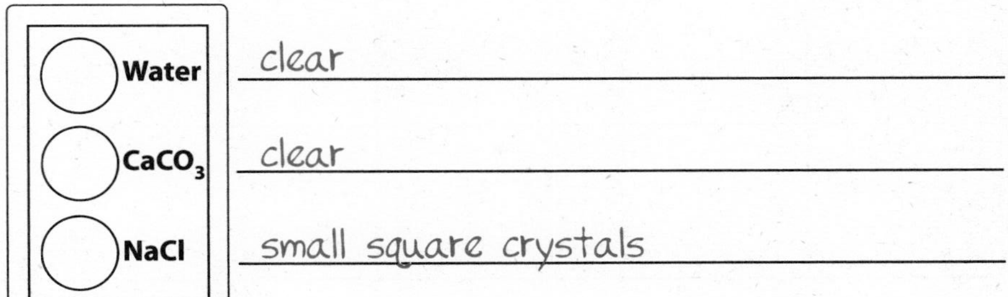

Water: clear

$CaCO_3$: clear

NaCl: small square crystals

Melt Three Materials

Prediction

Will margarine, wax, and sucrose melt in hot water? Record your predictions in the table below.

Procedure

Write your procedure and conduct the test.

Put samples of three substances into small cups—one sample to a cup. Float the cups in hot water. Observe the samples at regular intervals for phase change—solid to liquid. After 5–10 minutes, check substances that did not melt to see if they are soft.

Materials	Prediction: Will it melt?	Water temperature (°C)	Observations
Margarine		Answers will vary.	
Wax		Answers will vary.	
Sucrose		Answers will vary.	

Wax and Sucrose Questions

1. When wax melts, how do the wax particles change?

   The particles do not change, but they do change their relationship to each other.

2. Why do materials melt when they get hot?

   Energy transfers to the particles, bonds break, and particles move past one another.

3. What happens at the particle level when a material freezes?

   Energy transfers to the particles, bonds form, and the particles lock into position.

4. Look at the puddle of wax around the wick of your candle. Explain why it is solid now.

   Energy transferred from wax particles to air, bonds formed, and particles solidified.

This page is intentionally left blank.

Response Sheet—Investigation 8

A student watched his mom put a piece of wax in a pan. She put the pan on the stove. A minute later, the student looked in the pan and said,

Look, the wax is turning into water.

What would you tell the student to help him understand what happened in the pan?

The solid wax is not turning into water, it is melting. When a material melts, it changes from solid to liquid. Liquid wax has the same kind of particles as solid wax, but heat changes the relationship between the particles. When enough energy (heat) has transferred to the particles in the solid wax, bonds break between the particles, and they move over and around one another. The solid wax changes phase to liquid wax. The movement allows the wax to flow, making it look like water, but it is not.

FOSS Chemical Interactions Course, Second Edition
© The Regents of the University of California
Can be duplicated for classroom or workshop use.

Ice and Substances

White substance tested: ____________________

Amount tested (2 or 4 scoops): __________

Results

Time (min)	Temperature (°C)
0 (Start)	
2	
4	
6 (Final)	

Answers will vary.

Record the initial and final temperatures on the class results table. Calculate ΔT and record it on the class table.

$\Delta T =$ __________

Which substance(s) dropped the temperature of the ice the most?

Sodium chloride

Which substance was most effective? Sodium chloride

Questions

1. If you put a vial of room-temperature water in a cup of 0°C ice, will the water in the vial freeze? Why or why not?

   No, the room temperature water will transfer energy until it reaches 0°C. Then there is no energy transfer between the vial and the ice.

2. If you put a vial of room-temperature water in a cup of ice that is colder than 0°C, will it freeze? Why or why not?

   Yes, the room temperature water will cool to 0°C and continue to transfer energy to the ice until it freezes.

Phase-Change Summary

ENERGY TRANSFERRED TO THE SUBSTANCE

4. Sublime

1. Solid

5. Melt

2. Liquid

6. Evaporate

3. Gas

7. Freeze

8. Condense

9. Deposit

ENERGY TRANSFERRED FROM THE SUBSTANCE

This page is intentionally left blank.

Representing Substances

Substance name	Chemical formula	Representation	Number of elements	Number of atoms
Carbon	C	C	1	1
Water	H_2O	H O H	2	3
Carbon dioxide	CO_2	O C O	2	3
Sodium chloride	NaCl	Na Cl	2	2
Oxygen	O_2	O O	1	2
Sodium carbonate	Na_2CO_3	O C O O Na Na	3	6

Analyzing Substances

Substance name and Chemical formula	Representation	Number of elements	Number of atoms
Calcium chloride $CaCl_2$		2	3
Calcium chloride $NaHCO_3$		4	6
Ascorbic acid $C_6H_8O_6$		3	20
Carbon dioxide CO_2		2	3
Calcium carbonate $CaCO_3$		3	5
Citric acid $C_6H_8O_7$		3	21
Sucrose $C_{12}H_{22}O_{11}$		3	45

Thinking about Limewater

1. Limewater is calcium hydroxide dissolved in water. The chemical formula for calcium hydroxide is $Ca(OH)_2$. Use circles labeled with atomic symbols to draw what you think a representation of one particle of calcium hydroxide might look like.

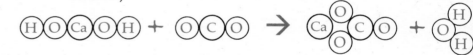

H O Ca O H

2. a. Use atom tiles to make representations of the particles that you think reacted.

   b. Rearrange the atoms to figure out what the white precipitate is.

   c. Draw representations of the reactants and the products using labeled circles. (HINT: The white precipitate does not dissolve in water. What white substance are you familiar with that doesn't dissolve?)

3. Write the limewater reaction using chemical formulas. Write the names of the reactants and products under the formulas.

$Ca(OH)_2 + CO_2 \rightarrow CaCO_3 + H_2O$

Calcium hydroxide — Carbon dioxide — Calcium carbonate — Water

4. Did new substances form? If yes, what are they? Yes. $CaCO_3$, H_2O

5. Did new atoms form? If yes, what are they? No.

6. Did new elements form? If yes, what are they? No.

Acid/Baking Soda Reaction Products

WARNING — This set contains chemicals that may be harmful if misused. Read cautions on individual containers carefully. Not to be used by children except under adult supervision.

1. What happened in the *vial*? Use chemical equations to explain.

$Ca(OH)_2 + CO_2 = CaCO_3 + H_2O$

2. What happened in the *bottle*? Use chemical equations to explain.

$NaHCO_3 + HCl = CO_2 + NaCl + H_2O$

3. Were you able to confirm all the products that formed during the reaction between baking soda and hydrochloric acid? If not, what else will you do?

No, the liquid in the bottle will be evaporated to see if the sodium chloride is in fact one of the products.

Response Sheet—Investigation 9

Grandmother ate too many chili peppers for supper. She moaned,

I need an antacid tablet.

Her granddaughter found the package of antacid (antacid means "against acid") tablets and read the label. The active ingredient was calcium carbonate. The granddaughter said,

This will give you some relief.

1. Explain why the granddaughter thought the antacid tablet would help Grandmother.

Stomach acid reacts with calcium carbonate. During reactions, starting substances (reactants) are changed into new substances (products). So when calcium carbonate reacts with hydrochloric acid, the acid is "used up." When the acid is changed into other substances, the pain caused by the acid goes away. (The acid is neutralized.)

2. Use chemical formulas to write the equation for the reaction.

$CaCO_3 + 2HCl = CO_2 + CaCl_2 + H_2O$

NOTE: Here are the formulas for some of the substances you have used.

CO_2	H_2O	Na_2CO_3
$CaCO_3$	HCl	$NaCl$
$CaCl_2$	$MgSO_4$	
$Ca(OH)_2$	$NaHCO_3$	

Citric Acid/Baking Soda Reaction

1. Explain why the same amount of gas was produced.

5 mL citric acid solution A + 3 *midispoons* baking soda → 30 mL gas

5 mL citric acid solution A + 6 *midispoons* baking soda → 30 mL gas

The amount of acid was the same in both reactions. The amount of product (gas) was the same in both reactions. The amount of acid determined the amount of gas. Therefore, the acid was the limiting factor, and soda was in excess in both reactions.

2. Explain why different amounts of gas were produced.

5 mL *citric acid solution A* + 3 midispoons baking soda → 30 mL gas

5 mL *citric acid solution B* + 3 midispoons baking soda → 15 mL gas

More concentrated acid (solution A) produced more gas. Less concentrated acid produced less gas. Again, the amount of acid determined the amount of gas. The acid was the limiting factor; the soda was in excess.

3. What might happen if you mix 5 mL of citric acid solution A with 1 midispoon of baking soda?

One spoon may not be enough to provide an excess of sodium bicarbonate. If that is the case, the acid will be in excess and the soda will be the limiting factor. The amount of product (gas) would be reduced.

4. What could you do to determine which reactant was in excess at the end of a reaction between citric acid and baking soda?

When bubbling stops, add a few drops of acid to the liquid in the bottle. If it bubbles, the soda was in excess. If no bubbles form, add a pinch of soda to the liquid in the bottle. If bubbles form, the acid was in excess. If no bubbles form, neither reactant was in excess. Both reactants were used up in the reaction.

This page is intentionally left blank.